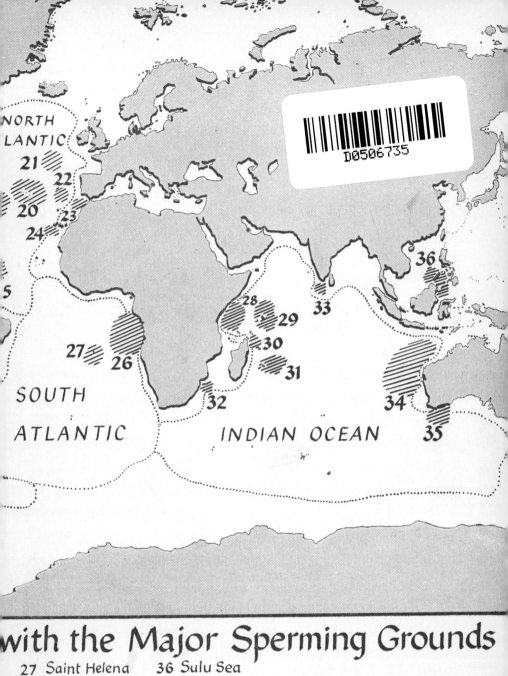

NORTH
ATLANTIC
21
22
20 23
24

5

27 26

SOUTH

ATLANTIC

28 29
30
31

32

33

INDIAN OCEAN

36

34

35

D0506735

# with the Major Sperming Grounds

27 Saint Helena
28 Zanzibar
29 Mahé Banks
30 Diégo-Suarez
31 Rodriguez
32 Delagoa Bay
33 Colombo
34 Coasts of New Holland
35 West Australia

36 Sulu Sea

▶ Locations based on a map prepared by
R. W. Richmond under the direction of
Charles Haskins Townsend from data
supplied by A. C. Watson, Nantucket
Whaling Museum

Miller Modified Mercator Projection

*Follow the Whale*

# By Ivan T. Sanderson

# FOLLOW THE WHALE

*by*
*Ivan T. Sanderson*

MAPS AND CHARTS BY THE AUTHOR

CHAPTER HEAD DRAWINGS BY
F. WENDEROTH SAUNDERS

## LITTLE, BROWN AND COMPANY
BOSTON            TORONTO

*Published simultaneously in Canada
by Little, Brown & Company (Canada) Limited*

PRINTED IN THE UNITED STATES OF AMERICA

TO

MY SMALL WIFE, ALMA,

IN MEMORY OF THREE HAPPY WEEKS

SPENT ON A VERY DEAD

SPERM WHALE

# Introductory

THERE seems to be a general impression that man's association with the whale began about two hundred years ago somewhere in New England, and that it came to an end sometime during the latter half of the last century with the passing of the square-rigged sailing ships. There even appears to be a general haziness as to why it ever occurred at all, apart from the desire on the part of some New England families to amass fortunes. Any such impressions are completely erroneous, for man has been following the whale for ten thousand years and he is still doing so today with even greater vigor and more deplorable success than ever before. Actually, the duration of New England whaling is almost negligible in point of time and quite paltry in many other respects when viewed against the whole sweep of whaling history. As an enterprise also it fades into insignificance when compared to the implacable modern industry, though in romantic appeal it will forever stand out as one of the greatest periods in the history of America and of man's conquest of the sea in general.

The literature on whaling is vast. Whole libraries have been written on the subject and fair-sized museums are devoted exclusively to the preservation of its accoutrements, while there are even "stuffed" whaling ships housed in large halls or embedded in concrete docks. Nevertheless, great parts of whaling history, and especially of the more ancient and most modern, have been completely ignored. Similarly, the literature on the whales themselves leaves much to be desired, and for two reasons. First, technical works are scattered and hard to assemble, while many popular works are riddled with contradictions. Second, it is only very recently that prolonged and accurate scientific investigations have been made of these most unapproachable and aloof creatures, and the results have not yet been published in popular form. Moreover, the findings of Mackintosh, Frazer, and others who undertook these studies at the Antarctic whaling grounds, have completely set at naught a very great deal of all that had been previously believed about the lives and habits of these animals. These discoveries go far towards explaining the remarkable plethora of contradictions found in many older works. As a result of these two shortcomings in the extant literature on both whaling and the whales themselves — namely that ninety-six per cent of the history is customarily ignored and that our knowledge of the whales per se has until very recently been more or less negligible — there is a deplorable lack of perspective in the popular conception of the whole subject. This is regrettable because whaling has played a part in our history that, in certain respects, is second to no other human enterprise, and whale products have always been and still are of very great importance to our economy.

The story that follows is an attempt to display this fascinating facet of human endeavor in some semblance of its entirety and in proper perspective by a process of corralling the forgotten and more neglected aspects of whaling history and the new discoveries about the whales themselves, and weaving them into a continuous web of narrative. It is primarily natural history, in both senses of that term. It is the history of man's conquest of the sea, a saga with a theme so inexorable that it can only be described as natural, and it is a natural history of a group of animals than which there are none more mysterious or romantic in the world. To follow the whale is to follow the whole course of one of the most important and significant aspects of our own history. It is virtually the story of the conquest of our planet.

Our association with whales is extraordinary in that we have almost nothing in common apart from certain anatomical generalities, and in some cases a liking for herrings, yet it began somewhere in the mists of prehistory and has continued unabated through the ages. The common denominator is the sea. The story is, however, unlike the stories told in other history books. It is not concerned with the rise and fall of empires, the glorification of human personalities, and the slaughter of nations. Apart from half a dozen names that stand out more in retrospect than through renown — names that few if any have heard, like Tiglath-Pileser, Ohthere the Bold, François Sopite, Christopher Hussey, Samuel Enderby, Svend Foyn, and Carl Anton Larsen — this is a history in which man is almost anonymous. Strangely enough, the animals are similarly retiring for, until recently, they have been just whales, as the men were just whalers. Yet the story is one of courage and drama, excitement and danger, romance and horror, and it maintains throughout an underlying motif of tragedy and pathos that is sometimes hard to tolerate. It is a saga of the triumph of the puny and of the twilight of the mighty.

There are several concurrent themes to this story that may best be postulated by means of six simple questions. Why did men go whaling; who among men have done so; when did they go; where did they go; how did they get there; and what did they find? Each question involves a different inquiry, but the answers, when found, mesh so exactly, like a warp and weft, that we can clearly discern a continuous pattern across the resulting cloth — a pattern that proceeds in an orderly manner by regular steps not only in point of historical time but also with respect to the men involved, the places they went, the ships they went in, and the whales they followed. However, if we are to appreciate this pattern fully, we have to see it in proper perspective, and in order to do this, we cannot just cut a block out of the middle of the cloth. We must view it as a whole, complete with its borders, so that the origin of the design and its ultimate fulfillment may be seen. It is, in fact, essential that we first obtain some concept of the time scale of the history of whaling.

Time is a relative thing and hard for man to comprehend. Our own lives are so short that the periods of time with which we must deal in this story have little meaning unless charted in some simple visual form and pointed up with high lights that are both notable and in some way susceptible to everyday comparison. The charts on pages xvii and 370 will perhaps make the matter clearer and demonstrate better than any words the immensity of whaling history.

To us, the date of the sailing of the first deep-sea whaler from Nantucket is something of the olden times, but to the captain of that vessel the landing of the first colonists on those same shores was just as ancient. To those colonists, in turn, the voyages of Cristoforo Colombo were already profoundly historic, and yet the first Euro-

pean — one Snorri Karlsefni — was born in North America, and on
that very coast to boot, just five hundred years before Colombo
sighted the West Indies. But you have to go back in time twice as
far again to find the man who gave us the earliest written record of a
whaling enterprise — to King Assur-Naçir-Pal of Assyria, who tells
us in a legend on stone of the exploits of his predecessor, King
Tiglath-Pileser I. Nor is that all; you must again double, or perhaps
treble, your journey back in time if you wish to stand contemporary
with the Stone Age men of the North Sea who left us the earliest
records of having followed the whale. If the Early Stone Age men
of Portugal went a-whaling with their huge harpoons, you must
step three times further back again into the mists of prehistory.

Then there is another matter that necessitates careful consideration if we are to obtain a proper understanding of the history and
significance of our subject. Whaling is a marine affair and must
therefore be viewed primarily from that angle. In order to appreciate the procedure, we must put ourselves in the place of the
whalers. It is essential, in fact, to forget the geography of land
masses, such as we learn in school and see in all our atlases, and observe instead the conformity and distribution of seas and oceans. To
do this, maps have to be constructed from what may be called an
aquacentric point of view, whereon oceans take the place of continents, shallow seas of islands, currents of rivers, strings of islands
that of mountain ranges, and narrow channels that of isthmuses.
Furthermore, the maps in our atlases are constructed upon projections that often give a quite erroneous impression of marine distances and directions, and of the relative positions of surrounding
land masses. All of them point north for no really valid reason. Not
even navigational charts show the seas in a truly aquacentric manner. What is needed, therefore, is an entirely new approach, of the
kind that the air age has forced upon global flyers (see Note on
Maps, page xix).

Just as the continents are fringed with promontories great and
small, and with a host of islands, so also are the oceans bordered
with gulfs and surrounded by a diadem of seas. There is a difference,
however, for a land-island, to be an island, must be entirely separated from the continental land, whereas sea-islands are of two
kinds. There are those like the Caspian Sea that are entirely sepa-

rated from the oceans and completely surrounded by land, but there are also others like the Scotia Sea which are almost entirely surrounded by water, but which nonetheless are clearly separated by shallows. This latter type, moreover, is of great importance and has a very real biological significance that can be displayed only on aquacentric maps.

These "sea-islands," or "sea-countries," as we shall call them, often have very distinctive climates and other environmental features, and they are often populated by most characteristic assemblages of animals. This may come as somewhat of a surprise to many, for it might seem logical to suppose that, water being a continuous medium, the animal life of the sea would spread indiscriminately hither and yon and, within the more obvious limits of temperature, depth, and salinity, become universal. This, however, it does not do, for these sea-countries display features just as unique to themselves as do any land-islands, and this predisposes much variation in their fauna, including the incidence of whales. Thus, when we come to investigate our sixth question — what whales did men follow — we find that the sea-countries to which they went and the particular ocean to which each was attached is of paramount importance.

Each of the major and many of the minor whaling industries have for this reason been concerned with a special kind of whale or group of whales. This has not, however, necessarily been dictated by the presence of those particular whales in the seas adjacent to the homelands of the whalers. The Dutch had to go to the ice front before they found the arctic right whale; the modern Norwegians have had to go to the Antarctic in pursuit of the rorquals; the New Englanders had to sail the whole earth to find the sperming grounds. The popular notion, therefore, that "whaling" simply means getting into a boat and going out to sea and harpooning a "whale" will have to be abandoned and a quite new concept adopted, for whaling in every case entails much more than just that. It means going to a particular sea-country, often at a definite time of the year, and following a certain kind of whale, in a very special way. It is particularly in respect to this ever-changing procedure that the history of whaling is so fascinating.

Whales, as will be seen presently, are of great variety and are not, it must be clearly understood, by any means all vast leviathans of the deep. There are some hundred species living on the earth today (see complete illustrated list in Appendix E) and the great majority of them would probably never even be called whales except by specialists. Most of them are quite small, and yet some of these, like the porpoises, blackfish, narwhal, beluga, and certain dolphins, have played a very important part in the life and economy of many races of men for thousands of years. Our story, however, deals mostly, though not exclusively, with a dozen of the larger kinds, namely the black and arctic right whales, the blue, fin, piked, and sei rorquals, the humpback, the gray whale, the sperm whale, the bottlenose whales, and the common dolphin and common porpoise. These are fully described as they appear in the narrative. The others are dealt with more briefly either in the body of the story, in the last chapter, or in Appendix E.

Finally, we should interject here at the outset a word of caution. We still don't know very much about anything, and our current ideas on the past are grotesquely warped in certain respects. Our cultural background in western Europe bequeathed to us a singularly lopsided view of ancient history and a strangely biased opinion of our own importance. Europe has been regarded by Europeans for over a thousand years not only as the hub of the universe, but also as the fountainhead of civilization. In point of historical and geographical fact, it is nothing more than a large, rugged peninsula at the west end of Eurasia, the greatest land block on earth, and the womb of culture, as possibly also of modern man himself. One, two, three, or even four thousand years of ascendancy by Europe or any other part of the world is of little real significance in the over-all sweep of history, and even our history is now being discovered to be much more ancient than was previously supposed possible.

Stone Age man in Europe, and his more cultured counterparts in other continents, was not nearly so stupid and primitive as we used to think. Jewelry was traded between Ireland and Crete two thousand years before Christ; the Koreans used ironclad ships centuries before we did; Indian princes sailed the open oceans with seven hundred retainers in one ship before the Greeks had invented a fore-and-aft sail; and rorquals were shot with harpoon guns a thousand years before Svend Foyn initiated the modern whaling period. What is more, all kinds of people were roving the oceans from continent to continent millennia before the peoples of western Europe had so much as put a mast in a coracle. Not until the lateness of our own times is appreciated, can any real concept of the past be obtained. And when we come to the history of the whales, we have to start thinking in altogether different terms again. In order to gain a proper perspective, therefore, let us turn from contemplation to action and follow the whale.

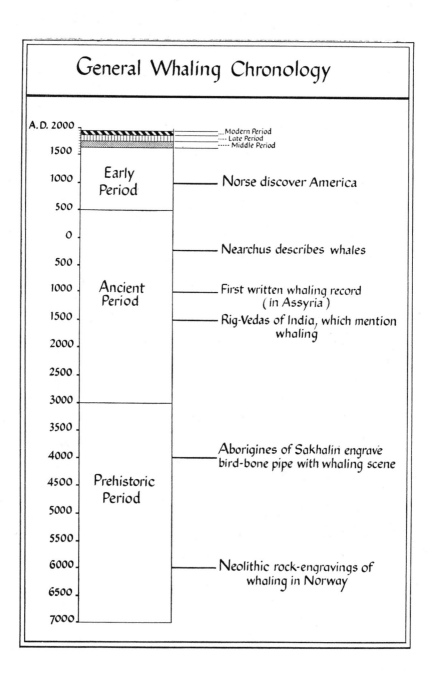

# General Whaling Chronology

| | |
|---|---|
| A.D. 2000 | ...Modern Period |
| | ---- Late Period |
| 1500 | ---- Middle Period |
| 1000 | Early Period — Norse discover America |
| 500 | |
| 0 | |
| 500 | — Nearchus describes whales |
| 1000 | Ancient Period — First written whaling record ( in Assyria ) |
| 1500 | — Rig-Vedas of India, which mention whaling |
| 2000 | |
| 2500 | |
| 3000 | |
| 3500 | |
| 4000 | — Aborigines of Sakhalin engrave bird-bone pipe with whaling scene |
| 4500 | Prehistoric Period |
| 5000 | |
| 5500 | |
| 6000 | — Neolithic rock-engravings of whaling in Norway |
| 6500 | |
| 7000 | |

# Note on Maps

GEOGRAPHY as currently taught in our schools is in many respects not satisfactory either from a purely cultural point of view or as a practical guide to the average man in the contemporary world. Comparatively little geography at all is taught today, and most of the other subjects presented to our young people sorely lack an adequate geographical background. That which is presented is sadly unimaginative and usually very biased in approach. Almost all popular maps and educational atlases devote ninety-nine per cent of their space to the political aspects of the world, and almost all maps are displayed from a single point of view physically — namely with the North Pole at the top of the page. This is often grossly misleading.

The coming of the air age has given great impetus to a reappraisal of our planet and to the construction of maps showing its surface from novel angles. In this, a few popular publications — we would single out news weeklies such as *Time* and *Newsweek* — have done great service by bringing to the public simple, lucid, well-drawn and often colorful maps viewed from all sorts of angles that present current political and geographical problems as they really appear to those faced with their solution. For instance, a map of a country as seen by a bomber-plane navigator often looks nothing like a map of that country in a school atlas.

Then again, the mere distribution of land and water and their altitudes or depths are not the only physical features of the earth that can be shown on maps, and most atlases devote some, if only minimum space to a few general features such as winds and ocean currents, human population, vegetation, and so forth. For the most part, however, the emphasis is upon land surfaces and very little space is devoted to any detailed picture of the seas and oceans. Recourse must be had to nautical charts, which are not normally available to the layman, and even these, being too full of detail, are often singularly uninformative about the more basic general aspects of the marine world.

There is also another matter that must be taken into account when we wish to depict history on maps. This is that the compass came into general use only during the thirteenth century A.D., at least in Europe, and prior to its introduction the concept of "north" was quite different from what it is today. North has been one of the cardinal points since early times in Egypt, but it was the least, rather than the most, important of them. The ancient world looked primarily east or west, and this brings us to another vital consideration. The world appeared different to every group of people in those days, depending upon where they lived, and this applies most especially to the dwellers on coasts of all kinds, and to mariners in particular. Straight ahead and left and right were much more important to the early navigators than north, south, east, and west. Thus, a Roman in Rome regarded North Africa as the World, with Greece behind him to the left, Gaul to the right, and Spain half right; to a Roman in Calabria, Egypt lay ahead, with Arabia and India beyond, while Greece was half left and North Africa right.

As we follow the whale, this approach to navigation must be borne in mind, because up to the time of the Basques it dominated all navigation and even thereafter retained great influence upon seamen of all nations, for they are a pragmatic breed and must rely for survival primarily on what they know by actual experience to be reliable. Even today in the most advanced stages of mechanical navigation your destination point is of more ultimate importance than the position of north. No true seaman, especially a whaler setting out after his quarry, sets up his chart with "north" straight ahead; rather, he slews the chart around so that it points to where he wants to go; then he can see at a glance what snags are in his way and which way to turn to avoid them.

This may sound so basically obvious as not to warrant statement, but it is surprising how seldom the concept is appreciated by any except navigators, and it is quite stunning what erroneous ideas we all have of the relative positions of land masses, islands and continents, seas, and other fixed geographical units. And to make matters worse, the maps we do have, if thus turned around to suit any particular voyage, are usually on projections totally unsuited to a proper understanding of these relationships. Nothing can be more misleading than a map of the world on the Mercator projection if viewed only in part, and from an unusual angle.

When delving into old records about the early voyages of the Basques, and reading the modern commentaries upon them with a view to summing up the theory that they reached Newfoundland and thus America before the time of Columbus (see page 140), but before I had drawn a map of the North Atlantic as seen from the Bay of Biscay, whence the Basques sailed, I had the preconceived notion that the achievement was well-nigh impossible because three thousand miles of open Atlantic intervened. Nothing can be further from the facts, as a glance at an aquacentric map of the North Atlantic (see page 138) from the point of view of a Basque codfisher will show. Such a map — drawn on a projection that shows actual distances and true directions — immediately reveals that the voyage to Newfoundland was "straight ahead" for nine tenths of the way and then "half left." Further, it can also be seen that almost the whole passage had been traversed *yearly* for at least four hundred years by the Norse going back and forth to their Greenland colonies — which they stopped doing only at the end of the fifteenth century — and thus entailed only an extra short hop across the Labrador Basin. This route had been followed previously by Thorfinn Karlsefni and others, five hundred years before. Finally, by following the everlasting and perennially reliable "Westerlies," the Basques would then be blown almost straight back to Iceland and thence to Ireland on a single tack.

The ten maps which will be found in the body of our story are designed to show the sea-countries concerned in whaling from this point of view. Each is provided with a series of notes on the particular points of interest it brings to light. There remains then the world map forming the end papers of this book. This is on a fairly standard projection and is orientated in the conventional manner with north at the "top." It also calls for some special comment here.

As our earth is a sphere, no true representation of it can be put upon a flat surface like a piece of paper. Something has to be grossly distorted, and it has long been agreed generally that the "top" and "bottom," or polar regions, are less important and should therefore receive the roughest treatment. And they do. The two-inch bands across the top and bottom of this map together represent a total area only a little larger than that of Africa! Nonetheless the wider band between these two fairly represents the comparative proportions of the remainder of the world. About fourth fifths of this is covered by water, and it is this part that interests us. The land masses, apart from some islands, are unimportant except for their names and general disposition.

On this map the most significant feature displayed, and, indeed, almost the only one, apart from the positions of the major sperm-whaling grounds, is the disposition of the oceans. Now, it must be clearly understood that an *ocean*, such as the North Atlantic, is not just the water area between Europe and Africa on the one hand and North and South America on the other. True, this *ocean* is con-tained within that body of water but an *ocean* is not just a body of water; it is a very definite geographical entity; it has most precise limits and a highly complex structure. Complete definition of an ocean would require a large volume, but the salient facts may be summed up as follows:

There are five true oceans — the North Atlantic, the South Atlan-tic, the Indian, and the North and South Pacifics, though the division between the last two is arbitrary in that you may separate them in any of four different ways according to the over-all criteria you choose to employ for the definition of the boundaries of an ocean. Then, there is a considerable mass of water at the top of the world which is normally called the "Arctic Ocean." Actually, we do not know whether it is a true ocean or just a vast sea, because we do not know what types of deposits cover its floor over that portion which lies below the permanent Ice-raft, and until we do know this, we can only apply a theory that disturbs many geomorpholo-gists.

Briefly stated, this is to the effect that the earth is really a sort of vast crystal and is trying to adopt a tetrahedral form — namely, a three-sided pyramid with an apex at the Antarctic and a flat tri-angular base around the North Pole. This would give us apices at four points, as we actually have in the land masses of northeastern Asia, Europe, North America, and the Antarctic. We should thus get three triangular continents depending south — and we have these in Asia plus Australia, Europe plus Africa, and the Americas — and three triangular oceans running up between them, which we also have in the Indian, Atlantic, and Pacific complexes. This would leave a flat triangular area at the top which should be filled with an ocean — the Arctic Ocean. We have just such a roughly triangular area of water there, but we still need to know at least one more over-all fact.

The true oceans are great areas of apparently permanent depression that have never been dry land. Their rocky bottoms are said to be covered with the second layer of the earth's surface, known as the *sima* (silicon-magnesium predominating), as opposed to the continents which are bits of the outermost layer, known as the *sial* (silicon-aluminum predominating). The continents of sial are said to *float* on the sima. The continental rafts are at present partially flooded or sunken so that a *shelf* extends seaward from all of them to a varying degree in all directions towards the oceans. They are notably wide off the southeastern coast of South America and to the east of Australia. These shelves are comparatively shallow, that is to say vis-à-vis the true oceans, but they are also clearly defined. Upon them, and upon them alone, are to be found what are called terrigenous deposits, namely, sediments derived from land surfaces and washed into the sea. Beneath the true oceans are only five kinds of silts, formed from meteoric material that descends from the sky, or muds derived from the coverings of tiny single-celled animals that die in the water above or from those of little free-swimming shellfish. The division between terrigenous deposits and these others marks the boundaries of the true oceans. All the rest of the water constitutes *seas*, which are something quite different.

The distribution and boundaries of the true oceans are of the utmost importance to a proper understanding of the natural history of whales and the history of their pursuit. Whales are not, as is often supposed even scientifically, cosmopolitan. Almost all of them are strictly confined to either oceans or seas — and very often to specific oceans or seas — while there are others that do not even enter the seas but are limited to the diadem of inlets, bays, estuaries, and other shallows that encircle them, just as the latter do the oceans. A glance at this world map will show that sperms are, except in a few cases, found predominantly in the oceans, even in that peculiar little arm of the Atlantic which extends into the Gulf of Mexico. On the other hand, the reason for the Australian and New Zealand bay whaling becomes abundantly clear from viewing this map and the one on page 327, which shows the nonoceanic connection between the Australasian and Antarctic land masses in more detail. Right whales avoid the oceans and travel around them from sea to sea.

# Contents

# PART V

## *The Late Period* 1700 A.D. to 1875 A.D.

# PART VI

## *The Modern Period* 1875 A.D. to 1955 A.D.

# PART VII

## *The Posthistoric Period* 1955 A.D. to 60,000,000 B.C.

# List of Maps

# Part One

10,000 B.C. TO 3000 B.C.

# The Prehistoric Period

# I

# Night Is Before the Dawn
## (Neolithic)

THERE is a place in the distant isles where the sun is long in coming. It is a place of meandering strands and flat, grassy islands. Low walls of ragged rock crawl out from the smoothness of the sands and plunge unconcernedly into the gently heaving waters. When the tide runs out, the rocks are girt around with a fringe of vivid-orange seaweed that makes sucking noises in the restless ocean swell. This place is mewed over by gulls and wailed at by curlews. Sheets of little pattering sandpipers wave back and forth with the swilling of the surf upon the golden shores, and endlessly flapping, spiky flights of terns shrill at the oncoming wind. Falcons rise from the labyrinth of grass to landward and beat into the air, crying harshly. The black of night is rent from time to time by strange lone cries, and usually the wind wails; but even if all else is quiet, there is forever the suppressed thunder of the ocean surf pounding upon these distant shores. The sun is long in coming even in summer when it goes away for such a little time and the night is bright with cold stars. The water between the isles hurries silently about, polished like jet, and the short grass scurries like the sea in a light breeze and casts back a miasmic paleness.

Comes now an eerie luminosity and the satin of the sky turns lucid. From everywhere at once an electric blueness floods the air. The pale strand picks up the ghostly light, but the grass-covered land melts into nothingness and the waters turn inky and heave in pallidness, reflecting the half-light. Birds stir in the air. A skein of huge black geese hurry by overhead, their leader honking orders that seem to echo in the dome of the sky. Great, snowy eider ducks and little back scooters stream across the water, dripping lines of black droplets upon its glassy surface. Scurries of petrels wheel about the channel and vanish out upon the ocean. Cruel brown skuas scream raucously aloft and plummet to earth behind the rim of the horizon. The little spike-winged terns are busy, endlessly rising and falling where the ripples break upon the beach, flapping always, whining shrilly, never getting anywhere but up and down upon their forked tails. A little procession streams by, cutting arrow-heads upon the waters, hardly visible in the half-light — a family of mergansers headed for the places of unwary fish. False dawn in the north is a time of stirrings, of soundless hurrying movements, of end-less comings and goings, of strange cries high in the silent crystal air, of armies taking their places, of feathered cohorts shifting about.

Then, round a low rampart of jagged rocks, a procession of large, black, pointed things sweeps out upon the immensely heaving waters of the channel. They are shaped not unlike great two-ended ducks. They scud across the oily waters and then deploy. More come from behind the low promontory. They cut swaths on the water. They are sharp, black forms in the blue light that isn't light. A rhythmical dipping and scraping they make, and lines of tiny water-drops spurt from them. They move silently across the channel, and the hurrying bird cohorts split before them and wheel aside to pass on in broken streams. They are little boats and they have men in them.

They are boats made of skins neatly sewn and stretched upon a light frame of bent and lashed sticks. They are pointed at both ends and are partly decked over fore and aft. They are very light and sit upon the water like dried leaves despite the husky men that squat in them and propel them with short paddles. They shoot forward smoothly, little ripples lapping against their sharp prows and swishing along their taut sides. There are two score of them strung out across the channel between the islands, moving slowly towards the open ocean. Now they form a great concave arc lying idle upon the waters, rising and falling on the immense smooth-surfaced swell that rolls into the channel, so that first they all vanish together as if they had never been, and then all rise again, black against the blueness of the sky. They wait silently.

There comes a lull in the endless passing of the birds. The gulls mew over the shore behind the wind, and the air is momentarily silent and aware. Then suddenly it is not silent. A loud puffing snort is heard; it is answered by others and there are unseen splashes upon the waters. Dark forms rise in some of the canoes, while others on the flanks of the formation begin silent, purposeful maneuvers. A goose honks loudly in the air above. There is another and nearer splash accompanied by a loud exhalation of air somewhere in the oily waters. Four of the canoes dart forward, icy blue ripples shimmering from their prows in the half-light. They converge swiftly upon a point, while the others close up the line of the arc behind. Three prolonged blowings suddenly break upon the tense silence; they are so close at hand that they seem to fill the crystal air with a sort of whistling vibration. A naked man rises in one of the advance canoes; his hairy arm goes back holding a thin streak poised against the depthless blue of the sky. A moment he waits, and then his arm descends and the streak is gone. There follows a moment of silence and then a spume of white foam shoots up from the black sea. Immediately more figures bob up in the other canoes and more thin lances are poised momentarily against the sky. Then they too shoot down and the water between the canoes boils into a fury of maddened churning and spray flies like bursting thistle seed. Smackings and bangings break out upon the waters where something breathing with gargantuan sighs, and gurgling horribly, now thrashes about. A canoe upends abruptly, standing for an instant like an obelisk above the water, and then suddenly and silently vanishes. The men never utter a sound but they bob up and down on the little maelstrom, their wet torsos now shining in the blue light of a brightening dawn.

The line breaks ranks and the canoes glide together, forming little knots upon the waters. Like turmoils break out at a dozen other points across the channel, and the air is all at once filled with wild ululations, hoarse man-shouts, and a frenzied splashing and slapping of the waters. The glasslike surface of the sea is rent by a dozen pools of disruption each of which is quickly surrounded by a ring of madly dancing things. These are inflated bladders, or skin floats, which the men in the canoes are feverishly tying to the lines trailing from the harpoons that have been sunk in the maddened sea beasts. At first these floats bob about disconsolately; then suddenly they rush together, dip deep into the water, and go careening off towards the open sea, dragging the canoes after them all together as if by magic. The canoes at first crowd and jostle each other amid a torrent of shouts and oaths, but then they slowly drop apart, one behind the other, and dance over the water like a sea serpent, twisting this way and that.

But watch the bobbing floats. Every now and then they stop their mad progress and come to rest, bouncing up and down while the waters settle to placidity. Immediately the canoes come up and form a circle around them. The men jump up, balancing themselves precariously and holding aloft long-shafted spears tipped with glistening white barbed points attached to snaking lines. They wait, wobbling about in their cockle boats, until a shiny black back rises slowly from the waters amid the floats. Then the keen shafts lance down from all sides and unutterable pandemonium breaks out once more. The water is churned to madness; the canoes are cast about or rush together in a welter of foam and spray. The men begin to paddle all together with a thumping rhythm, grunting in unison, and slowly they tow the whole watery disturbance towards the shore. The canoes strain against the thin lines and the floats dance about here and there, sometimes rushing forward and then again dragging back. Every now and then one of the harpoons pulls out of the quarry, a line suddenly goes slack, and a canoe drops out of the huddle. The line is hauled in and swiftly attached to one of the other canoes; then it goes taut again as its paddler adds his weight to the tow.

Sooner or later the paddler in the lead canoe gives a shout and spills out into the water. His canoe drifts idly away while he faces about and, bracing himself by digging his feet into the shifting sands at the bottom of the shallow water, he begins to heave mightily.

Slowly the other canoes approach him and their occupants tumble out also. Only one is left and he now drifts back towards the churning patch of water and the mass of bobbing floats. Then he stands up in his canoe and begins spearing repeatedly into the waters. Again and again his great lance jabs down and is withdrawn, for this is not a barbed harpoon but a heavy shaft terminating in a long cruel spearhead of polished bone with a point sharpened to the fineness of a needle. Bloody foam spatters the man's naked chest and drips from his hair, black as tar in the half-light. Then all at once it is over and the waters are still. The spearman gives a shout and the others run through the shallows, the lines over their shoulders, surf splashing from their flailing legs. The leader reaches down among the floats and, after feeling about for a few moments, heaves some black and shiny thing to the surface. This he half carries, half floats to the shore. It is dragged out of the surf and thrown up upon the sand. A man runs up the beach and, cupping his hands, gives out a long-drawn wailing cry and it is answered from afar by a man and from on high by a gull. Then a number of figures are seen bounding over the short tufts of grass and leaping the tidal ditches. They come from a distant group of huts and are soon pouring down on to the sandy beach. They form a circle around the wet, spindle-shaped corpse on the sand and a little boy squats down and pokes the creature in its tiny eye. The same scene is being enacted at half a dozen other points along the shore and on both sides of the channel.

THIS IS a scene that, with minor variations in background, actors, and costumes, has taken place somewhere in the world almost every day, year in and year out, since long before the dawn of history. The particular incident we have been witnessing reconstructs a morning ten thousand years ago by the chill waters of a sound in the southern part of the Outer Hebrides Islands on the fringe of the Atlantic Ocean off the west coast of Scotland. It was happening simultaneously at a number of points all around that cold, shallow body of water known to us as the North Sea, and it has been repeated upon those coasts almost countless times since. It was a porpoise hunt, the most primitive form of whaling and perhaps man's first major venture upon the sea.

Nor is this just an imaginary scene, something we have had to concoct to explain how man first followed the whale. The details of this picture are etched much more clearly and precisely than anything our unaided imagination could devise, because not only can we watch the very same process today on the islands of the Indian Ocean and on many other coasts, but also we actually have contemporary pictures of this prehistoric enterprise. What is more, these pictures are so vivid that they amount almost to written records and, like hieroglyphs, show an astonishing wealth of detail, such as the skin canoes, the barbed harpoons, the keen-pointed lances, and even the species of quarry that was hunted. Just to complete the picture for us, moreover, we have in our possession examples of these very artifacts that were once used and of the bones of the actual whales that were caught. The picture is living history.

There are still porpoise fisheries native to many lands. In Denmark porpoises were killed to the number of three or four hundred during April and May each year at Iseford in Zealand, as they entered the Baltic, and again in the fall at Middlefart some thousand were slain as they congregated to pass out of the Little Belt again, to go to the North Sea for the winter. There was a large porpoise fishery on the coast of Normandy in the tenth century, and in 979 A.D. King Ethelred II of England tried to encourage this by exempting the ships carrying the catch from the *tonlieu* tax when they reached English ports.

A curious porpoise industry grew up in the Bay of Fundy among the Passamaquoddy Indians sometime during colonial days. It seems to have stemmed from a much earlier and more primitive native fishery, for it was entirely in Indian hands and was carried on in canoes. Youths were specially trained for the profession and, while it took them many years to become adept, experienced hunters killed as many as a hundred and fifty porpoises in one year. The method adopted was to shoot the animals with smooth-bored guns loaded with a terrific charge of powder and heavy BB shot. Hunting was carried on in all seasons and was a most precarious procedure, for the hunter had to stand up in his flimsy canoe to shoot the animal, regardless of the condition of the sea, and then had to paddle quickly to it, spear it to death, and haul it into the canoe before it sank. This is no mean accomplishment when the animal is six feet long and spindle-shaped and the hunter is in a bark canoe on a rough sea, more especially in midwinter off the coast of New Brunswick. In fact, the whole business is strangely reminiscent of what must have happened when neolithic men set out at dawn in their little skin boats from the channels of the distant isles to await the coming of the porpoises.

Ten thousand years ago the lands around the North Sea were inhabited rather sparsely by a number of different peoples. Their origins are obscure but seem to have been quite diverse. They were modern men in the strict sense of that term, which is to say they were of a bodily structure in no essential way dissimilar to peoples found today in the same area. Some races or groups were powerfully built, others puny; some had narrow heads, others broad heads; some were tall, others short; but as a whole their range of variation did not exceed that of the modern inhabitants of western Europe. Only in their culture and their organization were they far removed from us.

These peoples were in various stages of Stone Age development. Some were comparatively advanced, especially those dwelling back from the sea in the larger land masses. These may even have begun already to imitate in rare copper the stone axes and other weapons or the ceremonial devices of their ancestors, a step that was to carry them forward to the age of metals. Along the coasts, however, dwelt peoples who seem not to have been so advanced. Whether this was due to sloth, resulting from the greater ease with which they could feed themselves on the bounty of the seashores, or to the fact that they were inferior people who had been driven to the coasts by more vigorous tribes coming from inside the continent, we are not sure. Most of them at the period of which we speak seem, however, to have made do with rather crudely chipped flint implements, with weapons of bone and wood, and with the most primitive pottery. They must have dwelt in huts made of driftwood, peat, or skins, for it is only later that we find foundations of dwellings constructed from stones piled together. They appear, in fact, to have lived much as the aborigines of Tierra del Fuego did until the last century — naked despite the cold of the winters, possessing only primitive umiak-like canoes, and sheltering from the weather behind miserable lean-tos or in primitive leaky huts.

Many of these coastal people developed a most curious habit. This appears to be a regular feature of man's climb upward and has been developed many times at different ages and among many races all over the world, and it still existed among the Amerindians of Tierra del Fuego. This habit is the accumulation of what we call "kitchen-middens." The term is derived from the Danish word *kjokken-moddings*, in which *kjokken* means kitchen, and *moddings* is equivalent to the Old English word *midding*, which means dunghill or refuse heap. Kitchen-middens are prodigious accumulations, sometimes of quite vast extent, of oyster and other sea shells, with some bones, bits of wood, stones, and other rubbish. They occur on many coasts — in Denmark in such quantities that they were once thought to be old beaches that had been raised by a general uplift of the land surface. They are found also in Ireland, on the coast of Cornwall, at the mouth of the Somme in France, all around Australia, in Tasmania, the Malay Peninsula, the Andaman Islands, and very extensively in South Africa, while the coasts of both North and South America are littered with them. These enormous refuse heaps are man-made and represent the garbage dumps of villages or settlements of primitive men. Sometimes they form long, meandering banks as much as ten feet in depth, two hundred feet wide, and nine hundred feet long.

Over these kitchen-middens there has been much discussion. The principal bone of contention has been whether the makers threw the refuse out of their front doors and kept moving their huts backwards as the heap approached too close, or whether they carted the shells in baskets to the end of the line and dumped them over the ramp. The experts will, however, presumably be debating this point until we ourselves revert to building middens once more. The point is intriguing but entirely academic. Nor does it apply at all in other cases where the makers seem to have been either more or less practical, however you choose to look at it, for they just pitched the shells out, any old where, so that the whole surface of the land is a lattice-work of ridges with cup-shaped hollows between, where the huts stood. Sometimes the ridges form simple rings that must have grown around isolated huts.

Kitchen-middens are of very great interest, for it is in them that we have found an enormous jumble of things that tell us much about their makers, including information on the whaling enterprises of these people of ten thousand years ago.

The method of examination of these structures entails cutting out and isolating square pillars of the refuse. For purposes of comparison it is arranged that these should be a yard square at the top, though they vary in volume, of course, according to the depth of the heap. The surrounding material is cleared away and the pillar is then taken apart item by item and catalogued; the results are most revealing. The main body of the heaps is invariably composed of shells. The most common species around the North Sea is oysters and it is thus manifest that these early seamen made this delicacy their staple diet. The Baltic Sea used to be more open to the ocean and was consequently more saline so that oysters were much more abundant in those days. With the oysters are found, in descending order of importance from the point of view of edibility, cockles, mussels, winkles, whelks, and some land snails, all of which are still eaten about those parts. Along with these shells are found the remains of crabs and many bones of herring, cod, and flatfish. There are also numerous bones of birds and mammals. For instance, from one group of three pillars examined, one contained 175 mammal and 35 bird bones, the second 121 mammal, 9 bird, and the third 309 mammal and 10 bird bones.

These bones found in kitchen-middens have been identified and tell us many more facts. The birds prove to be varied — the capercaillie, which is like a huge black grouse; ducks; geese; swans; and the now extinct great auk. There are never any signs of such species as storks, sparrows, or domestic fowls, from which we infer the latter were unknown. The mammals commonly represented are even more interesting. There are red deer, roe deer, wild boar, the extinct giant ox known as the aurochs, mice, dogs, foxes, wolves, marten, otter, water rats, beaver, lynx, wild cat of the species still inhabiting Scotland, bear, seals, and the porpoise, blackfish, and the killer whale. Note the last three. It is strange that the remains of moose, reindeer, bison, hare, sheep of any kind, or pigs other than the wild boar are not found. Certain bones of all skeletons are missing, which leads us to suppose that they were used as implements, or possibly for some religious purposes, and the longbones of the limbs are always broken at both ends. This was done to extract the marrow or, in the case of small examples, simply because the midden builders liked to crunch the heads just as many people do today. All marrow bones are, however, invariably opened one way or another.

Other even more interesting things are found in kitchen-middens. Those of the Stone Age occurring in western Europe contain numbers of crude flint implements and many animal bones still bearing marks obviously made by knives and scrapers of this material. Hearths of flat stones are also found, showing that oyster stews are as old as shipping. On the other hand, no trace of agriculture, cereals, or vegetable remains, other than charred wood and masses of sea-weed, has ever been found. The flint implements consist of axes, flakes of flint, and things which have been called "slingstones" but probably were weights for fishing nets. There are also a lot of bone implements of quite fine workmanship, such as pins, spear points, and many harpoon heads with sharp recurved barbs. There is also some very crude pottery.

These Stone Age sites were probably inhabited the whole year round and must have had much the appearance of the modern coastal settlements of the Lapps. The inhabitants were fishermen, hunters, and beachcombers. They had no agriculture and probably no domestic animals, with the possible exception of the dog, which they may have raised for food rather than for hunting. The exact dating of the kitchen-middens in Europe is still a matter of some debate and it is possible that they accumulated throughout an immense period of time. The probability of this conjecture is greatly enhanced when we consider that the making of such refuse piles has gone on ever since, in one part of the world or another, and is still taking place in some areas today. It has been estimated that some of those in Denmark were started about eight thousand years before the Christian Era, but others appear to be of much later date. Some experts believe that the principal period of their formation was from 5000 to 3000 B.C.

The builders in Denmark were a people known as the *Ertebolles*, from the place where their particular brand of pottery was first found. If their pottery is any criterion of origin, these people seem to have come originally from the Danubian basin, and to have been pushed right across Europe till they came to its western edge. They existed in what is known as the Mesolithic, or Middle Stone Age. The inhabitants of the other lands bordering the North Sea who indulged in whaling seem to have been of somewhat later date and of Neolithic, or Late Stone Age cultures. These are the so-called Brock and Wheelhouse Builders of Scotland and the isles and the Stone Age peoples who dwelt along the fjords of the Norwegian coast and who left us those pictures that speak so eloquently of their activities.

All these peoples used whale products from the earliest times, and it seems from the evidence that they actually went after the whales upon the sea. This is really a very astonishing thing to contemplate, more especially when we consider that they had only, at best, skin boats in which to do this. At the same time it becomes somewhat less amazing when we find that the Eskimos today go whaling in their "umiaks." These are tiny, narrow canoes made of the hides of the bearded seal, and it is probable that the neolithic boats were made of similar material, for there is much evidence of sealing activities by these people. The Eskimos of Alaska now hunt the largest whales — the arctic right whales — with iron harpoons and small explosive bomb-guns, but in other areas they still employ bone harpoons and confine their attentions to the smaller species. They also use floats made of inflated seal skins carefully sewn so as to be airtight, just as the neolithic hunters on the shores of the Hebrides did thousands of years ago. These prevent the whales from sounding and without them it would be virtually impossible, using skin canoes, bone harpoons, and lines made of hide, to land even a porpoise.

It is only logical to suppose, however, that before men went fishing in the sea, they learned about the animals that lived therein from dead specimens which they found washed up on the beaches. Stranded whales are even today fairly numerous around the coasts of Europe despite the great reduction in their numbers compared to ancient times, due to centuries of whaling. Official records of those stranded on the coasts of the British Isles have been kept for a number of years. During the period from 1913 to 1926 no less than four hundred and seven were reported. Of these, one hundred and seventy-eight were common porpoises, but seventeen other species were also represented and there was an average of four rorquals beached every year, most of them concentrated at the northern tip of Scotland and in the Orkney and Shetland Islands. We know, moreover, that whales have always been stranded on the seaboard of western Europe because their skeletons are frequently found in those deposits that have been accumulating since the last retreat of the glacial Ice-cap in bays and estuaries along the coasts. Notable among these deposits are those that have accumulated and still are collecting in, and gradually filling up, two inlets on the east coast of the British Isles known as the Firth of Forth in Scotland and the Wash in England. In the Wash, skeletons of the killer whale, bottle-nosed dolphin, and the common porpoise have been found and also, strangely enough, of the arctic right whale, which, since the dawn of the historical period at least, has been confined to the polar regions. Those found in the Firth of Forth deposits are mostly blue whales and finners, both of which are rorquals.

In prehistoric times this latter arm of the sea used to extend some twelve miles further inland as far as the site of the modern town of Stirling. It is filling up rapidly but at one time it was much more extensive and seems to have had a narrow strait about halfway in from its mouth. Whales apparently often passed through this neck with the incoming tide in pursuit of food and then, when the tide ran out, got beached inside. Several of these whales' skeletons have been found and four of them have given us most unexpected and interesting information.

The first record is that of a seventy-foot blue whale that was dug up in 1819 at a place called Aithrey. With it were found two crooks of staghorn, one of which was perforated by a circular one-inch hole, and both of which had obviously been fashioned and used by men. The second whale was discovered four feet below a layer of homogenous clay at Burnbank, near Blair Drummond, in 1824. With it was another deer's antler with a circular hole and with traces of a wooden handle that had been thrust through this and lashed to the horn. The third example turned up at a place called Meiklewood, in 1877, when a drain was being dug. It was also the skeleton of a large rorqual and, actually resting on its skull, was yet another perforated deer's antler, this time with a complete wooden handle still inserted through the hole. The fourth example came from Causewayhead in the same area and consisted of several portions of a skeleton of a large whale that had obviously been taken apart by men. The end of one of the ribs had been cut and shaped artificially and near it was found another tool made from a deer's antler.

Such evidence of early man's interest in stranded whales does not come from the Firth of Forth alone, for in East Jutland, during other drainage operations, the skull of a rorqual was discovered in an old beach deposit. When it was raised, eight stone adzes, two stone axes, and a number of flint flakes were found underneath. In England, bones of the common porpoise have been found in neolithic deposits in a cave some distance from the sea. They must have been carried there by men. There is also much other evidence that early men made use of whales that they either caught or found stranded.

Whale bones fashioned into various artifacts are constantly cropping up in prehistoric sites all around the North Sea. The ribs appear to have been used as rafters for huts just as — we shall see later — they still are today in other parts of the world. Basins made from the large vertebrae, and pigment pots from smaller ones, are numerous. They have been found in Scotland, the Orkneys, Shetlands, and Hebrides, and they appear again in later Bronze and Iron Age times in southern England. Combs, perforated mallets, and knife handles made from the bones of whales are common and, ironically, even a harpoon made of this substance was found in an Ertebolle midden in Jutland. In fact, worked whale bones are very common in kitchen-middens. There may also have been many other uses for this material, for we know that it was employed in ancient Ireland for making the frames of saddles and even in place of timbers for large rowboats. One can hardly imagine a more logical use for the ribs of the larger whales.

The most interesting tools made from the bones of whales are, however, strange, elongated, pancake-shaped objects with a number of notches, or nicks, on each side which have been unearthed in great profusion at some prehistoric sites. The elucidation of the purpose for which these were used has a rather amusing history. A large number of these objects made from the bones of oxen were originally found at a site named Skara Brae in the Orkney Islands and baffled their discoverers, who described them as adzes but asked, "What was there to hack with an adze on a treeless land?" No explanation was then forthcoming. Later, over a hundred similar heart-shaped slabs made of slate were found in a late Bronze Age level at a site at Jarlshof in the Shetlands. Then quantities made from the bones of whales, some of which were notched and some perforated and which were obviously intended to be affixed crosswise to the ends of sticks like an adze, turned up during the excavation of a "wheelhouse" at a place called Foshigarry on the island of North Uist in the Outer Hebrides. Then more were found in the Orkneys. Their purpose remained a mystery until precise analogies were unearthed on the shores of Hudson's Bay and in West Greenland at the sites of Eskimo settlements. These had wooden shaft-handles still inserted through the holes and bound on with sinews which had been preserved in the frozen earth. Finally, in 1937, it was discovered that identical implements were still in use among the Eskimos in Greenland. They proved to be adzes for stripping the blubber off whales!

Stranded whales were of the greatest value to prehistoric man. Though food can never have been really scarce for these shore dwellers, the northern winters were rigorous, storms undoubtedly prevented fishing, and, as we have seen, domestic animals and agriculture were unknown, at least in the earlier days. A stranded whale would thus provide a heaven-sent bounty to a Stone Age man. The oil would provide light and probably heat. "Blubber crackling" and the bones make excellent fuel, burning furiously and giving off much heat, and they were doubtless used for this purpose. Houses and perhaps boats were built with the ribs and long bones of the jaw and skull. The meat could be eaten fresh or, in cold weather, stored for the winter; it could also be dried for later consumption. Dried whale meat was used in the Faeroe Islands to feed cattle until quite recently. Other parts of the animal were even more valuable if we can judge by the uses made of them by the Eskimos and other primitive peoples. The skins covering the livers are made into drum heads; the guts are shredded and used as twine for sewing skins; the baleen is carved or softened in hot water and shaped into a great number of useful things. Sinews from the tail flukes were doubtless used then as they are today to bind stone and bone weapons and tools to shafts. In fact, whales must have been taken apart completely and every bit of them used by prehistoric man, and it is therefore surprising that we find any remains at all of those that were stranded in those ancient times. It is probable, in fact, that many more whales were stranded and used by Stone Age people than the remains we find today would indicate and they probably often served to tide a whole community over the winter.

We might have supposed that all bones of whales and objects made from whale products found in the sites of prehistoric habitation had eventuated from stranded whales were it not for the discovery of some very remarkable pictures in Norway. These consist of a considerable series of rock engravings of contemporary date, displaying in remarkable detail a whole array of scenes, together with numerous esoteric signs, symbols, and sketches, that indicate beyond a shadow of doubt that these intrepid neolithic seamen actually went out upon the waters and pursued the whales.

It always seems astonishing that early men made the effort to record, often in magnificently durable materials, just those very things which appear to be of most interest to us and of most use in interpreting history. The question as to whether the mammoth was contemporary with man and what it looked like was thus neatly settled by some considerate, palaeolithic cave artist who took the trouble — probably under a mystical or religious urge — to crawl into a deep cave in the south of France thousands of years ago, make a light, and draw the animals for us. Here, the questions as to how and when men first took to following the whale upon the open sea have likewise been answered for us with the neatest dispatch by some shivering neolithic fisherman who lived thousands of years ago on the fjords that debouch into the North and Norse Seas. It is a little uncanny.

These rock engravings are found in shallow caves and on exposed slabs of rock. They consist of the most amazing variety of depictions. There are masses of enigmatic signs that we cannot decipher; there are many representations of skin canoes with pointed ends and of human figures both sitting in them and standing beside them. There are also the plainly recognizable outlines of the beasts hunted, including elk, reindeer, bear, seal, water fowl, halibut, and whales. Twenty-nine representations of whales have been found and the identification of all but two or three of them is beyond doubt, for these ancient artists were keen observers of nature and knew their fauna much better than we do ours — they had to, if they were to survive. The one or two ambiguous drawings that cannot surely be identified may be meant to show rare species that were taken by chance. All the others are of the smaller species — porpoises, dolphins, blackfish, and killers — each of which can be made very distinctive by one who knows — the dolphin with a beak and sharply pointed dorsal fin, the porpoise with rounded muzzle, the blackfish elongated with blunt head and long flippers placed far forward, the killer barrel-like, parti-colored, with an immense dorsal fin and an even set of teeth.

These are the very species that are found in profusion in the kitchen-middens and other prehistoric sites. Hardly any remains of other whales occur therein, which seems to show that only those species were deliberately hunted. This is just what we might expect, for it is hard to conceive of even these intrepid seamen chasing the great right whales, rorquals, or sperms with bone harpoons and hide ropes in little skin canoes. The only surprise is the frequency of killer whales, both in the engravings and in the form of bones in ancient habitations. Obviously they were taken and yet they are the fiercest and one of the swiftest of marine creatures that hunt in packs and are deliberately aggressive. They grow to a length of thirty feet and have a terrible armament of teeth. These early whalers were bold indeed to hunt them with their primitive weapons.

Prehistoric rock painters do not seem to have indulged in these artistic flights for fun or simply to while away the time in the winter. All the evidence points to their having done these works for mystical purposes — either to thank whatever gods or fates they had for the conclusion of a successful hunt, or by way of supplication for profitable enterprises in the future. On the other hand, it has been suggested that they may have engraved these rocks by way of record and that the figures and symbols are a sort of primitive hieroglyphic writing which others could interpret and were put down for future reference or as tallies. This seems to be a not altogether farfetched notion, for the engravings contain a profusion of signs, symbols, and individual figures, all of which must originally have had some meaning to the artists.

In these engravings there is always a close association between the boats and the quarry that was hunted by means of them. Moreover, whenever skin boats are depicted, whales occur also, and in four cases either seals or halibut are also shown. It is altogether one of the strangest commentaries we have on the life of some of our earliest ancestors and goes far towards placing all that happened subsequently in its proper perspective. Following the whale, in fact, seems to be one of man's oldest activities and we must bear this in mind as we turn the pages of history and scan the amazing chapters that followed these crude beginnings.

The Common Porpoise (*Phocaena phocaena*) crops up from time to time throughout the whole history of western Europe, and it has played a noticeable part in the economy of several countries. The animal is the commonest form of whale found round the North Sea and is perhaps the easiest to catch. Its meat was once a standard article of diet in the British Isles, being so highly thought of that it was bought regularly for the royal kitchens of James V of Scotland, while in Tudor times in England it attained special rank because of Henry VIII's taste for it. We have the recipe for a sauce that was particularly recommended for the dish, made of bread crumbs, sugar, vinegar, and mint. Porpoises were regarded by the Church as fish and were therefore allowed to be eaten during Lent, when they were made into what was known as "porpesse pudding." One early writer, however, says of its meat that it is "of a very hard digestion, noysome to the stomack, and of very grosse, excremental and naughty juyce." This is a rather fearsome indictment but the alleged qualities are probably due to other unwholesomenesses indulged in by the worthy chronicler rather than to porpoise steak, which actually tastes like tough, dry beef. Nowadays the porpoise is taken only for its oil, of which each individual yields about three gallons.

It is one of the smallest whales, growing to a length of only about six feet, though some males of eight feet have been caught. The females are always smaller. In general color the common porpoise is white below and dark slate-gray or black above, according to the degree of wetness of the skin and the light in which the animal is viewed. The two colors blend but the flanks are somewhat streaked or mottled with gray. The flippers and tail are dark on both sides and sometimes the tail has a pinkish or yellowish tinge. The animal is of a beautiful spindle shape, with a rounded head and no beak. There is a triangular fin placed a little in front of the middle of the back measuring about eight inches along its base and four to five inches in height. The front edge of this fin often bears a line of small tubercles which are thought to be remnants of a body armor that clothed the terrestrial ancestors of the whales. The eyes are very small and the external opening of the ear, which is situated about two inches behind the eye, is no bigger than a pinhole. It has a half-moon-shaped blowhole on the top of the head but it does not blow a jet of vapor like the larger whales.

The porpoise has very stiff, rubbery lips, and the mouth is bright pink inside and contains a fleshy tongue which cannot be protruded. It has about twenty-five small teeth on either side of both jaws, arranged in regular rows and all the same in form. They are unlike the teeth of any other whale, being shaped like little spades with a peglike root and an expanded crown that may bear three distinct lobes. Porpoises feed on fish of various kinds according to the season and the area where they live, their favorites being herring, pilchard, mackerel, whiting, rock cod, and eels, but they also take squids and crabs, and they have been known to eat salmon. They consume enormous quantities of food and are not on the whole popular with commercial fisherfolk, but there is a belief current in many areas that it is unlucky to kill them. It seems that at times herds of them have virtually been tamed, so that they hang about shallow waters near shore, and when a school of fish appears, the people stir up the porpoises, which immediately dash off among the fish, eating quantities but often enough herding the rest right up on to the beach.

There is some interest in the origin of the name porpoise. The Romans seem to have called the animal alternatively *porcus piscis,* the "fat fish," or *marinum suem,* the "sea pig," from which most of our names for these animals are derived. Thus the Italians call them *porco pesce,* and the French used to call them *porpeis* or simply *porc poisson,* while the Old English spellings are *porkpisce, porpus,* or *porpesse.* Porpoises are also, however, sometimes called hogfish, sea hogs, or herring hogs. From the other stem are derived the German *meerschwein,* meaning sea pig, and the more usual French name of *marsouin.* The Laplanders call them *niser* and they have fished them since before the dawn of history.

The porpoises are coastal animals which apparently seldom venture far out into the open ocean. They like estuaries and often

ascend rivers for considerable distances after fish. In Europe they
have been caught above the locks in the Thames and have been seen
as far up the Seine as Paris. Their range is very extensive, for they
are found all round the coasts of Europe and in the White Sea,
though rarely in the Mediterranean, and in the Baltic numerously
only in the summer. They occur round Iceland and Greenland and
migrate up the Davis Strait in the summer as far as 69° N. latitude.
On the east coast of America they occur down to New Jersey.
There is also a porpoise in the North Pacific which has received
another name (*Phocaena vomerina*) but it is hardly, if at all, different from the North Atlantic type though, being distantly separated,
the two groups probably no longer mix. This race extends from
Alaska to the coast of Mexico.

Porpoises are gregarious animals, going about in herds or schools
of from fifty to a hundred together. They normally swim just below the surface and are propelled entirely by the tail, the individual
flukes of which perform a semirotary action like an oar being sculled,
while the flippers, which are only about nine inches long, are held
pressed against the body and are used only for breaking or turning.
Porpoises pair in the summer and the period of gestation is about six
months. The North Sea porpoises are known to pair in July and
August but young have been born as late as May in more northern
latitudes. The calves are about two feet six inches long when born.
Porpoises enclosed in stockades can be kept alive indefinitely provided the water is deep enough and they are given enough live food,
but several people have reported that, if the animals are too confined,
they utter the most heart-rending and plaintive cries night and day.
Altogether they give the impression of being rather sad and worried
beasts that delight only in their freedom and do not interfere with
us. Nevertheless, we have persecuted them for thousands of years.

# Part Two

3000 B.C. TO 500 A.D.

## The Ancient Period

## 2
# A Pale Glow in the East
### (*Phoenician*)

A PALE glow in the east presages the swift approach of the tropical dawn. The hot, dry wind that has blown throughout the night, and for so many days and nights before, straight from the arid wastes of Sind, holds the immense, blood-red sails taut against the crystal sky. The thin ropes of the rigging hum and murmur in their strain, while boisterous little gray waves, each flecked with the roseate glow of the eastern sky, lap and swish along the bulging sides of the great ship. The horizon to the west lies straight like a seam, glowering dark below with the departing night so that the ocean seems black and the edge of the sky above only its paler counterpart.

Two men stand upon the mighty vessel, silhouetted against the clear, pink luminosity of the sky. One in the forepeak scans the heaving ocean ahead with shining inky eyes. His skin is dark and reflects the ruddy morning glow; his hair is straight and black, and tied in a knot above his nape so that the wind may not bring it before his eyes. He wears a length of white cotton cloth around his loins, its end drawn up between his legs and woven into a knot upon his lean, flat stomach. The other man is at the stern, high upon a towering poop. He leans heavily upon a timber ten feet long that passes through a collar in an even greater beam, thrusting up through a huge wooden block in the deck — the post of an immense, straight, double-bladed oar that sweeps back, out, and to the right, away from the tall, curved stern of the ship.

This man is different. His complexion is a sickly yellow and deathlike in the gloom; it is set off by an immense black beard cut square and combed into a series of sharp horizontal and parallel crimps. On his head he wears a tall, cylindrical hat about which is woven a black cloth in the manner of a turban, with its depending end twisted around his neck. His body is clothed in a loose, ankle-length coat of many colors caught about the waist with a rough length of rope. His feet, hidden in the deep shadows below the tall gunwale, are shod in pointed slippers with upturned toes. Neither man speaks. The ship is silent, but for the moaning of the rigging, the lap of the waves, and the hiss of the wake. Neither man moves, though the mighty vessel is rising and falling gently to the pull of the everlasting wind.

The rosy flood from the eastern sky rushes across the bounding waters of the ocean, flecking wave-tops with flashes of vermilion and driving back the lowering darkness of the hot night. The sails are now as if on fire, and the halyards stand out like streaks of blood shot from the sky. The piled-up litter on the huge well deck below is vaguely lit with reddish light. A great white bird comes sailing out of the dawn, wheels silently about the tall foremast, and then suddenly rushes away in a long power glide towards the coming sun.

Abruptly the lean, brown man in the bows lets out an unearthly call. Despite the constant wind and the working of the ship, it seems to echo back from the very skies. The bearded one at the helm looks up, a heavy door opens under the foredeck, and brown faces, round black faces, slit-eyed yellow faces, and shining shaven skulls immediately appear from among the countless bales piled upon the main deck. Then again comes the long-drawn scream — "*Na* . . . *khi* . . . *reeeee* . . . *na* . . . *khi* . . . *reeeee*" — dying   away   in softness upon the hurrying wind.

Now there is feverish activity and a great hurrying hither and yon in the belly of the ship. Men call back and forth in a variety of guttural tongues; there is the clatter of iron, the squeak of wood on wood, the falling of heavy things, and a great running. As if by magic the two great blood-red sails stagger and flap, then move around together, and again come taut, filled with wind but standing at another angle. The waves now roar on one side but fall silent on the other. The helmsman pushes mightily against the steering timber, calling for others to assist him. Half a hundred heads crowd to the high bulwarks on the steering side. They shout; they gesticulate; and they point off across the sea.

Then an immensely bearded one, full six feet in height, comes clambering up a ladder to the poop deck and, shading his eyes from the blaze of the rising sun, scans the heaving ocean. He calls in a tremendous bass voice to the lean one at the prow; the lean one answers in a foreign tongue and points off to the northwest. Another man appears, running up the rigging to the masthead. He looks small like an Indian ape as he clambers hurriedly into the web of ropes lashed to the great cross-spar of the mainsail. He too shades his eyes and scans the sea. Then he calls down to the captain, and the captain calls to the helmsman, and the helmsman shouts at the four slaves who have joined him at the timber, and together they shove slowly across the deck. The mighty vessel veers creakingly away from the wind towards the north.

Meanwhile, small open boats have appeared from under the litter upon the bosom of the great well deck. Groups of seminaked men toil at them, casting aside loose objects, freeing the oars, and unlashing little masts. Hurriedly they carry these boats to the bulwarks and hoist them up on the rail. Others run aloft and cast down ropes which are made fast to these skiffs. Primitive blocks creak and the skiffs are hoisted overboard to dangle above the rushing waves, bumping against the ship's hull.

Not too far ahead now a great number of black shining things may be seen welling up from the deep, puffing, splashing, and then descending again among the waves. Every now and then one breaks clear of the surface, raising a pool of white foam. They are large ones, rather than great ones, but they are many. The captain spies them, and his dark eyes light and his heavy brows descend. He indicates steering directions to the helmsman by abrupt signals with his arm. He takes the ship to leeward of the multitudinous bobbing black things and soon he is running parallel to them about half a mile to the south. Then in a great voice he yells for the ship's company to cease their chatter and be silent. And silence comes, but for the moaning of the wind, the creak of the rig, and the bumping of the skiffs. Soon these also are silenced at another command from the height of the poop, and the great bulging vessel rides swiftly on in silence until it is somewhat beyond the dancing black sea-ones. At a further quiet command from the captain, it veers another point to the north so that its course will cut them off and intercept them. A hundred souls wait tensely.

Then, without warning, a long black form breaks through the waves right by the prow of the ship. It makes a blowing noise and immediately curves over into the depths again. The captain calls a command and three-score men leap over the bulwarks and swiftly slide down into the skiffs. But almost before they are safely in them another command rings out and the little boats are dumped into the churning waves. Keen-bladed knives flash in the sunlight, and ropes suddenly fly loose to be hauled aboard. The great ship slides through and away from the little boats like a shark that has dropped a litter of young ones. The little boats break out three pairs of oars each. All together they veer to the northeast and scud off into the morning sunlight.

And as they approach, the sea breaks up in a churn of foam mingled with great black bodies. Into this go the little boats, and from them flashes the glint of burnished copper and iron, and soon also there is blood. Bloody spray and foam fly; there are hoarse shouts of fearful men, long ropes taut into the sea, and the shattering of wood as boats are struck and capsize. The men are standing in the skiffs now, and stabbing to right and left with long lances. All is confusion spread out over four square miles of open ocean, a hundred miles from land.

Meanwhile the big ship has come about and wallows fitfully with her tall, curved prow rising and falling into the oncoming waves. Her great sails have dropped and lie, a tangled mass, athwart her waist. The rigging is crowded with the tiny forms of climbing men. The captain stands alone in the prow, signaling to the little boats as one by one they raise a white cloth and start pulling towards him. And as the first draws under the towering side, everybody on board crowds to the rail and peers down. Lines are tossed and willing hands leap into the sea to attach them to large hidden things that revolve just below the surface. And soon these things are hauled into view. The deck crew chant as they heave, and slowly the forms rise out of the waters high into the air. Then they are swung aboard and dropped upon the deck. More of the little boats pull slowly back to the ship until only two are left far upon the horizon. Neither raises the white cloth, and the remaining black sea-beasts have now all vanished. The sails are hoisted and the ship tugs slowly across the wind; immediately the last two skiffs alter course and creep towards her. But meanwhile there is an excitement drenched in blood upon the well deck of the ship.

Brandishing heavy knives, copper chisels, and hammers, men with almond eyes and soft brown skins set to work upon the mighty corpses. Pounding, slashing, and hammering, they work upon the mouths of the beasts, cutting out the great ivory teeth and handing them one by one to a tall, bearded man clad in a long coat and a turban who keeps a tally on a stylus and drops each tooth into a closed box. Long before this work is done the two remaining boats are alongside; ropes are thrown and they are ignominiously hauled aboard. Then the mainsail is reset and the ship leans determinedly before the wind. Slaves fall upon the toothless corpses with great knives. Later the oily blubber and flesh will be rendered into clear golden oil with which some of the older slaves may buy their freedom.

THE YEAR, by our modern calendar, is 2000 B.C.; the place is an imaginary point a hundred miles south of the arid Makran coast of what is now Baluchistan, midway between the mouth of the Indus River in India and Muscat at the mouth of the Gulf of Oman. The ship is an early, ocean-going, Phoenician bireme sailing back from India to its home port on the upper western shores of the Persian Gulf. Its crew is composed of sundry peoples nurtured in the countries around Mesopotamia, but its captain, helmsman, and artificers are Phoenicians. The pilot is a Dravidian from the Malabar coast of

India, and those sloe-eyed ones, who alone know how to cut the teeth from the sea beasts, are Egyptians. The sea beasts are whales of a species which was until recently considered exceedingly rare but which is now known to occur throughout the world. Their teeth have been discovered buried with potsherds and other artifacts in early settlements in southern Persia. These teeth were, for some reason, considered particularly valuable by the people of those countries in bygone ages.

This small whale, the False Killer (*Pseudorca crassidens*), was, until 1861, known to us only through fossil skulls dug up in England. Then it suddenly appeared on the coast of Germany, and subsequently has been found to occur all over the world, except in polar seas; whole schools have been stranded on rocky coasts in South Africa and Scotland in recent years. It grows to a length of about fourteen feet, never more than eighteen feet, is uniformly black in color, and is round and tublike in form. It has a rather small, recurved dorsal fin; the head is flattened above, rounded, and blunt in front, and is without a trace of a beak. The mouth contains eight to ten strong, blunt, peglike teeth on either side of both jaws. The eyes are small and the animal is altogether quite a gruesome-looking beast. It is thought that the sudden appearance of these whales off western Europe may have been due to a slow shift of the warm waters of the Gulf Stream towards those coasts, bringing with it the fish upon which this species feeds.

The Phoenician ships were, as far as we know and with the possible exception of those of southern India, the finest sea boats and the sturdiest built of any afloat at that time. Their prototypes about the Persian Gulf in very ancient days were little more than glorified rowboats, tublike, open, and undecked, with ungainly stem and towering stern, and without keels. They were propelled by oars lashed to the gunwales, and were originally only wooden exaggerations of the primitive skin boats used on the Euphrates River, grown in size but little else. These early types were made of cedar planks caulked with bitumen, and were propelled by ten pairs of oars. Very early, however, a mast that could be unstepped was added, and this carried a single, square sail, about the width of the ship, which was braced by four halyards, one from the masthead to the prow, one to the stern, and one to either thwart. Without a keel and with an outside paddle rudder, these ships must have been able to do little else but run free before the wind. However, the Phoenicians soon began experimenting. First they decked the ships over, and then they added a permanent mast. Next they increased the size until there were as many as thirty pairs of oars. They raised the freeboard and started affixing external fin-keels, while decreasing the beam in proportion to the waterline. The next stage was the introduction of two decks with the rowers in two banks, one above the other and both protected from the elements by being below decks, while the oars entered the vessel through holes in the bulwarks which were rendered weatherproof with leather collars. The evolution did not cease even here, however, but proceeded steadily through the centuries — the ships growing in size, more masts being added, experiments with lateen and regular fore-and-aft sails and numerous other nautical improvements being made — until we hear of large trading vessels that relied entirely on sail even in confined waters and dispensed with oars altogether.

The Arabian Sea is, comparatively speaking, a mild sea, for although it is subject to occasional tropical storms of great violence, and to some quota of bad weather of other sorts, it is not penetrated by any great ocean currents that bring masses of cold water to its hot surface, so that fogs are extremely rare there, and the skies above it are singularly free from clouds. It is a sparkling sea of azure waves and mellow countenance. There are sometimes wonderful mystic days upon this sea when the waters are almost colorless and so utterly smooth they lie like mercury under the torrential sunlight. Birds upon its bosom stick up like sooty periscopes and make pools of dissonance with their paddlings that may be seen for miles, spreading in rings like miasmic halos. A passing shark may cut a swath that opens to half a mile before it dissolves in the glistening surface, and some of the gulfs that extend from this sea into the hot lands that lie to the north often appear for days on end as if they were filled with molten silver. Yet throughout most of the year this sea is blown upon by steady winds. In the winter they come from India, are hot and dry, and are known as the northeast monsoons; in summer they blow from the region of Africa, are moist, and are very logically known as the southwest monsoons. The mild aspect of this sea-country fosters the growth of a teeming animal life that drifts and breeds in its warm tropical waters. Whales have always abounded therein and it was ordained that men should sooner or later meet them in that place.

It appears that this sea-country has changed little since men first settled upon its shores. The identity of these first settlers has been lost in the mists of time, but we find their crude stone implements scattered all along the arid strands of Oman and Makran, and more sparingly upon the Malabar coast of India. They have been called the Proto-Negroids and Proto-Dravidians, meaning simply those who went before the Negro peoples on the African side and those who preceded the Dravidians on the Indian side. Where these two types met is undeterminable, but they probably had much in common and mingled throughout the area from southern Arabia to Sind. There is still discernible a trace of this very ancient stock in the inhabitants of these coasts and, furthermore, the culture, or virtual lack of it, of some of the more isolated and backward among them today gives us perhaps a clearer picture of the lives of the original settlers than anything we may learn from digging up stone implements or from mere speculation, however profound it may be or upon whatever comparative researches it may be founded.

Some of these people still employ the most primitive kinds of boats that could possibly go upon the sea, or upon any other body of water for that matter. The fishermen of the coast of Muscat at the entrance to the Gulf of Oman make a craft called a *ramas* composed of three logs bound together with coconut-fiber ropes. There is no attempt to shape the logs, but they are chosen as far as possible with a similar curve, and the largest is placed in the center so that it sticks out of the water fore and aft. The boats are propelled with poles or paddled and there is as much water inside as out. On the Batima coast an even more primitive vessel known as a *shasha* is still in use. This consists of two large bundles of date sticks — the long, thin sticks of the palm's flower-bunch upon which the dates are borne — filled with strips of bark and masses of coconut fiber. These bundles are bound with coconut fiber, laid side by side, and their slender, pointed ends are brought together and firmly tied. The date-stick bundles are then joined by a kind of monstrous sewing along the center line, and a canoe-shaped structure results. These boats are about twelve feet long and can carry two people, who sit in them with water up to their waists. They are, however, extremely tough and pliable and see years of hard service in the great surf that pounds endlessly upon those shores.

Similar waterlogged craft are found along the Makran coast of Baluchistan among some very lowly tribes of fish-eaters who dwell there. These people were known to the classical writers as the Ichthyophagi and they appear to have lived then just as they do today. Nor do they seem to have changed at all in their way of life since earliest prehistoric times. They still make much use of whale products, and since theirs is a treeless land and there is no other building material available, the ribs of the larger whales are often employed as supports for their huts. They were using whale ribs thus in 300 B.C., because it was observed at that date by Near-chus the Greek, as we shall see later. The Shihuh of Cape Musandam on the southern shore of the narrow strait of Hormuz at the entrance to the Persian Gulf similarly use whale jaws for door posts and whale ribs as rafters. What is more, all these people still carry on a regular trade in the teeth of the smaller whales and dolphins, and this also they seem to have done since prehistoric times.

It is obvious that people dwelling upon a treeless and often absolutely vegetationless coast would turn to the sea for their food and for other necessities. It is also patent that they would then, as now, from time to time come upon whales cast up on the shore and would quickly discover, just as our neolithic ancestors did around the North Sea, the value of these great carcasses to their perpetually strained and inadequate economy. We have seen that scores of whales are stranded around the British Isles every year; the same thing occurs along the coasts of the Arabian Sea. *Ramas* and *shashas* are, moreover, just as seaworthy as skin canoes and umiaks, and in them the ancient peoples of the Arabian seacoasts followed the smaller whales beyond the surf, then, just as they do today. Here, as in western Europe, whales, of all the creatures to be found in the sea, were the most valuable to primitive man, and he appears to have been prepared to take any risks to capture them.

The story of man's conquest of the sea is one of the principal themes of our story and it must therefore be understood that the *shasha* in the East and the skin canoe in the West were not the only prototypes of all later ships. There was another contemporary point of departure, having an entirely different origin and quite another history, in which the whale did not at first figure but which later becomes of the utmost importance to our story. This was the shipping invented by the peoples who dwelt upon the banks of great rivers. These early navigators had only the river's current to contend with, while hazards such as storms, tides, and fog, that are of first importance to mariners, were to them of little or no account. The form of the first boats used on rivers depended upon the materials available for their construction. One was undoubtedly a circular, tublike thing made of skins on a wattle frame, like the boats still in use upon the Euphrates today. On the Nile a craft analogous to the *shasha* but made of bundles of papyrus-reed stalks was apparently the earliest form and may still be seen in use on the Sudds in the Sudan, while in India small log rafts, than which there could be nothing more primitive, are still employed in some areas. Thus we see that substantially the same three types of primitive craft originated both on the great rivers and on the open coasts — skin boats, fiber-bundle boats, and log-raft boats. The subsequent development of each on the sea and on the rivers was, however, not the same, though in many respects it took a parallel course and has now reached virtually the same ends, though even today we may still recognize certain differences in construction and design between the mighty steel descendants of the two types.

Thus shipping, as opposed to seamanship, has two quite separate origins, one maritime, the other terrestrious, and this is of the utmost significance to our tale, and to the whole history of whaling. These two types of shipping may be defined as the riverine-gulfine and the peninsular-insular, for the one started on rivers and then debouched into gulfs and other confined seas, while the other began on open coasts and promontories and then went directly upon the open sea towards other peninsulas or islands. It is impossible to say which is the older and they may have had contemporary beginnings, but while the riverine folk progressed faster in civilization, the maritime peoples seem always to have surpassed them in shipbuilding and in seamanship. This statement is perhaps a platitude, but it is, nonetheless, frequently ignored, while it alone often explains the collapse of empires and the sudden appearance of hitherto unheard-of peoples in ships upon the pages of history.

Long before the dawn of history, however, river craft had evolved to a point of considerable complexity and some efficiency, notably in Egypt. Masts and sails, permanently attached paddle-rudders, oars, and decks had been added. Hulls were made of wooden planks either lashed or nailed to ribs and were caulked with various substances. These riverine boats had also increased greatly in size and had already reached the sea. The Egyptians, being riverine people, were bad sailors and their ships were never more than colossal wooden imitations of their primitive papyrus-reed craft, although they were sometimes over two hundred feet long, were built of planks fastened to beautifully shaped timbers, and had other most advanced and complex features. They carried large, square sails on double masts, and their rigging was extremely complicated. They relied much upon oars and their ships were, in fact, monstrous galleys. The Egyptians never freed themselves from the ancient *shasha*-like design and they had to employ all kinds of strange devices to overcome the lack of timbers of sufficient length for the proper construction of their ships. For these reasons they clung to coastal waters and to inland seas, and it appears that not until the early fifteenth century, in the time of the Eighteenth Dynasty, did they even venture out of the Strait of Bab el Mandeb and creep cautiously down the Somali coast to Cape Gardafui.

The Egyptians thus had little if any tradition of things truly maritime and we have no evidence that they ever followed the whale, but there is a strange tale contained in an ancient papyrus, kept, at least until recently, in Leningrad, which may indicate that they knew of such activities in other lands. This is a romance known as *The Tale of the Shipwrecked Sailor* which tells how an Egyptian went to sea in a ship a hundred and fifty cubits long and forty cubits wide. He went south and was wrecked on a desert island inhabited only by a vast monster sixty cubits long. The story goes on to say, "Its beard was more than two cubits in length, its limbs were overlaid with gold and its eyebrows were of real lapis-lazuli." The kindly monster loaded the sailor with gifts which he took back to Egypt. Allowing for artistic license and the superstitions and fantastic beliefs of the age when it was written, there is a strong suspicion that this story concerns the discovery of a dead whale on some uninhabited isle in the Arabian Sea. The measurements by some estimations would fit those of a large rorqual, and the baleen of whales has repeatedly been referred to as their "beards" by those who have never seen the animals in the flesh. The limbs being over-laid with gold might well mean that they were covered with blubber from which oil that was golden in hue or which could be converted into good metal of the same color was extracted. The eyebrows of lapis lazuli, which, be it noted, is referred to as "real," may be either a flight of pure literary fancy or an exceptionally realistic descrip-tion, for it was an ancient belief that these stones were the lenses of the eyes of sea monsters.

The ancient Egyptians also had a name for the whale the spell-ing and meaning of which is of considerable interest. It was written:

SAN    EN    UATCH–UR

which may be transliterated as shown. This means literally "the bull of the sea" and it probably referred to the sperm whale, though it may also have been applied to dolphins.

Although the ancient Egyptians never ventured far out into the Indian Ocean, they obtained at the very earliest times articles of commerce that are clearly of Indian origin. Somebody must have been bringing these commodities to the Red Sea ports, and we are prompted to inquire who these carriers may have been. Now, as we have seen, the beginnings of seamanship on the Oman and Makran coasts of Arabia and Persia appear to have come to naught, for the inhabitants of those places are still today using the most primitive craft and seem never to have developed anything better. It appears, however, that on the southern coasts of India real sea-faring began at a very early date and it is possible that the first truly ocean-going vessels were constructed there. Unfortunately, we know very little about the early inhabitants of the Malabar coast. It was ever a rich and fertile land, and civilization, in which the whole population participated, started there in prehistoric times. Having ample wood at their disposal, these people seem to have developed quickly from such primitive beginnings as the *ramas*, the seaworthy boats in which they began crossing to Ceylon and to the more distant islands, like the Laccadives and Maldives, that lay off their coasts. Unlike the riverine boatsmen of the Nile, the Euphrates, and the Indus, moreover, the southern Indians seem to have struck out fearlessly across the open sea. Evidence of this has recently been brought forward by several Indian historians who believe that real seafaring and navigation actually were invented by the prehistoric inhabitants of the Malabar coast.

Seamanship such as this automatically brought man in contact with whales, and there are, as we have already seen, distinct indications that whaling was proceeding in the Arabian Sea in prehistoric times. However, we have to turn to another race of maritime people, who were bred on the opposite side of that sea, to get our first clear statements of a whaling industry in the ancient world.

Among the shipbuilders dwelling on the coasts of the Persian Gulf was a tribe destined to become a great nation, one of the greatest maritime powers of all times, and one of the most amazing cultural catalysts that history has ever seen. They were a Semitic tribe which later became known as the Phoenicians from the Greek name for the land they colonized on the shores of the Mediterranean, which they themselves called the "Land of Palms." Unlike the other coast tribes of the Persian Gulf, they seem never to have been piratically inclined but rather to have pursued the paths of peaceful trade and shipbuilding. Where they originally came from is not known, though the whole history of Mesopotamia from the earliest times records a constant drift of Semitic peoples from the deserts of Arabia into those fertile plains, and the Phoenicians may originally have come from the Arabian deserts.

However, about 2000 B.C. a contrary movement that was to continue for many centuries began in Mesopotamia — Semitic groups moving north and west in the direction of the Mediterranean. The Book of Genesis tells of one such exodus that carried the ancestors of the Jews to the Nile Delta. About the middle of the second millennium some of the Phoenicians appear to have migrated thus westward and to have reached the Mediterranean coast in that country we now call Palestine. There they settled down and built themselves several fortified harbor towns, the names of which were to become famous — Tyre, Sidon, and Arvad. It was once thought that the Phoenicians originally came from the Aegean region, but it is now known that they themselves recorded their homeland as being on the Persian Gulf and they appear always to have spoken of the Palestinian settlements as "colonies." They brought with them their skill as shipwrights and immediately set to work to create a merchant fleet on the new sea, and from 1500 B.C. until the coming of the Romans, a period of more than a thousand years, these amazing people maintained their maritime commercial supremacy despite the rise and fall of empires and rivalries and vicissitudes of many other kinds.

While the Phoenician colonists were thus engaged, there arose in Mesopotamia a great empire. The Assyrians were also a Semitic people who had come into the fertile valleys from the western deserts and had wrested them from their previous inhabitants, conquering far and wide and consolidating their power around their great capital of Nineveh. By the year 1100 B.C. their conquering armies reached the Mediterranean under the banner of their King Tiglath-Pileser I. They arrived by way of modern Syria, conquered its Hittite inhabitants, and then pressed on southward to the borders of the Phoenician colonies. Here they found something very new and strange to them, which appears to have made such an impression on King Tiglath-Pileser that he ever afterwards ranked it above all other things encountered during his campaigning. Indeed, its strangeness made such an impression on the Assyrians that more than two hundred years later it was still being discussed in their home country. What King Tiglath-Pileser, the landsman, found in the land of the seafaring Phoenicians was a fully fledged whaling industry.

We learn from cuneiform inscriptions on a broken obelisk which is now in the British Museum that Tiglath-Pileser boarded a Phoenician whaling ship at the port of Arvad and with his retinue went to sea in pursuit of whales. What is more, he witnessed the capture of a large *nakhiru* — an Assyrian word meaning "the blower" —

which is now known from comparative etymological researches to signify especially the sperm whale. The exact text reads: "Ninip and Nergal, who bravery love, the beasts of the field have entrusted to him, and in ships of Arvad he rode; a blower in the great sea he slew. Wild bulls destructive and fine . . ." Ninip and Nergal were the intrepid Phoenician whaling captains; "he" was King Tiglath-Pileser; and the "great sea" was the Mediterranean.

The larger whales are not now common in the Mediterranean but skeletons of right whales have been found at the sites of this ancient Phoenician whaling industry and sperm whales still occur in that sea and probably were much commoner then than they are today. That the whale killed in Tiglath-Pileser's presence, and which was of paramount importance to this Phoenician industry, was the sperm whale is confirmed by the discovery of statues in bas-relief of two very obvious, square-headed, spouting sperms placed on the gates of the city of Assur by King Assur-Naçir-Pal, who reigned two hundred years later, from 884 to 860 B.C. It was also under this king that the Assyrians renewed their western conquests and finally overran the whole eastern Mediterranean seaboard. The wily Phoenicians, however, unlike the other tribes, did not attempt to defend themselves but voluntarily joined the empire and paid tribute. This tribute, moreover, is detailed in certain Assyrian and Phoenician records that have come down to us, and among many things listed appears "the teeth of *nakhiri* and dolphins," which were very highly prized by the conquerors. One Assyrian text of this time says: "*Seni na-khi-ri bi-nu-ut tehamti ma-da-ta-su-nu am-khar*," which means, literally: "Teeth of blowers, the produce of the sea, their tribute I received."

Phoenicia was always the center of a remarkable industry manufacturing ivory ornaments of highly skilled artistry. Ancient Egyptian and Assyrian nobles collected ivory then just as wealthy people do today, and some of these collections have been found. They are known as Phoenician ivories because those people were always the past masters at the art. Elephant ivory was then rare and the Egyptians used hippopotamus teeth. The Phoenicians used the teeth of the sperm whale, which is some of the finest ivory known. Ivory was, in fact, at that time commonly known as "whale's bones" — not "whalebone," be it clearly understood. It seems the smaller but more numerous teeth of the dolphin were likewise in great demand for a number of ornamental purposes.

The oil was also a valuable commodity and there are several references in Phoenician texts to the export of this to countries as far away as Egypt. This whaling industry persisted on the coast of Palestine for many centuries and was apparently as much of a surprise to the Romans as it was to the Assyrians. Unfortunately, we know nothing of how it was organized, how the whales were taken, the oil, teeth, and other desired products extracted, nor anything of the exact kind of ships that were used. One point that we would specially like cleared up is whether the whales were cut up at sea or towed to shore for processing. Whichever procedure was followed must have presented extraordinary difficulties, for the sperm whales have to be held afloat after death. They were probably killed from small boats launched from large merchantmen, but what kind of harpoons or other weapons were used we do not know and can only guess. The Phoenicians had most efficient winches and may have hauled the carcasses ashore, for it seems from vague references made to this industry by classical writers that the skeletons of these creatures were always to be found around their ports in great numbers.

It was probably from this local whaling tradition that the Biblical story of Jonah and the whale derived. This is a very curious tale, fraught with contradictions and impossibilities, and appears to have a foreign origin, for the Jews were never a seafaring people. First we may inquire why Jonah, when ordered to go east, went west. His objective was Nineveh, which lay far inland to the east, and yet we find him setting out on a ship into the western sea at Joppa, which was a seafaring place and one of the centers of the whaling industry. What is still more suspect is that the story of his vicissitudes is distinctly reminiscent of a very much older Assyrian fable that later gave rise to various sea-monster stories in the *Arabian Nights*, and it has therefore even been suggested that it was given as an excuse by Jonah for his long and otherwise unaccountable absence. Others believe that the whale merely indicates the name of a Phoenician ship, or even of a tavern, upon which, or at which, the worthy Jonah sojourned a long while. The original text does not mention a whale but uses a word meaning actually "the great fish."

There is, moreover, a great deal of misinterpretation or frank mistranslation in our versions of the Bible: the word used for leviathan, for instance, would be better translated as crocodile, and behemoth means a hippopotamus.

If the whole story was a fabrication to explain an awkward absence, there is no further necessity to wrangle about the business of Jonah being swallowed by the whale, over which there has been endless debate, and not only among theological purists. Most whales have throats far too small to swallow even a salmon, let alone a prominent Israelite. However, the sperm whale, which, as we have seen, was probably the common species of the eastern Mediterranean and the animal on which the local Phoenician whaling industry appears to have been founded, can swallow very large objects.

Moreover, a story of a whale swallowing a man might well have been current even in those days, for there are several modern reports. One was published quite recently with due solemnity in the trade journal of one of the biggest modern corporations. In 1758 a man was said to have been swallowed by a large shark in the Mediterranean. The captain of the ship fired a cannon ball at the shark and the man was vomited up alive and rescued. In a German book published in 1895, a whaleman named James Bradley was said to have been swallowed by a whale which was caught and killed the next day. It was immediately opened and the luckless Bradley taken out of its stomach, still alive but entirely comatose. It is said that he lay in a swoon for hours and was found hard to revive, though this is not difficult to imagine, and was out of his mind for three months afterwards. According to the account, he then revived completely and was entirely normal.

You may make what you like of such accounts, but if they are current today, they were probably rife in the time of the worthy Jonah, and whether he underwent such duress himself or not, they could certainly have provided him with a perfectly classic explanation for his temporary disappearance.

## 3
# The Glow Spreads West
### (*Graeco-Roman*)

THE WATERS sparkle and dance, sun-drenched and wind-tossed. The whole world seems to be a sprightly symphony in blue: blue of every conceivable shade from the deepest azure at the bottom of the wave troughs to the miasmic, powdery blue of the blown spray. Upon the waves dance little waves, and upon them still smaller wavelets, each crimped with flashing ripples. The dome of the sky above is of a deep, liquid aquamarine filled with sailing, fleecy clouds that stream to the east like galleons of the Gods. Everything below glitters under the torrential sunlight as if interwoven with threads of gold.

Upon the bosom of this dancing sea a slim little vessel pitches lightly, its immensely tall, sharp prow chopping into the blue waters and slicing them into a gash of almost incandescent whiteness in which the spume roils and hisses. The vessel too is painted blue — blue of a clarity and cleanness normally seen only on the surfaces of glazed Persian pottery — and, in keeping with the sea foam, its low rail and tall, slender spars are of a glistening white. Its face —

for it has a face, with a sharp, keen nose, and two great lozenge eyes painted on either side of the prow — has a somewhat frowning and most determined expression. As the prow dips into the blue waters, the bow waves separate like tapering white mustachios, and every now and then the sea rises to the pupils of these eyes, so that the face appears to leer over the waves.

Upon the upturned point of the prow flutters a long pennant in the form of a silvery fish, and upon the lower stern post a small carved bull's head stares through blank white eyes at the scurrying wake. There are two tall masts braced to the low rails by a multitude of thin white cordage, and two enormous pale-blue sails of quite indescribable shape but pointed sharply to the sky balloon far out over the water to the leeside. The whole vessel is canted at a crazy angle upon her seaward tack.

Aboard the boat seven sun-tanned men with mops of jet-black, wavy hair, immense shoulders, and strangely narrow waists crowd the windward rail, clinging to the shrouds and literally riding the waves as the vessel rises and falls over the bounding waters. They wear tightly fitting trunks of many colors and most complex patterns, with lines of stars and twisted whorls, and floral designs woven into crosslines of bright shades upon a dark ground. They also wear metal bracelets at their wrists and above their elbows, and large rings in one ear lobe. Their features are keen, their faces narrow, and their noses straight and slender. As they ride along they chant softly to the breezes and scan the glittering sea with their dark eyes. And so the hours pass while the wind stiffens.

Then suddenly, as one man, they leap to the rail top and balance precariously with their bare feet upon its slim edge, shading their eyes with their hands from the glare of the sun. They chatter excitedly while one drops to the bottom of the boat and draws the bung from a large earthenware amphora. Taking a tarnished silver cup from a place of safekeeping under the gunwale, he fills it with red wine, holding the amphora under his arm and bracing his knees against the gunwale. Then, as he reels back to the rail, carefully balancing the cup, the others drop back into the boat and, forming a rough circle, close their eyes and place their right hands over their faces. The bearer of the wine raises his voice in a loud chant and intones certain holy and mystic words. Then, placing a white cloth over his head so that he cannot see, he feels his way to the rail and pours the wine into the sea. This done, the men raise a shout and fall to work.

The Gods have been propitiated and the spirit of Him who sometimes resides in the body of the "Lamb of the Sea" has been appeased. These are simple fishermen, but they are devoutly conscious of the ways and the feelings of the Gods. Also, being men, they know that what they are about to attempt is but the ritual slaughter of the earthly body of the best disposed of all the Gods, who is friendly to all mortals but especially so to those men who go upon the sea. Thus they are now free to proceed with the work at hand. They seize tridents, long lines to which massive bales of cork-oak bark are attached, and a bundle of white fish net.

Two, bearing tridents, clamber quickly to either side of the bow, while the linesmen arrange themselves amidships holding the cork bales, and two others make the net ready aft on the windward quarter, piling it so that it may be tossed instantly into the sea. Sail is somewhat shortened, and those in the bow raise the tridents high above their heads and poise their cruel, sharp points forward and downward at the glistening waves which are parted by the onrushing boat. And thus the tableau holds for many moments while seven pairs of eyes watch the blue waves immediately ahead with a fierce concentration. Somewhere in those waves are sleek bodies that rush along as if propelled by some mechanical device unknown to these simple men. Sooner or later those sleek forms will one by one rush to the surface and curve gracefully out into the air. One by one they will come, like children playing leapfrog, all in a straight, evenly spaced line, the big ones in front, the little ones at the back.

And then all at once they do come. Out of the spume at the very point of the boat's prow shoots a dark-blue spindle. With the utmost ease and grace and apparently without any effort, it simply darts ahead of the rushing boat and sails into the air. And down into the middle of its tight, shiny back goes the keen, barbed trident, driven with all the might of the muscled man above it. The Sea Lamb falters in mid-air and then, curving desperately to the right, smashes into the oncoming waves, sending a column of glistening white foam into the air. Immediately a shout is raised, the shaft of the trident rushes away over the waves, and the line leading from it goes taut and rips one of the bales of cork out of the hands of a man amidships. At the same time those aft start to pay out the fish net. This has a multitude of little cork floats spaced evenly along one edge and heavy stones along the other, and as soon as sufficient of its length is in the water, it just pulls itself off the stern of the boat.

But by now the second man has cast his trident. This sails away to the other side, sticking up out of the waves like a flagpole. Another cork bale goes overboard. Now the first man casts again, and then again. Ten times they cast and six times the line yanks a cork bale overboard. Then, suddenly it is all over. The next tridents remain poised on high; the wind calls in the rigging; the timbers of the boat squeak and work; the spray hisses; but the Lambs of the Sea have passed.

Far behind now, the six cork bales bobble about on the waves, sometimes throwing up spume, sometimes disappearing below for many seconds. The net is all overboard and straggling behind like a silver serpent in the wake. Its drag has slowed the boat considerably despite the strong wind. All hands then leap to the sails, and the helmsman braces his feet against the gunwale and pushes the tiller far over the side of the vessel. With a great flapping of canvas, the slender sea chariot comes about, right into the wind, and then instantly lays about on the other tack and goes scudding off, tossing spray. The trailing net curves into a great half-moon.

Then there follows a long tense period of maneuvering as the helmsman circles the six bobbing bales, round and round in ever-decreasing compass, until the long, trailing net almost closes itself and all the bales but one are milling around in the middle. But the maneuver is not yet over, for just as the net closes, three of the bales vanish below and minutes later bob to the surface far off outside the net. Only two are left within. But now it is too close to maneuver with sails alone, and they are dropped. Oars are broken out and the boat suddenly reverses across its own wake in a backward rush, driven by the rowers, who stand facing the stern. The net forms a loop around one of the bales and suddenly goes taut, then is lashed furiously about, being pulled first this way, then that.

Two of the crew now have hold of it and they rapidly haul it aboard. Then, after only a few minutes, something rushes against the boatside; the trident shaft rises out of the water waving crazily and blood darkens the white foam with a crimson stain. More hands jump to help, and with a mighty heave a great body comes over the side and is dumped into the well of the boat, where it flaps and bangs about, raveling the net and knocking over equipment.

A man leaps upon it, straddling its back with his legs, and baring a short, broad dagger, makes but one hard thrust. The Lamb of the Sea lies still. Then the men quickly unravel the net and cast it overboard again. The oars are unshipped once more and the boat starts forward into the waves. Meanwhile, he who has dealt the deathblow again takes out the tarnished silver cup and, holding it beneath the head of the animal, makes another slash with the knife so that warm blood flows. When the cup is full, he takes it carefully around the vessel, smearing a little of the blood on the prow and the stern post and handing the cup to each of the crew, who moistens his lips with the blood and wipes a little on his forehead so that the spirit of the holy fish may enter his soul. The cup is then washed in pure fresh water and returned to its place of safety until another Lamb of the Sea is hauled aboard, when the whole ceremony is repeated.

It is many hours, however, before all six of the cork bales are retrieved, and many times the boat has to circle the last of them before it is safely in the net. Five of the bales bring with them an exhausted Lamb of the Sea. One of these, which is small, is already dead, and over this no ceremony is performed, for the God spirit, if it ever resided therein, must already have departed. Instead, a special prayer of forgiveness is said as the animal comes aboard. The sixth bale has only a length of rope attached to it, and the trident has gone.

And now the sun is already low upon the horizon and the wind is dropping. The sails are set and the oars work rhythmically to help them. The slender boat knifes across the waves to distant land, low upon the horizon and apparently stretching forever to either side. This is the island of the Keftiu, better known to us as Crete. There will be rejoicing and feasting and much music when the seamen reach the great stone jetty of their home port, for they bring food that is not only good but also holy.

WOULD that we could name these hard-working but pious fishermen, but this sea hunt, the like of which must have taken place countless hundreds of times throughout the length and breadth of the Aegean Sea for perhaps a hundred centuries, occurred too long ago. It was a regular practice among these seafaring people, and we know somewhat of how it was accomplished from much later references by the Greeks, and more especially from many exquisitely colored murals found in the temples of Cnossos in Crete, and from scenes depicted on vases of the period. Here, seven thousand years after the neolithic people of the North Sea learned to harpoon the porpoise, and a thousand years after the Phoenicians first sought the *nakhiri*, we stumble across still another ancient whaling industry, and in another sea-country. Mariners, it seems, must always follow the whale.

The Minoans of Crete, or the Keftiu, as the ancient Egyptians called them, developed a high culture at an extremely early age, contemporary, in fact, with those first beginnings that we have noted in India, in Mesopotamia, and along the valley of the Nile. At the dawn of the third millennium before our era they had already developed most competent ships and were sailing the open sea. In contrast to the ancient Egyptians, who were essentially a riverine people, the Cretans were peninsular-insular folk par excellence who appear to have abhorred coastal navigation and to have set out directly across the eastern Mediterranean to trade with other lands. Their pottery and other wares appear in Egypt, intermixed with the relics of the earliest dynasties, whereas they do not appear on the nearby coasts of Asia Minor until much later, which seems to indicate that the Keftiu pioneered the route to the mouth of the Nile. Certainly they maintained a tremendous trading port at what is now Alexandria, for an enormous harbor has been found there which must have been built by Egyptian slave labor, but which was obviously constructed under the guiding genius of some truly seafaring people who were certainly not Egyptians. Centuries before the coming of the Dorians, who overran Greece and overthrew this wonderful Minoan civilization about 1700 B.C., these fearless people had reached Sicily, the west coast of Italy, and perhaps even Spain, and they certainly sailed the Black Sea.

Their ships appear to have been their own original development from ancient neolithic prototypes. They had extremely high prows which, if the representations on coins, vases, and wall paintings are to be believed, always bore pennants in the form of a fish or dolphin. These craft were long and slim with little freeboard, and rose to a graceful transom aft that was sometimes tapered to imitate a fish's tail. They were propelled by a long bank of oars but sail was used from the earliest times, and before 2000 B.C. one or even two extra masts had been added. These sails were, technically speaking, "squaresails," but the Cretans had a clever way of reefing them diagonally so that they could be very close hauled; thus their fleets could probably sail several points closer into the wind than might be supposed. Had these people lived on an archipelago by an open ocean rather than in a virtually landlocked sea, the course of history might indeed have been very different, as we may gather from consideration of the accomplishments of the Greeks, who fell heir to so much of their culture, including their art of shipbuilding, and who, when the opportunity came, themselves performed the most extraordinary feats of seamanship. It is, moreover, to these people, the Greeks, that we must now turn, for upon our particular topic, as upon almost any other that one might wish to choose, they had so very much that was worthwhile to say. But first a word about the Lamb of the Sea.

The dolphin is a frolicsome little whale which, in its boisterous and apparently uninhibited ways, seems to have delighted men's hearts since the earliest times. Nothing could be less warranted than the silly habit we have unconsciously adopted of attributing our own emotions to animals, for we have not a single iota of evidence that they appreciate any of our feelings or that any of their behavior is prompted by the same stimuli that activate us. We assume, for instance, that an animal defends its young because of what we choose to call parental love, though we do not know precisely what that emotion is, nor why it should be; we believe that the robin perched atop the dogwood sings out of sheer exuberance, but it may just as well do so as a warning to other robins to keep off its beat or merely because it is suffering from some infestation of intestinal parasites. Nevertheless, there are instances of animal behavior that appear to be quite inexplicable unless we assume that animals sometimes experience sensations such as we ourselves feel. The ancients of the Mediterranean, with their delightful naïveté, assumed that the dolphin frolicked in the blue waves because it felt happy, and that it did this especially around ships because it liked men above all other creatures. There is nothing really harmful in this idea; it is charming, whether its causes be rightly or wrongly deduced.

Despite the fact that a certain kind of fish known in technical parlance as *Coryphoena*, which changes color when dying, is sometimes called by English-speaking seamen "dolphin," the animal to which this name applies by right of some two thousand years of precedence is a small whale (*Delphinus delphis*), the animal which has given its name to one of the principal families of the *Odontoceti*, or Toothed Whales. There are several members of the genus, varying considerably in size and in the number of their teeth, but apparently all are confined to more limited localities than the common species. One from the Molucca and Torres Straits delights in the name of *Delphinus rosiventris;* and it is just that, for its underside is rosy pink in color. The common species has an enormous range throughout the warm and temperate seas of the world and extends also to high latitudes by following the Gulf Stream to the Finmark coast. It is particularly common in the Mediterranean and Black Sea and is well known to all the inhabitants of those areas, apparently having made a great impression upon them since the earliest times.

The dolphin may, in some respects, be said to have symbolized the maritime nations of the Mediterranean just as the eagle did the land powers. It grows to a length of about eight feet, is spindle-shaped, and has a rather puglike, rounded head to which the distinct, six-inch beak seems to have been affixed as an afterthought. The upper parts are shiny black or dark gray, sometimes with a bluish sheen, and the underside is white, often suffused with bands of gray-green. There is a black ring round the eye which, together with the distinct groove between the beak and the forehead, gives the animal a rather notable expression that doubtless had a great deal to do with the unusual personality attributed to the beast by the ancients. There is a sharp dorsal fin and the flippers are also rather narrow and acute.

The dolphin has from forty to sixty teeth in each half of each jaw, making a total of some two hundred in all. They are small, conical, pointed, set close together, and slightly recurved, and they interlock exactly. The animal eats fish and swallows them whole, head first. In contrast to the bumbling porpoise, dolphins prefer the open water to the coastal shallows, and pursue their food in companies, sometimes of enormous numbers. They are extremely swift animals, having been observed to keep up with a ship doing eighteen knots and then suddenly to dart ahead and disappear into the blue. Their strength, or rather their "drive," is quite phenomenal. One that had been caught around the tail by a chance slip-knot in a rope set off for the open sea down a channel, towing a twenty-three-foot motor launch, and traversed a three-mile course between marking buoys known to the fishermen in the boat at a rate of slightly over five knots, and this when the tail, which is the animal's "propeller" and sole device for causing forward movement, was hindered by the rope dragging the boat!

A single youngster is born at a time. It is about two feet in length and has the distinction of bearing a small mustache composed of half a dozen hairs on each side of its snout. The mother is most solicitous of her offspring, keeping it beside her always, and for a long time even feeding it with stunned fish when it is being weaned, which was another habit that delighted the ancients. Despite the fact that prehistoric fishermen knew the dolphin had lungs, breathed air, bore its young alive, and suckled them with milk, they persisted in classing the animal as a fish. However, its many unfishlike ways, and notably its warm blood, never ceased to mystify them, and these characters, combined with its habit of accompanying ships, soon convinced them that these creatures were endowed with a special intelligence akin to their own and that, as a result, they were particularly solicitous of man's welfare. Nonetheless, they fished for the poor animal on account of its teeth, which were used for personal adornment, for its meat, which they sun-dried and salted as described by Xenophon, who ate some and made a number of extremely unflattering remarks about its toughness and subsequent unwholesomeness, and for its oil, and especially that of its liver. That gullible old Roman gentleman, Pliny the Elder, whom we shall soon meet more intimately, records that people boiled dolphin livers to obtain an oil which was highly efficacious in the removal of "lichens and other leprous spots." We may well wonder if the spots in question were not the outward manifestations of some vitamin deficiency that was counterbalanced by the vitamin content of the livers and if, therefore, the whole procedure was not a forerunner of our modern fish-liver-oil industry.

It appears that the barbarian tribes living on the coasts of the Black Sea maintained a regular and extensive dolphin-fishing industry even prior to 3000 B.C., and this was known to those bold peninsular-insular mariners, the Cretans. The fishermen of the Aegean islands also netted dolphins and hunted them with tridents to which lines were sometimes attached so that the practice became, in one respect, a minor whaling enterprise. In other areas, however, the dolphin was most sacred and was not allowed to be molested. It early became a prominent figure in the folklore and mythology of the Aegean, and even in the pantheon of the Minoans, for it is represented on seals, pottery, gems, and many other artifacts from the earliest times of Cretan and Mycenaean civilization.

Altogether, the Minoans delighted in the dolphin and some of the most exquisite paintings of it have been found on the walls of what is known as the Queen's Megaron in the palace of Cnossos in Crete. These dophins are quite realistic and are shown frolicking upon a pale-blue background with the sea indicated by wavy lines. They appear also in rather cruder form, again painted on a pale-blue background, on the floors of the Great Megaron Palace at Tiryns in association with some very realistic representations of octopus and other shellfish. They also appear on burial jars, and in some early Mycenaean shaft-graves in southern Greece ostrich eggs with plaster dolphins appliquéd on their surfaces have been found. These eggs had a religious significance, representing birth and future life, while the dolphins represented the termination of life, for these animals were believed to carry away the spirits of the dead. The dolphin's connection with the cult of the dead is lost in the mists of antiquity but in the Aegean area it early became associated with the Dionysus legend.

The earliest representations of the dolphin in the art of the eastern Mediterranean are not always easily recognizable because the artists regarded the animal as a fish and appear to have muddled it with the tunny. Also, they drew from memory rather than from the animal itself, and they had great difficulty with the perspective of the horizontal tail. They were often doubtful as to the animal's exact appear-

## The Arabian Sea, as Seen by the Ancients

This map displays most of the world known to the Minoans, ancient Egyptians, Greeks, and Romans, and may be employed to view this world from the angle of those four peoples. To a certain extent it also shows the outlook of the Sumerians, Assyrians, Babylonians, and Phoenicians, and by turning it upside down you may see half the world as viewed by the ancient Dravidian Indian navigators. The essential feature, from the point of view of the eastern Mediterranean civilizations, is that India was straight ahead, with Egypt, Nubia, and Ethiopia on the right, and Arabia, Mesopotamia, and Persia on the left. Further, Libya (or Africa) bounded the world on the right and Cathay (Asia) on the left.

The route to India was neither difficult nor adventurous to the Romans, apart from the fact that they were inland seamen and bad sailors. It simply followed an ancient sea route laid out over three thousand years before by Dravidians and Sabeans, and later by Phoenicians and Greeks. Advantageous winds carried the creaky, overstuffed ships down the Red Sea, and then straight across the Arabian Sea to India, provided one sailed at the right time of year. The return was accomplished just as easily by taking advantage of the Monsoons blowing the other way. Looked at this way, these Monsoons blow straight from right to left, or vice versa, across the course.

Whales of several kinds are very common in the seas depicted, and the classical voyagers could not have failed to see them. Industries founded upon them, apart from the Phoenician sperming in the eastern Mediterranean, were concentrated around the Arabian Sea.

## Map 1 The Arabian Sea, as Seen by the Ancients

Miller Modified Mercator Projection
Scale 1:40,000,000

•••••••••• The Roman Route to India
ooooooooooo The Voyage of Nearchus

ance and gave it two dorsal and four ventral fins like a fish, while they sometimes added a gill slit. In their more elaborate representations, the body is sometimes greatly elongated and the dorsal fin is shifted forward so that it becomes a sort of crest, like a cock's comb. There was also a convention which persisted until Christian times, and which to a certain extent still remains with us, that the dolphin should be shown in a crescentic form with the back arched into a semicircle and the belly concave. Actually the animal cannot bend to this extent, even when leaping free of the waves. It gives the impression of doing so, however, because when so engaged, the head and tail are turned down and the whole animal describes an arc. Pictures of dolphins thus curved do, moreover, give the impression of movement and speed, and this was greatly appreciated by the highly artistic Mediterranean peoples.

It is also upon the subject of dolphins that we come to the first matter-of-fact and contemporary treatises on any whale. Further, these writings contain not only descriptions of the animals but also mention of the uses to which they were put by ancient man. As it is our intention to follow the whales as well as the whalers, we may therefore turn unreservedly to these records that were so obligingly compiled for us by those ancient moderns, the Greeks, with their somewhat puckish erudition.

In 326 B.C., Alexander of Macedon reached India and conquered the rich Indus valley. He had every intention of proceeding into the Ganges valley and subduing the whole subcontinent but his ragged army was utterly exhausted by years of meandering campaigns through half of Asia, and he was persuaded to turn back. He divided his forces, putting all those that he could find in the ranks of his army with any knowledge of the sea under the command of one Nearchus, whom he instructed to build a fleet and sail back to Mesopotamia along the Makran coast, keeping in touch with his army as it moved west through Persia. A very large number went with Nearchus and it is manifest that sufficient shipping to transport this host could not have been assembled or built if the country in which they found themselves had not been versed in seamanship. It appears, moreover, at least by the account of Arrian, that the Indians built eight hundred ships for Nearchus, and this in a surprisingly short time. Some of them were of three hundred tons burthen.

Megasthenes, writing of India at this time, states that the Emperor
Chandra Gupta, who reigned from 321 to 297 B.C., divided his government into six ministries and that the first of these was a Board
of Admiralty. Although we have no exact historical record, it appears that the seafaring prowess of India, which we glimpsed centuries before, had continued to develop along its own lines. We know
that by that time there were already Indian colonies in Pegu, Sumatra, Java, Borneo, Cambodia, China, and perhaps even in Japan.
The sculptures on the Burubudur in Java show large vessels with
multiple sails, and although this monument was built some centuries
later and after the Kalingas of the east coast of India had colonized
that island, these vessels could not then have been a new invention
and must have been preceded by an old and vigorous seafaring tradition.

The voyage of Nearchus was notable as an historical accomplishment. What is more, the accounts of it left by Arrian and by Strabo
contain some illuminating descriptions of whales. One of the most
interesting of these states, "What most alarmed them was the magni-
tude of the whales, which occasioned a great commotion in the sea
all at once, and raised so dense a mist by their blowing that the sailors could not see where they stood. But when the pilots informed
the sailors that they were animals which would quickly take themselves off on hearing the sound of the trumpet and the clapping of
their hands, Nearchos thereupon impelled the vessels in the direction
of the surges which obstructed their course, and at the same time
frightened the animals with the sound of the trumpet. The whales
dived, and then rose again at the prows of the vessels, so as to furnish
the appearance of a sea-fight, but they very soon made off. Those
who now sail to India speak of the size of these animals and of their
appearances, but say they do not come either in shoals or frequently,
but are scared away by shouts and the sound of the trumpet. They
state also that they do not come near the shore, but that the bones of
those that die, bared of flesh, are readily cast ashore by the waves and
furnish the Icthyophagi with the material for the construction of
their huts. The length of these whales, according to Nearchos, is
'23 orgyiae.' "

From this we infer that a school of large whales was a novel sight
to the Greeks, and this in turn bears out the oft-repeated contention

that the larger species were never common in the Mediterranean. It has been suggested that the school encountered by Nearchus was comprised of humpbacks, which are still prevalent along that coast.

The voyage was fraught with difficulties. Food ran extremely short, and the fleet completely lost touch with the land army despite Alexander's sanguine belief that they could keep in close contact. Nearchus, however, had sensibly shipped an experienced Indian pilot, a man of Baluchistan whom he found at Mosarna and who knew the whole route to Mesopotamia. The pilots referred to in the passage above were obviously Indians and they undoubtedly had complete charge of the navigation. As we have seen, this sea route had been followed for several hundreds, and perhaps for some thousands of years by the Indians, so that considerably more was known about it than the Greek chroniclers of the voyage give us to suppose, and Nearchus was probably never in any great danger of getting lost.

After entering the Persian Gulf and passing the Bushire Peninsula, the fleet came to the mouth of a river, probably the modern Rud-Hilleh, and the record states that there "at the River Granis, near which was a palace, a stranded whale fifty cubits in length was observed, attended by a great number of dolphins, larger than are ever seen in the Mediterranean." This passage has been interpreted in two ways. It could mean either that a school of some smaller species of whale had been stranded along with the big specimen, or that the carcass was still fresh and was being mauled by a number of sharks. The Greeks were never quite clear as to the distinction between dolphins and sharks, and they sometimes spoke of the former as having the mouth under the head, so that the animal had to turn over on its back to grasp its prey.

The whales were undoubtedly one of the sights that most impressed the inquisitive Greeks upon this first excursion of theirs into eastern seas. Nor did their interest flag from that time on. Aristotle had already compiled his great works on natural history, and knowledge of these things was current among the better-educated Greeks. The extent of this knowledge was, as has been noted, quite astonishing, and displays extraordinary powers of observation, evidence of most careful compilation, and the existence of a very free and rational outlook upon all matters zoological. Aristotle's work *The*

*Animal Kingdom* contains most interesting passages on the whales. For instance, he states:

Thus the dolphin is directly viviparous, and accordingly we find it furnished with two breasts, not situated high up, but in the neighbourhood of the genitals. And this creature is not provided, like quadrupeds with visible teats, but has two vents, one in each flank from which milk flows; and its young have to follow after it to get suckled and this phenomenon has been actually witnessed. The Dolphin, the whale and all the rest of the Cetacea, all that is to say, that are provided with a blowhole instead of gills are viviparous. That is to say, no one of all these fishes is ever even seen to be supplied with eggs, but directly with an embryo from whose differentiation comes the fish, just as in the case of mankind and the viviparous quadrupeds.

The dolphin bears one at a time generally but occasionally two. The whale bears one or at most two. The Porpoise in this respect resembles the dolphin and, by the way, it is like a little dolphin in form, and is found in the Black Sea: it differs, however, from the dolphin as being less in size and broader in the back; its colour is leaden black. Many people are of the opinion that the porpoise is a variety of the Dolphin. All creatures that have a blowhole respire and inspire, for they are furnished with lungs. The dolphin has been seen asleep with his nose above the water and when asleep he snores. The dolphin and the porpoise are provided with milk and suckle their young. They also take their young, when small, inside them. The young of the dolphin grows rapidly, being full grown at ten years of age. Its period of gestation is ten months. It brings forth its young in summer, and never at any other season; (and singularly enough, under the Dog Star it disappears for about 30 days). Its young accompany it for a considerable period; and in fact, the creature is remarkable for the strength of its parental affection. It lives for many years; some are known to have lived for more than 25; and some for 30; the fact is, fishermen nick their tails sometimes and set them adrift again, and by this expedient their ages are ascertained.

The allusion to the seasonal disappearance of the dolphin is thought to be not entirely zoologic but to refer to the occultation of the heavenly constellation to which the name of the dolphin had been applied. For the rest, the description adheres quite strictly to ascertained fact, with a few minor exceptions, notably that of the length of time that it takes the animals to reach maturity, which, from recent researches, seems to have been very much exaggerated. Aristotle then goes on in another passage to discuss the breathing apparatus of the *Cetacea,* saying:

> But the dolphin is equipped in the most remarkable way of all animals: the dolphin and other similar aquatic animals including the other cetaceans which resemble it, that is to say, the whale, and all the other creatures that are furnished with a blowhole. One can hardly allow that such an animal is terrestrial and terrestrial only, or aquatic and aquatic only, if by terrestrial we mean an animal that inhales air, and if by aquatic we mean an animal that takes in water. For the fact is the dolphin performs both these processes; he takes in water and discharges it by his blowhole, and he also inhales air into his lungs; for, by the way, the creature is furnished with this organ and thereby, and accordingly, when caught in nets, he is quickly suffocated for lack of air. He can also live for a considerable while out of water, but all this while he keeps up a dull moaning sound corresponding to the noise made by air-breathing animals in general; furthermore when sleeping, the animal keeps his nose above water, and he does so that he may breathe the air.

In this passage the worthy philosopher has strayed somewhat from the narrow path of accuracy, for the whales do not, of course, inhale water in the manner that fishes do, and their spout is only warmed air, heavily charged with water vapor. Further, there is no evidence that dolphins sleep with their heads out of water, though specimens kept in confinement have been seen to rest for considerable periods with their muzzles flush with the surface. At one time, also, there was dispute as to whether they made a moaning noise, but in this Aristotle seems to have been quite correct. When this Greek writer comes to describe the habits, as opposed to the morphological attributes, of these animals, however, he definitely goes awry, for reasons that may be more clear if we recollect the place this animal had grown to assume in the fables and religious beliefs of the Greeks. On these subjects Aristotle wrote:

Among the sea fishes many stories are told about dolphin, indicative of his gentle and kindly nature, and of manifestations of passionate attachment to boys in and about Tarentum, Caria and other places. The story goes that after a dolphin had been caught and wounded off the coast of Caria, a shoal of dolphins came into the harbour and stopped there until the fishermen let the captive go free; whereupon the shoal departed. A shoal of young dolphins is always, by way of protection, followed by a shoal of large ones. On one occasion a shoal of dolphins, large and small, was seen, and two dolphins at a little distance appeared swimming in underneath a little dead dolphin when it was sinking, and supporting it on their backs, trying out of compassion to prevent its being devoured by some predaceous fish. Incredible stories are told regarding the rapidity of movement of this creature. It appears to be the fleetest of all animals, marine or terrestrial, and it can leap over the masts of large vessels. This speed is chiefly manifested when they are pursuing fish for food, then if the fish endeavour to escape, they pursue them in their ravenous hunger down to deep waters; but, when the necessary return swim is getting too long, they hold in their breath, as though calculating the length of it and then draw themselves together for an effort and shoot up like arrows, trying to make the long ascent rapidly in order to breathe, and in the effort they spring right over a ship's mast if a ship be in the vicinity. This same phenomenon is observed in divers, when they have plunged into deep water; that is, they pull themselves together and rise with a speed proportional to their strength. Dolphins live together in pairs, male and female. It is not known for what reason they run themselves aground on dry land; at all events, it is said that they do so at times, and for no obvious reason.

This is a strange mixture of fact and fancy. Dolphins do appear to be somewhat "affectionate" among themselves — doubtless a manifestation of a strong herd instinct — but their supposed attachment in some cases to young boys might well be regarded as pure fantasy. Nonetheless, there have very recently appeared authenticated stories fully illustrated by photographs of just such attachments between individual boys and dolphins. Dolphins are solicitous of their young but almost certainly do not support them when dead, or even when injured. They are swift and leap far out of the waves but never over the masts of even the most paltry ships. Aristotle's description of their diving and respiratory apparatus is poetic but not altogether unsound, for they do indeed behave like divers. Despite these defects, Aristotle's description is somewhat remarkable as having been written twenty-three centuries ago.

Strabo, writing later of Ceylon, which he called Taprobane, says, "They say it is an island lying out in the sea, distant from the most southern parts of India . . . that there are found around its shores cetaceous animals [whales] which are amphibious and in appearance like oxen, horses and other land animals." This passage was later elaborated by the Roman writer Aelian, who, in his *History of Animals*, says, "This sea is reported to breed an incredible number of fish. They say whales also frequent this sea though it is not true they approach the shore lying in wait for tunnies. The dolphins are reported to be of two sorts." Strabo even has information on the Ganges and quotes another Greek, one Artemidorus, whose writings are lost, saying, "The Ganges descends from the Edomoi Mountains towards the south. To one of its affluents he gives the name of Oidanes, which breeds crocodiles and dolphins." It is indeed an astonishing thing to read these rather matter-of-fact remarks, written over two thousand years ago, and to find in them such intimate references to the wildlife of places as distant as Ceylon and Bengal. It brings home to us the extraordinarily rational attitude of the Greeks towards exploration, geography, and the natural sciences. The whole business, moreover, becomes positively prosaic with the advent of the Romans.

Egypt came under the Roman domain in 30 B.C. and the Romans, with their customary efficiency, set to work to make the newly acquired territory a paying proposition. With consummate adroitness they immediately opened the ancient trade route to India, though they did not themselves attempt to sail this but left the whole business to the Greeks. In this we see the genius of the Romans, who, in contrast to the Greeks, always avoided doing anything themselves that they could persuade somebody else to do for them, particularly if it was something which they did not wholly understand. Thus, we find the influence of Rome extending, within a comparatively few years, far beyond the confines of Europe to distant parts of Asia.

There were many Roman chroniclers of this expansion, ranging in attitude from that self-satisfied country gentleman, Horace, who liked to stroll among his cypresses, to the revoltingly successful general, Caius Julius Caesar, who was wont to "throw a company of Balearic slingers" across rivers to the discomfort of some Gallic tribe that was only trying to defend its crops, its maidens, and its territory. But eventually Rome had to breed a Pliny. A really successful civilization must sooner or later, and inevitably, produce such a type.

Gaius Plinius Secundus, commonly known as Pliny the Elder, who lived from 23 to 79 A.D., penned a whole shelf of volumes into which he gathered information upon practically everything he could lay his hands on, a most astounding assemblage of facts gleaned from any and every source quite irrespective of their merits or veracity. Never was there more entertaining reading, not even in our own small predigested periodicals. In Pliny anything may be encountered — word-for-word plagiarisms from Aristotle and the older classics, the shrewdest observations upon current events, and the most arrant nonsense that any gullible idiot could unearth from under Egyptian stones or from the darker recesses of barbarian fetishism. In this outpouring we find, moreover, many items of the utmost interest that reveal the wisdom and beliefs of a successful empire and display the accumulated knowledge then current in the world.

Pliny goes into the details of the trade route to India with some care. The chapter is not, but might well be, headed, "How to Get to India and Back in a Year." It lists by name the winds to be used, specifying that the journey should start from Cape Fartak in Arabia, using the west wind Favonius, or Hippalus, and that the course should be steered to Patale on the Malabar coast. The return is to be made in December, using the southeast wind named Vulturnus. Pliny then goes into the marvels to be encountered on this journey and the wildlife of India. Would that we had space to give some of his descriptions of the latter; that of the rhinoceros is hard to beat even in modern literature. We must, however, confine our narrative to what he had to say upon our own particular subject, the whales, which in some respects surely cannot be surpassed in any other work, ancient or modern. This delicious publicist, whom many persons of lesser mentality have presumed to call naïve, launches out with altogether carefree abandon to deal with the whole matter of whales in a most comprehensive manner. There can be no question, moreover, but that he succeeded in accomplishing exactly what he set out to do and that, in the doing of it, he carried the early Christian world along with him for a number of centuries.

He starts off with the axiom that the greatest beasts are in the sea. This would seem to be irrefutable. He then goes on to say, "But the most numerous and largest of all these animals are those found in the Indian Seas; among which are balenae [whales] four *jugera* in extent, and the Pristis, 200 cubits long." This is all very well but for the fact that the Roman measure, the *jugerum,* happens to be one of area for measuring towns and encompassed a space of 240 by 120 feet. Not content with this little flight, however, the worthy Pliny then goes on to state that there were in the Ganges River in India eels 300 feet in length and, perhaps worked up by this statement, he proceeds to give a most convincing account of a large peninsula in the Red Sea which projects "into the deep and forms a vast gulf. In the recesses of this becalmed spot the sea monsters attain so vast a size they are quite unable to move." There then follows a more or less word-for-word quote from Arrian regarding some people called the Godrosi who dwell on the Makran coast and who make "the doors of their houses with the jaw-bones of fishes, and rafter and roofs with their bones many of which were found as much as forty cubits [73 feet] in length." Here we see a rather shrewd elaboration of the original description of the Ichthyophagi, the novel points of which must have been taken from some other authors now lost to us, but Pliny cannot resist the temptation to go into the matter of size, like certain modern guidebooks.

For all this, Pliny is full of topical information; in fact, he was really a newspaperman at heart and is much better when he is doing a straightforward job of reporting. He tells us of a sudden land subsidence during the reign of the Emperor Tiberius that left a school of some three hundred whales, or "sea monsters," on the mud flats by the island of Lagdunum. These, he says, had white marks in the place where horns should have been. They were probably a school of killer whales, which have white marks on either side of the head that were mistaken for horns in earlier times and may have given rise to the belief in the *aries marinus,* or "sea ram." Pliny also remarks, in passing, and in a delightfully chatty manner, that "Turranus speaks of a monster that was thrown up on the shore at Gades, the distance between the two fins at the end of the tail of which was 16 cubits and its teeth 120 in number; the largest nine and smallest six inches in length." This appears to have been a sperm whale.

Even more delightful anecdotes follow which give us a very interesting sidelight on a matter that we observed as having been current many centuries before. Pliny states that "M. Scaurus, in his aedileship, exhibited at Rome, among other wonderful things, the bones of the monster to which Andromeda was said to have been exposed and which he had brought from Joppa, a city of Judaea. These bones exceeded 40 feet in length, and the ribs were higher than those of the Indian Elephant, while the backbone was a foot and a half in thickness." So startled was the worthy reporter by the size of these remains that he apparently collapsed into straightforward and honest description without exaggeration. He must, in fact, actually have had somebody measure the exhibits. The interesting point to us is, however, that these remains came from Joppa, the town from which Jonah set out and one of the centers of Phoenician whaling since the second millennium. It is, moreover, reported by Pliny as well as by others that there were still at that time many signs of this industry in the ports of Palestine, while the chains which were said to have been used to bind Andromeda could be seen affixed to the rocks at the harbor mouth of Joppa. These latter were probably the attachments for a boom used by the Phoenicians in defense of that port. Pliny also has some chatty remarks to make on the subject of an animal he calls the Orca, which, from certain passages that we shall see immediately, we should have no doubt in referring to the animal bearing that name today, namely, the killer whale. His best tale is about one that appeared on the coast of Italy and which, it seems, he himself saw killed. His story is:

> An Orca has even been seen in the port of Ostia, where it was attacked by the Emperor Claudius. It was while he was constructing the harbour that this orca came, attracted by some hides which, having been brought from Gaul, had happened to fall overboard there. By feeding on these for several days it had quite glutted itself, having made for itself a channel in the shoally water. Here, however, the sand was thrown up by the action of the wind to such an extent that the creature found it quite impossible to turn round; and while in the act of pursuing

its prey, it was propelled by the waves towards the shore, so that its back came to be perceived above the level of the water, very much resembling in appearance the keel of a vessel turned bottom upwards. Upon this, Caesar ordered a great number of nets to be extended at the mouth of the harbour, from shore to shore, while he himself went there with the praetorian cohorts, and so afforded a spectacle to the Roman people; for boats assailed the monster, while the soldiers on board showered lances upon it. I myself saw one of the boats sunk by the water which the animal, as it respired, showered down upon it.

There are those who have doubted the necessity of employing the Praetorian Guard to dispatch anything so small as a killer whale, and who have therefore suggested that the beast in question was a sperm whale, the back of which, suddenly appearing amid the surf, would much more resemble the bottom of a Roman boat. However, taken in conjunction with other remarks made about the Orca by Pliny, it seems improbable that even he could have so lightly transferred the identity of the beast.

On the subject of the dolphin, that animal so beloved of the Mediterranean world in general, Pliny waxes really magnificent. Having stated that this animal is even swifter than the birds, he proceeds to copy the majority of Aristotle's facts about its appearance and habits, but then goes on with the utmost blandness to say that "the back is arched and the nose turned up [*simus*, in Latin]. For this reason it is that they all recognize in a most surprising manner the name 'Simo' and prefer to be called by that rather than by any other." The word *simus* actually meant "pug-nosed," or "pug-faced," and was applied to a breed of dogs not unlike the King Charles Spaniel. These look very much like black-and-white Pekinese and, when seen in profile, are somewhat reminiscent of the dolphin.

Not content with this little flight of fancy, Pliny goes on to state that the dolphin is very friendly to man and that it is "a lover of music as well, being charmed by melodious concerts and especially by the notes of the water-organ." In elaboration of this he tells several stories of dolphins that loved music and musicians, but most of these seem to have been borrowed from older writers imbued with those ancient fables already mentioned. One concerns a dolphin caught in the sea and put in a lake which became very fond of a small boy who used to feed it bread. It came to the shore whenever the boy called and, after being fed, took the boy on its back and carried him to school at the other end of the lake. After many years, however, the boy died but the dolphin continued to come every day to the place where it had been fed and was very sad until it pined away and died. This seeming fable has only within the last few years been confirmed by a photographic record of a boy-dolphin companionship.

Another of Pliny's stories was apparently widely current in Rome at that time and seems to have been at least based on fact. It concerns a dolphin at a popular bathing beach on the north coast of Africa which was tamed by the local inhabitants and which fed from their hands. A Roman proconsular official then tried to go one better than the locals and gave the animal a bath in scent or some form of perfumed oil, whereupon it passsed out cold for a number of hours and floated at the surface of the water as if dead, but finally revived and made for the depths, where it remained *in camera*, and doubtless in mortification, for some months. When it returned, it became so famous and so many tourists came to see it that they forced up the cost of living locally to such an extent, and caused so much trouble with their pilfering and souvenir hunting, that the locals killed the beast.

Pliny also tells us of the uses made of dolphins by fishermen, and recounts how people at Narbonne called them when the mullet were running out of a certain narrow channel to the sea from a large salt-water lagoon. Nets were erected and the dolphins apparently patrolled the outside, driving the fish back into the shallows where they could be captured. This story also has recently been rendered more credible by accounts of similar behavior by another species of dolphin in Australia.

Pliny also mentions briefly two other small cetaceans, one of which he names the Tursio (perhaps the *Tursiops*) and which, he says, "bears a strong resemblance to the dolphin; it differs from it, however, in a certain air of sadness." This is a rather delightful statement. His remark about the other species is highly interesting from a zoological point of view and is really a quite astonishing historical record. This reads: "In the Ganges, a river of India, is found a fish called a Platanista; it has the muzzle and the tail of the dolphin and is of the length of 16 cubits." Apart from a quadruplication of the size, this is undoubtedly a description of the Susu, the animal to which we now apply the scientific name of *Platanista gangetica*.

This is perhaps the most curious and specialized of all the whales. It lives in the muddy waters of the Indus, Ganges, Irrawaddy, and Brahmaputra rivers and ranges from the tidal estuaries to the foothills and up all the tributaries of those rivers as far inland as there is water and no rock barrier in the stream. It appears to migrate up and down the rivers to some extent, going farther inland in the hot season. It feeds on fish, prawns, and shellfish for which it grubs about in the mud at the bottom. It can stay under for two minutes but usually rises regularly and quietly at short intervals to breathe. At other times it may become very active and leap clear of the water. The name "susu" is in imitation of the noise it makes when breaching to effect its extremely quick exhalation and inhalation of air.

Susus grow to a length of about nine feet, but one caught in the Jumna River was twelve feet long. They are entirely black, rather elongated little whales with a distinct neck, so that the head is movable. In place of a dorsal fin they have a slight elevation just behind the middle of the back, and the flippers, instead of being tapered like those of almost all other whales, are triangular, narrow at the base, and cut off square at the end. The head is round and swollen in front, due to two large, bony crests on the skull, but is prolonged into a great bill rather like that of the gharial crocodile, which inhabits the same rivers. This beak, or bill, is laterally compressed, half as long again in the female as in the male, slightly expanded at the tip, and armed with some 120 teeth. These are long, pointed, recurved, and so close together they almost touch at the base in front, but become gradually smaller, more widely separated, and more laterally compressed as they approach the back of the jaws. As the animal advances in age these teeth become worn down until they are just flat-topped, cylindrical pegs. The whole mouth structure is very singular and is devised for probing in the mud and for grabbing the quick things found there.

The susu has other oddities. The eyes are minute and rudimentary, the whole eyeball being no bigger than a pea; there is no lens and the optic nerve is reduced to a thread. The external opening of the ear is about the size of a pinhole. The blowhole, unlike that of any other whale except the La Plata River dolphin, is a single longitudinal slit. Susus are usually solitary animals but they occasionally travel in pairs and are sometimes seen in great numbers in certain stretches of rivers where food is plentiful. The inhabitants of various parts of India eat the beast. It is strange that this, one of the most obscure of all whales, should have been one of the first to be given a name and individual mention in the world's literature.

Pliny also makes some observations upon the whales of the western seas and the Atlantic. He states that the Balaenae, or true whales, penetrate the Mediterranean but are more common off the coast of Spain, though "not before the winter solstice because they retire at periodical seasons to calve in a large bay." This, as we shall see later, refers to the Bay of Biscay and was an accurate observation upon a fact that had great bearing on the future history of western Europe. He says that there is also in the western seas the Orca, "which cannot in any way be adequately described, but as an enormous mass of flesh armed with teeth." This animal he rightly reports as attacking the female whales when they are sluggish with calf, and herding them on to shoals when they make a dash for the open sea, which is their only means of defense.

He concludes by saying, "The largest animals that are found in the Indian Ocean are the Pristis and the Balaena, while in the Gallic Ocean the Physeter is the most bulky inhabitant, raising itself aloft like some vast column, and as it towers above the sails of ships, belching forth as it were a deluge of water." The scientific name given to the sperm whale is, for this reason, *Physeter*, and it is indeed to the western oceans that we must now turn in order to follow the whale. The world of the ancients only glimpsed these monstrous creatures; we are now to view them at very much closer quarters.

# Part Three

500 A.D. TO 1600 A.D.

## The Early Period

# 4

# Half-Light over Cold Seas

## (Norse)

THE VALKYRIE are riding high this day, for the dark clouds rush across the sky at such a speed that from the bottom of the fjord it would seem they must surely rumble and roar upon their passage. But all below between the two-thousand-foot cliffs is still and silent. The blue smoke from the roof openings of the big house curls languidly into the air and hangs in translucent wraiths by the cliff faces. It is ever mysterious that, although the wind may be blowing in a tempest outside upon the sea and high above the mountains, the air in the deeper inlets of the fjords may still remain almost motionless. Sound too is often absent, as though the fjords were a vast crypt, so that the screams of infants in the peat huts echo across the water, and the lowing of a cow may be heard miles away up the valley.

It is dark also, although the day is well advanced and the winter still two full moons away. The clouds racing across the narrow sky-light of the fjord are low and rain-soaked, and the waters, as they always are at this time of the year, are almost black. Only inland, at the head of the valley and beyond the long, narrow, blue lake, is there any brightness, for there hangs the bluish whiteness of the glacier, depending like an immense glistening tongue from the mighty snow fields above. Around it always is the brightness of reflection, so that even the dour rock faces of the mountainsides on either hand seem lightened and the meadows on the valley bottom shine vividly green. Looking up the valley is like looking up through a window at the land of the Gods, a vista leading directly to Valhalla itself.

Then from far off down the fjord towards the sea and beyond the first sharp bend which shuts off all view, because there the mighty cliffs seem to curve and clash together, there comes a sound. It is a steady rhythmical sound, a thudding interspersed with a creaking, the sound of a fast-approaching boat. Rapidly it draws nearer and louder as it is amplified by the walls of the canyon. Figures appear out of the doorways of the big house; people come running down the pastures from the mountainsides; a horseman comes galloping down the valley from the lake; and children gather swiftly on the stony, boulder-strewn beach. By the time the boat appears round the bend in the fjord, the whole village is gathered on the shore.

It is the skutaboat of Thorvald the Long with every man aboard laboring at the oars, even three to an oar amidships, and Biarni the Yellow standing in the bow holding a trumpet of cow's horn in his hand. The oarsmen grunt as they pull in unison and Thorvald beats out the strokes on the gunwale with his left hand and a club, while with his right hand he feathers the steering oar. Now Biarni raises the horn to his lips and gives a long-drawn blast. This is the announcement of something very important afoot and a call for all men to come quickly. The crowd waves and the children shout. The skuta drives up the fjord amid the surging sweeps of the sculls, and Biarni cups his hands and yells, "*Seigval . . . seigval . . . seigval . . .*"

Now, all the boats had left before dawn to go down to the sea in search of the cod which are running in great numbers inside the islands and it is a full day's pull with the oars to the mouth of the fjord and the open sea. Why is it, therefore, that the skuta of Thorvald the Long returns so soon, calling out that seigval, or cod whales, are coming? Most of the people do not know, but some of the older men do. It has been many years since anything so exciting has happened and so, even before the boat strikes the steep boulder beach, they begin shouting orders. It can mean only one thing and this that the boats have met a school of seigval chasing the cod into the fjord and, sending the swiftest boat back to announce the happy event, have formed a ring beyond the whales to the seaward and started to drive them inward. If by their shouting, banging on the water with oars, dropping nets with long pieces of cloth, skin garments, and sails tied to them, and by rapping on the boat hulls they can panic the whales, the whole school or herd may well forget the codfish in their madness and rush headlong up the fjord. Should this happen, the village must be prepared, and certain important posts must be manned.

There are only ten young men left in the village, and only twenty more come to join them in Thorvald's skuta; the rest are women, children, and old men. All of them must therefore help, so those who do not know what has to be done now crowd around Biarni as he leaps from the boat because he is the son of the Lawgiver himself, and therefore naturally takes command.

Dividing the people into two parties with an equal number of old ones, women, and children in each, Biarni takes charge of one group and turns the other over to Thorvald. Men are ordered to run immediately to the Long House and bring all the harpoons and lances that are there. The children are sent to search for shields and hammers, the women for ropes, and the old men, who know what is afoot, for the great spears for the catapults. When all are reassembled with this gear, a shout is raised and the two parties race away from each other round the horseshoe end of the fjord and thence along its two steep sides towards the sea.

There are paths cut out of the rock faces along these ways that lead first up, then down, and sometimes almost to the water's edge. They are narrow paths and the two parties string out, single file, with the children straggling behind. The paths reach a mile down the fjord and then rise to prominent rocks almost immediately opposite each other just where the canyon begins to turn. Here are cunningly concealed defensive posts that have often stood the settlement in good stead, for from them arrows and spears may be showered down upon any who wish to reach the end of the fjord. At these places are kept a pair of huge ballistae, or catapults, with walrus-hide thongs and a battery of sycamore-wood springs, brought from the far south. These primitive engines shoot immense ironheaded spears with twelve-foot shafts three inches in diameter. What is more, when pointed somewhat downward they can shoot these shafts almost right across the fjord.

Now Biarni holds up his hand for silence and instructs the young men each to take two of the women and some children and disperse themselves below the ballistae on the steep cliffs and about the edge of the water. They are then, he tells them, to remain silent even after the sound of the boats is heard approaching up the fjord, and particularly so if any whales should pass by. Nor are they even to move until the signal is given, whereupon all but those carrying ropes and nets are to climb along the shore banging the shields with the hammers, throwing stones into the water, and shouting. Those with ropes are to await the arrival of the boats and then cast their lines to them, and so move slowly with them, forming a solid chain of boats and nets from shore to shore behind the whales, cutting off their retreat to the sea.

When the companies are gone and have taken their places, all is once more silent but for the occasional slap of a hand on a face or a bare arm as the countless mosquitoes become intolerable with their biting. But the waiting is long, especially for the little children and when everyone is straining his ears for the first sounds of the on-coming multitude. The two companies wait, and wait, while it grows darker, the clouds rush ever faster across the sky, a light cold rain begins to fall, and the moaning of the storm above is heard even in the depths of the fjord. Will they never come?

But at last Biarni, who mans the ballista on the north side, which is a little in advance of that of Thorvald and from which place he can see farther round the curve of the canyon, leaps to his feet and holds up his right arm. All faces are turned to him, and now they hear too. From far away yet, but now clearly, come the yells and the shouts and the horn blasts of a great company. The ships are coming. Will the seigval come also?

Then to everyone's amazement a huge form suddenly bursts out of the still waters of the fjord. It blows like a bull and then it whistles shrilly, and a puff of vapor rises into the air from where the waters roil. Then it is gone. The whales are indeed coming and their leader is already only a mile from the end of the fjord. Will he sense that he has entered a trap and turn about to rush among his fellows, warning them, or will he cast himself upon the stony beach? None can tell and nobody dares move or make a sound lest the whale turn about immediately. But he has sunk into the depths and is not seen again, while the uproar from the boats draws swiftly nearer. Now the hammering on the hulls may also be heard and soon also the splashing of oars and then all at once a host fills the fjord and the air is rent with sound. And there, right before them, milling around on the surface or poking their great pointed heads out of the water against the rocks, are the seigval — a good hundred of them, already packed close together and rapidly becoming frantic, as is plain for all to see, for they are swimming not as upon the sea in some order but in all directions and in a most disorderly manner.

Now the boats are alongside the rope men and Biarni's arm descends with a mighty crash upon the key of the ballista. There is a loud "thwang" and a whirring sound as the great spear arcs out over the water, and immediately the uproar is multiplied tenfold as the shore parties now add their voices to those of the boatmen, rocks shower into the fjord, and the women set up a terrific clatter with the shields. The panic-stricken seigval surge forward all together, churning the dark waters to foam, while one of their number, pierced by the harpoon from Biarni's ballista, leaps almost clear of the surface. Blood showers everywhere, and sensing this terrible danger, the whales rush headlong up the fjord.

But what is this? Something comes boring along the surface of the water towards them like an upturned skuta propelled from beneath by all the forces of evil in the depths. It is the old bull seigval. He knows now the trap into which the herd has been forced, and he is intent upon making a dash for freedom. Before the boatmen can brace themselves, he is among the oncoming horde, and then by his greater weight he has driven through them and strikes the nets and ropes which are drawn between the boats. These become entangled in his flippers but his great tail still drives him forward and all at once it happens: the two center boats are drawn madly together and crash in a mass of foam. There is the sound of splintering wood and one of them upends, caught in a web of ropes. The head

of the seigval rams into it at the water's surface and splits it asunder.
Men fall from it like little peas from a pod.

Now all is confusion. The great ballistae "thwang" shaft after
shaft into the melee, rocks shower down from the canyon walls,
and the men in the boats break out long lances and begin stabbing
at the frenzied beasts. Slowly the whole company moves forward
toward the beach despite the breakthrough of the leader and the
smashing of two boats whose occupants are left to fend for themselves and to swim to shore. And as darkness descends and the rain
comes down in singing showers, there is a great shout from the
hoarse throats of the whole community, for all at once the seigval
rush madly on to the rocky shore, literally piling one upon another
in their desperation. Moreover, there are so many that those behind
cannot reach the shallows and mill around until speared to death by
the boatmen, who now wield their battleaxes as well as their iron-
shod lances. The waters of the fjord are red with blood and the men
are spattered with it. The boats are drawn together in a tangled
mass of ropes and nets that will take days to unravel.

Only slowly do the excitement and the noise die down, and it is
black night before the last boat is securely tied to the upturned
flipper of a dead whale. Flaring torches are now lit and affixed to
poles driven into the flesh of the whales and the pebbles of the beach.
The whole settlement assembles and the Lawgiver mounts the prow
of one of the beached skuta. Raising his hands, he calls for the men
to assemble, and when they have done so, he begins to name them
by families and by the number in their families. And this goes on
far into the night despite the rain, for all must be told, so that the
oil from the mountain of captured whales, when it is boiled down
and purified, may be divided equitably among all, for such is the
custom of the men of the fjords.

THE NORSEMEN of the fjords of Norway are often, though altogether erroneously, called "The Vikings." Actually, they were for
the most part the direct descendants of those bold neolithic seafar-
ers whom we saw incising records of their whaling enterprises on the
rocks of these same fjords almost ten thousand years previously.
Their leaders, however, formed an aristocracy of quite another race

who originally migrated from central Asia about the beginning of the Christian Era, bringing with them new gods and certain strange customs. These Asiatics, Asia-men, Aesirmen, or Aesir, were polygamous and they followed set rules about the division of their land and property among their sons.

They were so prolific, moreover, that in a few centuries there was not enough land in the north for all the sons of these jarls and petty kings, and the young noblemen took to roving the sea. This was called by them "viking," or "going a-viking," and became a national habit which resulted in widespread conquests, eventually extending from Scandinavia to Constantinople in the east, and to Canada in the west. They even raided Morocco, and Norse freebooters interfered in the affairs of every European country bordering a sea or penetrated by a river large enough to sail upon.

About the year 890 A.D., King Alfred of southern England, who was a great scholar as well as a lawgiver and warrior, wrote *A Description of Europe*, which was an Anglo-Saxon translation of a Latin work by a Spanish presbyter named Paulus Orosius of Tarragona, compiled in the early fifth century and entitled *The Compendious History of the World*. To Orosius's work King Alfred added any new knowledge that he could find about northern Europe, all of which north of the Rhine and the Danube he called collectively *Germania*. With this he included an account of the voyage of a Norseman named Ohthere. This name is often spelled Octhere, Othere, or Ottar, but these are inaccurate, for the name seems to be derived from *oht*, meaning fear or dread, and *here*, an army. The tale begins: "Ohthere told his Lord, King Alfred . . ." and this seems to imply that Ohthere was actually employed by, subject to, or at least allied with the English king, although the latter was the most stubborn foe the Norse ever encountered. It is even possible that Ohthere actually made the voyage after consultation with King Alfred, and that he returned to report as closely as possible what he found. He certainly brought special gifts for the king and other objects as material evidence of his statements. Ohthere was a nobleman of Nordmanna, or Halgoland, which lay to the south of Sciringes near the modern Koughille in northern Norway. The province of Trondheim, or Drontheim, is today the northernmost in Norway, and it is now divided into three provinces — Trondheim in the south,

Nordland in the middle, and Finmark in the north. In Ohthere's day Halgoland, which is now the southernmost district of Nordland between the island of Lekoe and Cape Kunnen on the Arctic Circle, was the most northerly populated area in Norway. It is a magnificent country of towering mountains and rocky islands.

The principal reason for Ohthere's voyage was to discover new herds of walrus, which were of some considerable importance to the economy of the Norse, especially to their shipbuilding industry, for it was from their hides that the sturdiest ropes for riggings were made. The Norse knew all about the animals of the sea and recognized that the walrus and the whale were mammals and that they were related, as their names for them showed. They called the walrus the *hval-ros*, or "whale-horse," though in King Alfred's script it is written *hors-hwael*. The voyage was made around the northern tip of Scandinavia and down into the White Sea, where plenty of walrus were found. The account of this voyage given by Ohthere to King Alfred and recorded by him in his *Description of Europe* contains a passage that opens a little window on one of the less often mentioned activities of the Norsemen, namely that of their whaling enterprises. It goes as follows:

> The Biarmians told him (Ohthere) many stories, both about their own land and about the other countries around them; but Ohthere knew not how much truth there was in them because he had not opportunity of seeing with his own eyes. It seemed, however, to him, that the Finlanders and the Biarmians spoke nearly the same language. The principal object of his voyage, indeed, was already gained; which was, to increase the discovery of the land, and on account of the horse-whales, because they have very beautiful bone in their teeth, some of which they brought to the King, and their hides are good for ship-ropes. This sort of whale is much less than the other kinds; it is not longer, commonly, than seven ells; but in his own country (Ohthere says) is the best whale-hunting; there the whales are eight and forty ells long and the largest fifty; of these, he said he once killed (six in the company) sixty in two days. He was a very rich man in the possession of certain other animals as well, which constituted the principal wealth of his people — namely, such beasts as are naturally found wild. He had then, when he

came to seek King Alfred, six hundred deer all tamed by himself, and not purchased. They call them Reindeer. Of these six were stall-reins or decoy deer, which are very valuable amongst the Finlanders, because they catch the wild deer with them.

The Biarmians were the inhabitants of the district of Perm in northern Russia, bordering the White Sea. There has been much supposedly erudite discussion among scholars as to the correct interpretation of this passage. The Scandinavian ell is divided into twenty-four inches, and the lengths given, of seven ells, or fourteen feet, for the walrus and fifty ells, or a hundred feet, for the larger whales, are quite accurate, the latter being well within the compass of the larger rorquals. The historians, not being acquainted with the history of whaling in Norway, have found it impossible to believe that one man in the company of either six other persons or even six other ships, as some read the passage, could have killed sixty of the larger whales in two days. It is not generally known, however, that a very special type of whaling has been practiced since time immemorial in the fjords of Norway, whereby whole schools of whales are allowed to enter narrow channels and are driven far into deep inlets where they become crowded together and cannot turn. They are then panicked and often dash right up into the shallows at the head of the fjords and are stranded.

This practice is still followed in various places and there is even a special industry based on the capture of the lesser fin whale, or *seigval*, in two bays near Bergen. Wide-meshed nets are used to cut off the animals' retreat, though more to frighten them than in any attempt actually to hold the whales, which are far too strong to be restrained by any net. In olden days when the whales were thus corralled, they were shot with heavy arrows from huge crossbows, and when weak from loss of blood, were harpooned and hauled to the beaches. The hunt sometimes lasted for eight or nine days and nights before the whole school was landed. This species, also known as the Little Piked Whale (*Balaenoptera acutorostrata*), is the smallest of the rorquals and not very much larger than the extremely rare pigmy right whale, the smallest of all the whalebone whales. It has a world-wide range but prefers to stay near coasts. The Scots call it "piked" because of its pointed dorsal fin, while the Scandinavians call it the cod whale, and it is known to North American whalers as the "sharp-nosed finner."

It grows to a length of only some thirty feet and has a very sharp, narrow snout and a pointed dorsal fin placed rather far forward for a rorqual. In color it is very striking, being a dark gray to bluish black above and ivory white below. Like all the rorquals it has pleats on the throat, but these are extremely numerous and the outer two on either side, together with the lower jaws, are black, in marked contrast to the glistening white throat. The most distinctive feature of this animal, however, is the broad, pure-white band that crosses the upper side of the otherwise black flippers. The baleen is small, only about eight inches long and almost pure white; there are some 320 plates.

In the summer the little piked whale is found in the polar regions, but in winter it comes south and is a seasonal visitor to Norway, where it assembles in considerable numbers. It enters the Baltic and is occasionally taken in the Mediterranean. In the North Pacific it migrates back and forth through the Bering Strait, and in the polar ice fields it hunts in the channels between the floes, where it has the habit of standing straight upright with its head out of water. It is a fish-eater and likes to travel singly when it will often follow ships for days on end. In coastal shallows it darts along in pursuit of fish where there would not appear to be enough water for it even to float. It has a feeble little spout like that of the calves of bigger species, and it has been observed that it often associates with the larger rorquals. Pebbles have sometimes been found in the stomach of this animal and it has been suggested that they may be used to crush the rather bulky food eaten by these whales, like the stones in a bird's gizzard, for these whales, of course, have no teeth or other masticating device and yet are known to swallow quite large dogfish. Various species of piked whales have been described, but they all seem to be, at most, local races, with the possible exception of one from the coast of India which is known only from skeletons but which appears to be somewhat larger and to have more bones in its neck.

In Norway, shoals of white-sided dolphins were until quite recently also hunted by this same process of herding. On one famous hunt in 1834 no fewer than seven hundred of these dolphins were killed in one day, the thirty-first of December. The White-sided Dolphin (*Lagenorhynchus acutus*) is one of the most strikingly colored of all whales, being black above and white below with a broad band of yellowish brown between, in the middle of which is a large white patch. There are then two pairs of jet-black stripes, one extending from the tail forward through the colored flanks to merge with the dark back just in front of the tall dorsal fin, while the other passes from the flippers, which are also black, to the eye. The upper side of the beak is always black and the chin and throat yellow or cream. White-sided dolphins grow to about nine feet in length and assemble in enormous schools of up to two thousand. They are a North Atlantic form extending from the polar ice front in summer as far south as Massachusetts on the American side and the British Isles on the European. They are herring-eaters and the jaws are armed with a large number of very small teeth.

In view of this ancient tradition of whale and dolphin herding along the coasts of Norway, it is quite possible that Ohthere may have been referring to this procedure, and a catch of sixty large whales, such as he mentions, would then indeed be memorable, even to him. It is possible also that the whales of which he spoke as being commonly taken in his country were the black right whale, because an eighth- or ninth-century grave made of stone slabs which was excavated at Hundholm in his home country of Halgoland contained, among other things, some tongue bones of this species. It appears, moreover, that the Norse also used a large ballista, or sort of super crossbow, for shooting whales. This was wound up by a winch operated by two men and shot an extremely heavy harpoon bearing a tremendous iron head which was made in one piece with a long collar that fitted over the front half of a wooden shaft of three-inch diameter. This would account for the Norsemen's apparent ability to take the larger whales, and perhaps even the rorquals, which sink when dead but which could be held afloat by such heavy gear, provided it was attached to ropes that were strong enough. Ropes, as King Alfred tells us, were made of twisted walrus or seal hide, but the Norse also had lines of bast and twisted cow hair. Hemp was unknown. Multistranded ropes of seal hide are extremely strong, and one would probably be quite sufficient to keep

the largest whale afloat until other lines could be attached, or to tow
a small boat when a whale was struck. This ballista is a strange an-
ticipation of the modern harpoon gun which was invented a thousand years later by a descendant of these Norsemen named Svend
Foyn, of whom we shall hear more later.

As we have noted, the history of whaling is concerned with the
activities of a number of maritime peoples. The reasons for this
specificity are often obscure and sometimes quite inexplicable: one
people will make whaling their major industry and a basic part
of their economy, while others, living on the same coast, will not
attempt to do so. It is therefore not only of intrinsic interest, but
also of paramount importance to a proper understanding of whaling
history, to know just who the people were who went whaling,
where they came from, and what they did. Enough is known of the
history of the English, Dutch, and New Englanders, for instance, to
warrant only brief allusion to their pasts, but when we come to other
peoples or races, such as the Phoenicians, Japanese, Norse, and particularly the Basques, we must digress more widely.

The origins of these peoples were until fairly recently shrouded
in the profoundest mystery and much mythological nonsense. Modern archaeological studies and other researches have now, however,
placed at our disposal many facts concerning their origins which
go far toward explaining their subsequent behavior. From these we
now find that much of what we formerly believed about these
peoples is either untrue or unimportant, while certain other aspects
of their culture is of the greatest significance. Most outstanding
among such characteristics — especially of the Norse and Basques —
are their comparative lack of imagination, on the one hand, and their
intense realism and practicality, on the other. These characteristics
manifested themselves in behavior that has nearly always been mis-
interpreted. Thus neither of these people seems ever to have been
in any way interested in exploring for its own sake.

The great voyages that opened up vast new areas of the seas,
oceans, and distant lands by the Norse were never considered by
them to be contributions to geographical knowledge, nor were they
designed as such. Like Biarni Heriulfson, who, as we shall see later,
first reached the mainland of North America, and that by mistake,
they were so disinterested they often did not even land, let alone

explore. When they did return later in search of such newly sighted coasts, moreover, they did so solely for the most practical purposes, such as to find new sources of food or other raw materials. Both Basques and Norsemen were primarily fisherfolk, and to them whales were the most valuable "fish." They went anywhere after these sea products and thus only incidentally discovered new lands. Even the British and Dutch were far more interested in finding sources of animal oil than in discovering a northeast passage, and this was desirable only as a new route to the spices and other luxuries of the Orient. A rounded picture of these odd and comparatively rare maritime peoples is thus a substantial part of our whole story, and the origin of the Basques, Japanese, and Norse is of just as much importance as that of the blue, sperm, and bottle-nosed whales. Unless you know where the people concerned came from and how they lived, you cannot possibly understand, for instance, why the Scots built icebreakers or the Norwegians are today milling about the Antarctic in vast floating factories.

It was in shipbuilding, however, that the Norse made their greatest contribution to history and it was through their seafaring example that western Europe was first stimulated to assert itself. The Norse used two kinds of craft known rather logically as "long ships" and "round ships." Both were clinker-built of oak on a frame of numerous strong, naturally curved timbers that were gutted to receive the planks. The timbers were grown crooked deliberately by being tied down when saplings. The planking was bolted and riveted together from the inside, and then lashed to the frames with withes made from tree roots. These ships were caulked with three strands of corded cow hair laid in when they were built. Both types were double-ended and they were virtually without keels. Bowsprits were unknown and there was no rudder post, steering being effected by a large outside oar which was always on the "starboard" — meaning the "stars" for navigation and the "board," or oar, for steering. Apart from these points, the two types differed considerably. A great deal is known about the long ships because of the Norsemen's habit of burying their sea kings in their own boats under a mound of earth known as a *howe*. Four of them have been dug up in a very fair state of preservation. The round ships are even better known, for they are still built today on the coasts of Norway, where they are now known as Northland boats. The long ships were the war vessels of the Norse, but they were also used as pleasure yachts on the *viks*, or bays, of Norway, by the kings, jarls, and other nobles, and by their ladies. The most famous of all was Olaf Tryggvason's *Long Serpent*, which was a hundred and forty-eight feet long, had thirty-two pairs of oars, and carried three hundred men. The ultimate of all long ships, however, was that built by King Cnut in England which had sixty pairs of oars, carried five hundred persons, and was a third the length of the *Queen Elizabeth*.

Of more interest to us, however, are the round ships, for it was in these that the Norse made their great voyages of exploration and went a-whaling. They were also of various kinds and sizes but were mostly built to the same plan. They relied more on sail and had oars only fore and aft for use in entering ports or bucking river currents. They were usually of about fifty tons' displacement and carried up to fifteen tons of cargo. There was a forecastle for sleeping and a small poop deck, and the two were connected by narrow covered passages along either side of the central hold, which was undecked but covered with a skin tarpaulin when filled with cargo. There was accommodation of a cramped kind for a crew of from fifty to sixty. Women often went along with their men, though in lesser numbers, and many a Norseman was born upon the bosom of the ocean in the narrow forecastles of these sturdy ships. Life aboard the round ships was not gentle. Only two sparse meals were eaten each day, usually consisting of porridge and dried fish but sometimes supplemented by bread, butter, and cheese. Water was often foul and was replaced by ale when it was available. The Norse also had the wise habit of drinking the blood of freshly killed sea birds.

Round ships lacked keels and had a central mast, and they were very much broader in the beam than the war vessels. They would not at first sight appear to be very handy, and they could probably only run free or sail, at most, one point into the wind, but they seem to have been most excellent sea boats. They had much more freeboard than the long ships and so were able to brave the ocean at its worst. They were known as *knorr* or *kaup-skip*, which meant "trading ships," though the name *byrding*, or "ship of burden," was also applied to them, and when they went on long ocean voyages they were called *haf-skip*, or "deep-sea ships."

Since the compass was unknown in those days, we may well wonder how the Norse sailed regularly, and usually unerringly, back and forth all over the North Atlantic, arriving at tiny oceanic islands time and time again in all winds, both fair and foul, and despite currents, drifts, and various other factors of which they probably knew little.

If we look at a map of the North Atlantic in an ordinary atlas, especially one drawn on Mercator's projection, we may well be mystified and greatly amazed at the seamanship of the Norse. If, however, we redraw this map from a purely aquacentric point of view, and upon what is known as an "equal-area projection" centered about the North Pole, and then turn the whole thing round so that it may be looked at from the angle of a Norseman going "west viking," we shall see many things that were simply not apparent before. For instance, starting from the Wick and proceeding northwest, one comes first to the Orkneys, then the Faeroes, then Iceland, and finally to Greenland, all in a straight line. Provided one doesn't veer to starboard after leaving the coast of Scotland, one is certain to make land by sailing in any direction. Then, if it starts to get too cold, one knows that one is going too far north. Similarly, coming home, one simply keeps straight ahead by the stars and, after leaving Iceland, veers to starboard for Norway or to port for the British Isles. Looking at a map of the North Atlantic in this way goes far towards explaining the voyages of discovery of the Norse, for it will be seen that they simply kept on going in a straight line as far as possible.

The Norse estimated their speed and distances by the number of twenty-four-hour sailing periods between known points, and it has been calculated from recorded voyages that the *kaup-skip*, for all their apparent clumsiness, made on an average about six to six and a half knots. Using these *kaup-skip* and the simplest navigational rule — namely, to keep going straight ahead — the Norse sailed regularly back and forth over the North Atlantic, culminating in Harald Hardrada's polar expedition in the eleventh century. Iceland was originally discovered, however, in the first half of the ninth century by a Dane named Nadd-od while on his way from the

## The North Atlantic, as Seen by the Norse

The people we call the Norse were Central Asiatic landsmen and did not really understand boats or the open oceans. They arrived in western Europe only about the beginning of the Christian Era. All their sailing was done for them by the descendants of the ancient Stone Age peoples of Scandinavia. To the latter, vikingism was a matter of thousands of years of island hopping, but, although they seem to have already reached the Faeroes, Britain, Portugal, and even Africa, by this procedure, they had not had reason to expand further. Norse population pressure, land hunger, and food shortages, combined with the fishing enterprises of these neolithic peoples, forced them far beyond.

While Norse vikings went in all directions, even east up great rivers to found Russia, or Røssland, and although they circumnavigated Europe and finally arrived in Byzantium on the Black Sea, the major expansion was to what we call the "west," which was to them "straight ahead." Thus, they hopped to Iceland and thence to Greenland, and from there they made voyages to the right in pursuit of whales and fish, to the left to New England, and probably also straight ahead into Hudson's Bay. Nothing came of the last two efforts, probably because of the waning of the population pressure behind them, which made these trips almost voyages of exploration. The farthest advance may have been to Minnesota, as shown, but this could at best have been just what the famous "Kensington Stone" states it was — a search party looking for Greenland colonists who had disappeared west long before in search of wood and a place where they could grow foodstuffs.

There is nothing inexplicable about these Norse voyages. They simply island-hopped straight ahead and seldom had to cross a hundred miles of open water, while the winds and tides helped them.

KENSINGTON STONE
MUCH DEBATED RUNIC
MARKER LEFT BY KING
MAGNUS ERICSON'S
EXPEDITION OF 1362 A.D.
IN SEARCH OF LOST
GREENLAND EMPIRES

CANADA

VINLAND

NOVA
SCOTIA

HUDSON'S
BAY

LABRADOR

NEWFOUNDLAND
(Markland)

HELLULAND

BAFFIN ISLAND

GRAND
BANKS

DAVIS
STRAIT

BAFFIN BAY

ARCTIC
ICE-RAFT
(TODAY)

LABRADOR
BASIN

NORSE SETTLEMENTS

GREENLAND

×North
Pole

NORTH
ATLANTIC
OCEAN

DENMARK
SEA

EAST
GREENLAND
SEA

AZORES
ISLANDS

ICELAND

GREENLAND SEA

JAN MAYEN
LAND

FRANZ JOSEF
LAND

NORSE SEA

BARENTS
SEA

SPANISH
BASIN

NORTH
SEA

SCANDINAVIA

LAND OF THE BIARMIANS

SPAIN

FRANCE

EMIGRATION OF THE AESIR

KINGDOM
OF THE
ABBASSIDS

?

## Map 2  The North Atlantic, as Seen by the Norse

Polar Azimuthal Equidistant Projection
Scale 1:45,000,000

⟵⟵⟵  Main Viking Routes
⟵--- Known and Conjectural
Explorations

Faeroe Islands to Norway. He was blown off his course to the north and made a great sweep to the west, ending up at almost the right distance but exactly in the opposite direction to that which he desired. Then, in 900 A.D. one Gunbjorn, while on his way to Iceland from Norway, got blown off his course, missed his objective entirely, and landed up on the coast of Greenland. These were purely fortuitous discoveries; later voyages were not.

The Norse had fine ships and they sailed sea-countries that lie between two great oceans — the North Atlantic and the Arctic. It was almost inevitable, therefore, that they should follow the whale. That they did so, we know not only from Ohthere but also from several other contemporary records and from material objects found in their burial *howes* and other places. There is, for instance, in the *Heimskringla*, — the "Bible" of the Norse, composed by the great Icelandic literary genius Snorri Sturlasson, in 1100 A.D., in which the whole history and tradition of the race is recorded — a saga of one Grettir the Strong, containing a delightful passage in which we are told of the stranding of a large rorqual at Rifsker in Iceland and how all the important people who were able went to it. The Icelanders were noted for their feuding and general irascibility at all times, behavior that finally brought their splendid little democracy to ruin and lost for them their most treasured possession, their freedom. This story in the saga of Grettir is almost a parody of these national shortcomings.

The story goes, "The first to arrive was Flosi and the men of Vik who at once began to cut up the whale, carrying on shore the flesh as it was cut out. Then there came the men of Kaldbak with four ships." This ominous note being struck, the writer takes a flight of fancy on related subjects and then goes on to say that the leader of this second party, one Thorgrim, laid claim to the whale but was challenged by the men of Vik and was outnumbered. But, "Then there came a ship across the fjords; it was Svan of Hol from Bjarnfjord with his men and he at once told Thorgrim not to let himself be robbed." Thereupon the inevitable happened and a fight began. Flosi and the men of Vik were getting badly beaten up when one Olaf appeared with the ships of Drangar and saved them. A general melee followed in which all parties participated lustily. From a rather ribald verse composed later about the affair, however, we learn, somewhat to our chagrin, that these stalwarts went at each other with strips of rotten whale blubber — "most unseemly," as the ancient poet pointedly observes.

There appears to have been a considerable whaling tradition in Iceland, and it is to this outpost of the Norsemen that we must now turn to continue our tale. There came to Iceland in 960 A.D., from Jaeder in Norway, a noble family. There was among them a son named Eric, called the Red, who was then only ten years old. This lad grew up to be even more rowdy and obstreperous than the normal Norseman and, while still in his late teens, got himself into such a maze of brawls and feuds over women, his inheritance, and practically everything else that he had to find a ship and leave the country. He gathered a few rather unwilling followers and went off to the west, as the story tells, "in pursuit of whales and other sea creatures." By these activities he lived for three years. He then returned to Iceland and started propagandizing the country he had been exploring, calling it Greenland simply to make it appear more attractive, for he had resolved to settle there. He set about trying to collect volunteers to join him in his colonizing, and in this he seems to have been very successful, for in 985 or 986 A.D. he set out with twenty-five ships carrying seven hundred people and large numbers of cattle, horses, and other supplies. Only fourteen of the ships reached the promised land, but, led by Eric, they settled at a point some distance up the Davis Strait on the west, or inner, side of southern Greenland and set to work to lay out a colony by the old traditional methods of the Norse.

From the first, Eric was the leader and chieftain, and in time he became a sort of monarch by right of tradition. The colony prospered and more people came, until in its heyday some hundred years later it probably numbered about four thousand souls divided up into two main and several subsidiary settlements. It proclaimed itself a free state and had a checkered history which lasted for five hundred years, the last Greenlander being found dead in 1540, lying outside a miserable hut, clothed in the typical Norse cape and hood, and clutching an old iron dagger in his hand. He was found by a Dutch whaling captain very appropriately named Jon Greenlander.

The Greenland colonies traded many things with Europe, including the furs of polar bear, fox, and seal, the skins of walrus, and the ivory from their tusks. The Greenlanders also carried on most industrious whaling enterprises, as the many bones of these animals found during the excavation of their settlements indicate. They regularly took the black right whale, the ca'ing, or blackfish, the white-beaked dolphin, and the narwhal. This was a summer activity because of the dark and intensely rigorous winters, and the whole able-bodied male population took part. Fleets were formed and went up the straits into Baffin Bay as far north as Melville Bay at 76° N. latitude, and then crossed to Lancaster Sound. On occasion also they seem to have gone west round the south of Baffin Island and into Hudson Strait. The whales caught were processed on the spot and the products loaded aboard the round ships and freighted back to the settlements. Blubber oil, dried meat, ivory from teeth, and bladders and guts, which were soaked and inflated like balloons to be used as floats, were the most useful items to the colonists.

Walrus and narwhal tusks were reserved for foreign trade, those of the latter being exceedingly valuable in Europe. Narwhal tusks were sold as the horn of the unicorn, and it is probable that most people in Europe believed they were just this. As such they were thought to be very powerful and almost universally applicable medicine, being ground down and made into potions to overcome feminine modesty and resistance, to cure corns, heartburn and sore eyes, and for a variety of even more magical purposes. They were also used for making thrones, especially episcopal thrones, and for other ornamental objects in monasteries. They had a regal connotation and were taxed accordingly.

Although the narwhal has always been taken both for its very high-grade oil and for its tusks, Greenlanders seem to have been the only people in the West who ever made it the basis of a regular industry, and the majority of the narwhal horns that came to Europe for many decades originated with them. Similarly, their regular hunting of the White-beaked Dolphin (*Lagenorhynchus albirostris*) seems to have been unique and was probably quite fortuitous, the animal just happening to be very common in their sea-country, while they needed it for food. This species is a gregarious fish-eater, growing to a length of about nine feet, and ranges throughout the North Atlantic down to about the forty-fifth parallel on the

American, and the fifty-fifth on the European, side, though it also enters the Baltic.

By reference to the map on page 87 it will be seen that this northern bow of the Atlantic forms a distinct "province" made up of a number of sea-countries that are confluent and lie between the polar ocean to the north and the North Atlantic Ocean proper to the south. As we shall see, many species are more or less confined to this belt and to the other interoceanic provinces between the temperate and polar seas, which are the principal abodes of all whales and in which all major whaling industries are situated. Within this area the white-beaked dolphin migrates north to the polar seas in the summer and south into the cold temperate waters in the winter. It is a common animal and associates in schools of up to fifteen hundred individuals. It is very like the white-sided dolphin but has a two-inch white beak, a slightly more swollen head, a more sloping back fin, and longer flippers. It is black above and white below, with a large white spot behind the eye and two elongated white areas within the black of the flanks, which are sometimes mottled gray. There is also a white area on the back behind the blowhole. There is, however, considerable individual variation in these markings, and sometimes the animal's back is shot with purplish blue. There are about a hundred small, regular teeth surrounding both jaws.

The Narwhal (*Monodon monoceras*) is the most amazing of all whales and in some respects the most extraordinary of all living mammals. It is a small species, growing to a maximum length of about sixteen feet, is cylindrical in shape with a blunt rounded head, a small tail, little rounded flippers, and a ridge one inch high along the back in place of a dorsal fin. It has a single crescentic blowhole. In color it is very singular. The young, which are about five feet long when born and very carefully tended by their mothers for a long period even after weaning, are usually uniformly dark gray, but the adults develop all manner of dapplings and leopardine spottings of gray on a creamy background. The females are always more intensely spotted than the males but there are some very pale individuals of both sexes, and the oldsters turn almost pure white. The underside is less spotted and lighter. It is believed that this coloration provoked their name from the Danish *narhval,* and the old Norse *nahvalr*, which is derived from *na-r* meaning a corpse. The Dutch whalers called them *eenhorn* or *hoornvisch* by reason of their most distinctive feature, their tusk.

Narwhals have no visible teeth, their jaws being horny and used simply for crushing and not for masticating the fish, squids, cuttles, and crustaceans that they eat. There are, however, in both sexes two amazing tusks that are greatly modified canine teeth which point forward and lie horizontally in the bones of the upper jaw. In the female these remain hidden within the jawbones throughout life, but in the male either one, which is then invariably the left, or both grow into tremendous, long, straight spears with a number of grooves and ridges that extend spirally to the tip like a corkscrew. The strange thing is that this twist is always sinistral, or to the left, and even if two tusks are developed, the grooves on both turn the same way. These tusks may often be more than half the length of the animal, and specimens up to ten feet long have been recorded. One tusk, eight feet long, had a basal girth of seven and a half inches; they are devoid of enamel and have a central pulp cavity that extends almost to the tip.

The question as to what their use may be to the animal itself has caused a great deal of debate. One observer noticed that the males fenced with them, holding their heads out of the water and crossing their tusks like rapiers. It has been suggested that they are used to spear fish, but in this case the female, who has none, must fare rather badly, and we would also like to know how the animal gets the fish off its spear. Narwhals have been seen crowding air holes in the polar ice in order to breathe, and it is believed the tusks may have been developed to keep these holes open during rapid freezes. The structure is, however, undoubtedly a secondary sexual character like the cock's comb.

The narwhal is an exclusively polar animal seldom seen outside the Arctic Circle. It is found all round the coasts of the Arctic Ocean and travels about in family parties of up to twenty individuals. Sometimes narwhals gather together in enormous herds to migrate north, as has often been observed in the Davis Strait. They are now greatly reduced in number, the result of centuries of persecution, but they are still more common between Europe and America than between America and Asia. They are exceedingly fast swimmers and are said to make a number of strange noises. Occasionally they gurgle, and sometimes they give a shrill whistle, but this is believed to be made by the air being evicted from the blowhole and is a sound common to several other whales. A deep roar or short, low-pitched blast is, however, definitely produced by the mouth and may be the mother calling her young.

One case of twins is recorded. The narwhal has never been known to attack man or ships, or to attempt to pierce canoes with its tusk as does the swordfish. The blubber oil of narwhals is much superior in quality to that of all other whales, and this, combined with the tusks, made them valuable to the Greenlanders above all other products of the sea. At the same time, the meat is very palatable, and a great delicacy, a *mattak*, is made by boiling the skin until it is reduced to a jelly.

The lonely Greenland colonies, distant as they may appear to us, were not the ultimate outposts of the Norsemen. They made trips far to the west and south. These were not attempts to colonize but merely to search for timber for shipbuilding. The most notable occurrence during these efforts was probably the birth by the wife of one Thorfinn Karlsefni of a male child who was named Snorri — the first European known definitely to have been born in America and who saw the light of day almost exactly five hundred years before Cristoforo Colombo reached the West Indies. Only one definite attempt at colonization on the mainland of America was made by the Greenland Norse, and this was doomed to failure by the very character of its leader, an atrocious woman named Freydis, a daughter of old Eric the Red. She murdered half her crew in cold blood and antagonized the Amerindians. After that, there is a prolonged silence of nine hundred years but for one dim glimmer that was brought to light at the end of the last century and which has even now not been fully accepted as an historical record. This is the so-called "Kensington Stone," found by a distant descendant of the early Norse, one Olaf Ohman, under an ancient aspen stump in Minnesota, in 1898. On this, in crude runic script but in a very distinct later form of the Norse language which could hardly have been forged, it is recorded that a mixed band of Scandinavians, searching for the lost Greenland colonists under instructions from King Magnus Ericson of Norway, met disaster there in the year 1362 A.D.

It is a strange fact that this great continent, once it had been discovered by such a vigorous and expansionist race as the Norse, should not have been conquered and colonized, but instead lay fallow for another five centuries before it was even "discovered" by the European world. How drastically, and perhaps for the better, the history of the world might have been changed if this land had become a great Norse empire, and had been called *Erica* after the sturdy old whaler rather than *America* after a rather paltry latecomer from the Mediterranean who either only sailed up the Mississippi or never reached the northern continent at all. From our point of view, however, there is a fitting epitaph to the efforts of the Norsemen in the New World which is to be found in the *Flatey Book* — one of the most important early Icelandic documents known — for it concerns the whale, in pursuit of which Eric the Red first came to this continent.

It appears that when Thorfinn Karlsefni's group reached Leif Ericson's camp they were very short of provisions. To their joy a large stranded whale was discovered nearby and they immediately set about cutting into this and trying out the blubber. According to the *Flatey Book* version, they also ate the meat, but all became violently sick. Now, there was an inveterate old reprobate on this expedition, a confirmed pagan named Thorhall, who had given as his principal reason for coming along in the first place the fact that he wanted above all to find wine, which was sorely lacking in Iceland and Greenland. Finding that there was no wine in the new land and that it was even the wrong season for the much-vaunted "grapes" of America, he decided to go home. He left in a small auxiliary ship, taking nine others with him, and got lost. He was finally wrecked on the shores of Ireland, where he is said to have composed a poem, one stanza of which is recorded as follows:

Those who will may bide in quiet
Let them praise their chosen land,
Feasting on a whale steak diet,
In their home by Wonder Strand.

# 5
# Half-Light over Warm Seas
## (*Japanese*)

THE BOAT of Masatoshi Komuro appeared suddenly out of the pale gray mist between the island and the headland. It swung right, under the overhanging, flat-topped pine trees, as it headed into the narrow bay. The girls on the beach were the first to see it, for almost everybody else was working indoors drying things that had become sodden during the long period of rainy weather. It was still early in the morning, and none of the boats which had left for the fishing grounds late the evening before, when the rains had stopped, should have been returning so soon. The village was almost without fish because the weather had been so bad, and the farmers were waiting eagerly for supplies so that they could get back to their early planting. At first the girls thought there must have been a serious accident of some kind to have caused Masatoshi, of all men, to come rowing home in such a hurry. They all gathered at the water's edge.

As soon as the boat was within hailing distance, the steersman stood up in the stern and, cupping his hands, started shouting to the girls on shore. At first they could not even hear, let alone understand, what he was calling, but then the always unpredictable Iiye, who was known to have set her cap upon Masatoshi, ran along the beach to the flagpole, which she climbed as nimbly as a squirrel, and, wrapping her legs around its very top, started waving to the men in the boat. Iiye had strange ways with the men, and she, far beyond any of the other girls, understood in turn their ways, despite the displeasure of the older women, who were frankly horrified at her behavior and were always predicting her early demise in all manner of dire ways. The men in the boat waved back to her in such a way that she promptly understood their hurry and immediately called down to the other girls the single exciting word, "*Kujira*." But the silly girls simply stood there repeating the word one to the other, until Iiye slid down the pole and went flying up the beach to the village calling out wildly the news that Masatoshi brought word whales had been sighted. Immediately people began to pour out of all the houses and the children dropped their games and went running to the beach.

Now, it was fortunate that none of the men on shore had left the village for the farms inland, because it would have taken a long time to round them up to man the many boats that had not gone fishing, and the little fleet that was already at sea would have been left not only shorthanded but in a quite useless position, because none of them had carried whaling equipment, this being not yet the normal time for the northward spring migrations of the whales. It was still far too early, but the weather had been so unusually warm for the season, and the rains had been so excessive, that almost anything could be expected. Thus it was that, long before the boat of Masatoshi reached the beach, the men ashore, assisted by the younger women, were already assembling all the harpoons, ropes, and floats by the water's edge, while the children shoved the long, sharpended, open boats into the water. Meantime another party was hauling the great net out of the warehouse.

It was made of root-rope cable an inch and a half thick most cunningly knotted to form a giant mesh two feet square, and it was a hundred feet long and nearly fifty wide when spread out. Nobody remembered any longer when it had been made and even the oldest men could not say when certain well-known splices had been put in it, but it was the proudest possession of the village, and was always kept in the best of repair. It had been several months since it had last been wetted, and it was very stiff. The gang had to wait until all the boats had been launched and all the gear assembled before they had enough hands to move it. By then Masatoshi had jumped ashore, gabbling away in great excitement.

Iiye was immediately at his side, elaborating on all that he said, although it is not the place of unmarried girls to speak when menfolk are talking, but nobody rebuked her, not only because they were so excited, but because they had all learned long before that their best efforts would be to no avail. Iiye, although only seventeen, was taller than anybody else in the village, and she had a sweet, friendly, and most courteous disposition, but she was irrepressibly ebullient, had not the slightest respect for any custom or tradition, and, being as strong physically as any man, did almost exactly as she pleased. The girls as well as the men adored her, and backed her up in anything she did, for it is an ancient tradition in Nippon that outstanding women make the best leaders, which is more important than that they should keep silent. So it was that Iiye ended up giving orders to all who would listen.

Nevertheless, furious argument broke out as to what was to be done, and this might have continued all day, for the manning of the oars was a most important point in the lives of these people, when one of the children gave a shout of glee and pointed to Masatoshi's boat. In it sat Iiye at the left forward oar, smiling quietly, her chin resting on her hands.

At this the men burst out laughing, but the older women set up a deplorable wailing, while the children ran about screaming, "*Yuki-masho*," which can best be translated as, "Let's go." And the children prevailed over the wailing women, for the men made a concerted dive for the boats, and before the ancient ones' counsel or commands could be heard, they had pushed off, Iiye pulling the lead in Masatoshi's boat with a stroke that put the other oarsmen to strenuous work. And so the fleet of more than twenty boats strung out down the bay, Iiye in the lead boat, and the big boat of Jindo San, with Masatoshi at the helm and filled with the net, trailing behind. The mist closed upon them beyond the headland and they disappeared into a bright, white, clammy gloom that blanketed the heaving bosom of the sea which was as slick and oily as a wrestler's skin.

The steersman in the lead boat was young Daikyo Miyoshi, Iiye's brother. Not even the more experienced hands could understand how, on that eventful day, he steered the boats to the fishing fleet which waited off shore, for he not only took them through the blanket of fog for many miles out to sea to the point where the mist suddenly thinned and gave way to brilliant sunshine, but he also brought them directly to the other boats waiting beyond.

These were now strung out for miles, the nearest just outside the fog bank to landward, the farthest well beyond the horizon. The whales had been encountered in the fog, traveling leisurely north-wards, and had obviously — from their unhurried progress and con-stant, gentle blowing — been feeding. They were seis and they had yearlings with them. However, they turned seaward just after Masatoshi's boat departed into the fog to fetch the gear and help necessary to attack them, and the only thing the others could do was follow them by stringing out to the limits of vision and contact. At one time they had thought the whole thing a lost cause because the whales went so far out to sea, but now they learned by signals that the animals had turned about and were heading slowly back towards the coast. What is more, they were still undisturbed and apparently quite unaware that humans were watching them.

As soon as the two fleets joined up, the more experienced men had their boats rowed together around Jindo San. While they waited, the whales slowly moved shorewards, and one by one the other boats, that had been strung out over the ocean watching them, came in to join the crowded fleet. By the time the big boat ar-rived, they were almost all assembled in a tight knot, and Jindo San stood up and shouted out his suggestions so that all might hear and understand. And this time even Iiye was silent and listened atten-tively, for not only was she fully aware of her position in their midst on sufferance, but she was also a very intelligent person and had often listened to her father and others when they had recounted their experiences hunting the *kujira*. Then, at a signal, the fleet de-ployed and moved off northward in a double line, with the big boat in the middle, in order to intercept the whales at a tangent as they moved slowly back towards the coast. Nobody spoke and they all tried their hardest not to let their oars clatter or even squeak, for the *kujira* is a very shy and sensitive creature, and is easily disturbed. Half an hour later the lead boat, steered by one Naosuke Tomada, raised a signal in the form of a piece of cloth on a long bamboo pole and waved it in the general direction of the northeast. This indicated that the whales were breaching in that quarter and were still heading towards a position that would coincide with the line of advance, but other signals indicated that more speed would be needed to get to that point in time. Every steersman immediately gave a brief command, and all men bent to their oars.

Very soon a lot of funnel-shaped, white fountains of spume could be seen rising from the sea in groups of four or five, one after the other. It was the whales spouting, and they were not more than half a mile away. Then Jindo San gave a command by two strokes on a small gong; this carried clearly across the waters, and every oar came to rest so that the boats just drifted forward in formation. This was the critical moment, for should the whales notice them and take alarm at their presence, they might turn about and go charging out to sea, while if they continued and did not by mistake come up under a boat, they might pass right under them. Time seemed to stand still while the whales kept breaching, blowing regularly, and rolling below again as they moved ever closer to the boats.

Now, Iiye and her brother were on the inner line about the middle of the fleet, only two boats from the big one commanded by Masatoshi and next to that of Jindo San, and it was soon clear to all that it was precisely to this point that the leading whale was heading. The boats roundabout, therefore, began to turn their prows to the ocean so that they might present the smallest obstacles to the oncoming beasts and at the same time allow the harpooners, standing ready in the bows of the inner line of boats, to take the best advantage of every second that might elapse from the first breaching of the animals between the boats and the time when the oarsmen could get within throwing distance of that spot. In this, Iiye's position as forward oar in her boat suddenly became of first importance, but she was so strong and so eager that her first pulls, though made with skillful silence, were so deceptively powerful she brought the boat about almost singlehanded, and they were in position long before any of the others. At that very instant the lead whale broke the surface directly ahead of them. Her brother gave a single order and the boat literally jumped forward, the little harpooner known as "Naze," because he was always asking questions, poised in its bows. Before any of the oarsmen knew what had happened, a harpoon was fast in the animal, the line had leaped overboard carrying the inflated skin float behind it, and Daikyo had brought the boat around in a tight turn. Then he too seized a harpoon, and leaning right over the head of his first oarsman, he cast it almost directly downwards.

As if lightning had struck it, the whale came to life with one tremendous heave that projected it straight out of the water, and as it went it took the float which was attached to Daikyo's line clean out of the bottom of the boat. And, as this went, it caught Daikyo in the small of his back and punched him abruptly overboard. Then two things happened. The first whale headed straight for the big boat, while a second whale breached right alongside. Another man had already seized the steering oar in Daikyo's place and the harpooner, Naze, had another implement ready, which he cast, and he once again made fast. This second whale sounded immediately, leaving a whorl of blood on the surface.

The first whale, pulling two floats, rushed over the sea and passed right by the big boat, from which three more harpoons were thrown. Two of these took, and this caused the animal to turn suddenly and come straight back between the two lines of boats. It was only then that those in the surrounding boats saw Daikyo swimming for the big boat, but right between the whale and one of the floats. What happened next could not have been avoided, so quickly did it take place. The monster had turned almost a complete circle, and as it rushed off, the line pulled round Daikyo in a tight loop and he was jerked off over the surface in a cloud of foam. That was when the men of many boats lost considerable face which they never really recovered, for as the whale passed Daikyo's boat, they were amazed to see somebody dive overboard directly upon it.

That one helps one's friends is an established tradition, but diving into the sea to combat an infuriated *kujira* in this cause is not considered either sensible, practical, or even worthwhile. When, therefore, the onlookers realized who had so dived, they held their breaths and their oars and even their harpoons, for it was Iiye who had disappeared below the surface. And thus they waited quite immobile until the whale breached again farther up the line, and Jindo San let out a roar. Then harpoons flew and men leaned furiously upon their oars, everything forgotten but the work at hand. Nobody had time to think about a lost friend and his stupid sister.

The whale had been in difficulties from the start, but it was now becoming frantic with no fewer than eight harpoons fast in its blubber and seven floats holding it back. It was Jindo San who first noticed that one float was missing, and as soon as he had shouted orders to Masatoshi for the net to be put overboard, and had assembled a sufficient number of boats in a rough circle around the whale to drive it towards this trap, he took a quick look around. To his amazement he saw, somewhat astern and just visible in the outer fringes of the fog which they were rapidly approaching, not only the missing float but also two heads bobbing about in the water beside it. Blinking his extremely small black eyes under their heavy lids, he sucked in his breath with a tremendous hiss and murmured to himself, "*Ara!*" and then more thoughtfully, "*Oya!*" which may be said to mean, first, "Well, God bless my soul!" and secondly and literally, "By jingo!" Then he turned his attention to the taking of the whale.

This proved easier than anyone could have expected, for the crazed beast was easily turned, and being too weak already to breach any more with any force, it just charged straight into the net. This did indeed cause the total loss of the smaller boat holding the net's other end, for the animal's rush was still so powerful that it hauled the two boats together, and the smaller one simply caved in, was swamped, and came apart while its occupants jumped overboard or leaped for the big boat. The whale then tried to sound, but the pull of some two dozen floats, the great net, and the big boat were too much even for its vast bulk and strength, and it just floated up to the surface, where it was immediately stabbed from all sides by the now assembled boats, the men using every implement available. It died within minutes.

Meantime the fleet had broken up and become widely dispersed. Two other whales were fast farther up to the north; the boats to the south were scattered far and wide; while a few lone bladders careened across the sea. Jindo San at last found a moment from his duties as leader of the expedition to look around for the missing float with its bobbing heads. To his amazement his eyes fell upon them only a few yards distant from the assembled boats, and he let out a most unusual roar and pointed for all men to see.

Every man stopped what he was doing to look, and there they saw Iiye paddling slowly towards them, one hand on the float, the other clutched around her brother's neck. And when willing hands had fished them from the waters and had laid out Daikyo, whose body was ringed by a livid welt of bleeding flesh and exposed ribs, and had done what they could for him, the men turned to the girl. The end of the line attached to the float showed plainly how she had saved her brother. It was cleanly cut, which could only have been done with a sharp knife. Iiye still had that knife clutched between her teeth when they pulled her from the sea.

The men were very silent and they went about their business industriously, fastening the lines to the floating whale. Then they rowed for seven hours back to the bay, and nobody said a word. Iiye rowed also, while little Naze tended to her brother. It was dark when they reached the village beach and almost dawn by the time they had drawn the three whales killed to the foreshore. Then the men from all the boats which had been near that of Daikyo assembled, with Jindo San at their head and, forming a body apart from all the rest, they called to Iiye to come from her house. They bowed to her, something not normally done by grown men to an unmarried and young girl, and they asked her forgiveness in formal and most humble terms. Then, without waiting for any reply, they went quietly away to their houses. Only Masatoshi remained, and everybody recognized that it was his duty to do so. He approached Iiye in silence, took her by the hand, and led her to the house of her aging father.

THE inhabitants of the islands of Nippon are a mixed race in the narrower sense of that term. Originally there was a most ancient Stone Age stock inhabiting these islands which were then invaded by another people emanating from the nearby continent who subdued and then partly exterminated and partly absorbed them. Next came a second wave of more cultured folk who overran the southern part of the archipelago, wiping out all whom they found there and driving the remnants of the original inhabitants and the previous invaders into the northern islands. The original race has now completely vanished, while the remnants of the first invaders have been almost eclipsed by absorption in the northern islands.

Nippon is the name given by the Japanese and sundry other peoples to an archipelago which they collectively inhabit off the eastern edge of Asia. Today, the political unit we call Japan is confined to only three of the six intrinsic parts of this archipelago. These are known respectively as Kyushu in the south, Honshu, with the island of Shikoku, in the middle, and Hokkaido in the north. The other three portions of the archipelago are the Ryukyu Islands, which stretch south from Kyushu to the great island of Taiwan, or Formosa, which lies close to the mainland of China and is inhabited by people basically allied to the Chinese; the large island of Sakhalin, lying against the coast of Amuria to the northwest; and the diadem of islands known as the Kuriles, which stretch northeast to the southern tip of the peninsula of Kamchatka.

The accompanying map displays all the essential features of the area as seen by the Japanese. If you want to recognize it, you should turn the page exactly ninety degrees clockwise and then you will see it as it appears in our school atlases. Seen either way, but thus lopped off from the rest of the vast continent of Eurasia, it will probably look rather startling to all but geographers because we have always thought of Asia as ending with China to the east, off the coast of which lies only Japan. Almost invariably, all that lies "above," or north, of China — according to our silly way of looking at the world — is either simply ignored, or entirely left out of our maps. Nevertheless, the triangular piece of land that juts out east over the Pacific, and which lies north of China, is actually slightly larger than the United States, while one of its rivers, the Lena, is longer than, and a second, the Amur, almost as long as, the much-vaunted Mississippi complex. This is a gigantic land of mighty mountains, vast plains, and endless forests, inhabited today, as it has been since the fifth millennium B.C. at least, by a large number of tribes which are grouped into several related units or nationalities. The area of which we speak is roughly triangular and stretches from 120° E. to 170° E. and from 75° N. to some 40° N. about Pekin. It is nearly two thousand miles wide from west to east across the

## The West Pacific, as Seen by the Nipponese

The Japanese, or the people we call by that name today, although originally a seafaring race of migrants, were not true mariners until comparatively recently. They did not employ sail until this millennium, and there were periods in their history when the building of ships, as opposed to little boats, was prohibited by law in order to prevent the people from leaving the country. Nevertheless, they have since become a great sea power and expanded widely over the northern Pacific.

The people who inhabited their islands before they came were great seamen though still living in the Stone Age. They appear to have been related to the eastern Siberian Mongoloid peoples, the Eskimos, and possibly some of the Amerindians. All these people went whaling in small skin kayaks, like the present-day Eskimos and the neolithic peoples of Scandinavia in Europe. They obtained many whale products and exported some of them to China, to the south, by the overland routes shown on this map.

The essential features of the world looked at from the viewpoint of the Japanese have always been, first, their position upon a continuous barrier of islands off the main Asiatic coast and completely fencing it in and, second, the vast, hot, ocean river known as the Kuro Siwo which flows out of the South China Sea via the straits north of the Philippines. This creates the climate of their isles, cuts them off from the open Pacific Ocean beyond, and diverts almost all their attention to the left — that is, to the northeast — which leads to western North America. To what extent this may have carried the Japanese, or those who dwelt in their islands before them, to the coasts of America is not known, but many cultural features are held in common by all the early peoples of these coasts, notably their whaling practices.

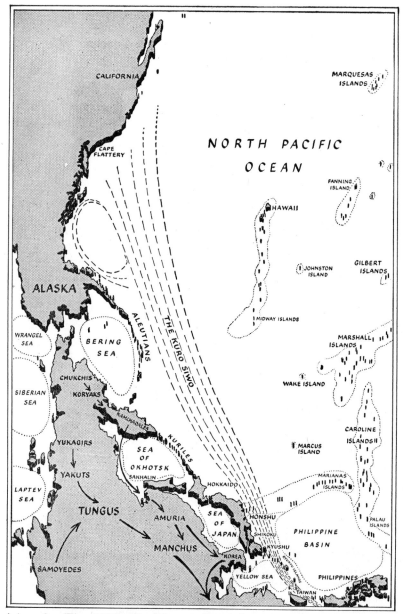

Map 3   The West Pacific, as Seen by the Nipponese

Bohn Projection
Scale 1:68,000,000

➤ Narwhal and Walrus Ivory Trade Routes
of the Middle Ages

top, twenty-five hundred miles from north to south, and three thousand miles in length along its eastern face. Very little, comparatively, is known about it by anybody except the Russians, who an-
nexed the major part of it in the last century but have only got
around to examining it in what detail they can devise during the
past quarter century.

In many respects the seaboard of this subcontinent is startlingly
like that of western Europe, but in reverse, or, rather, mirrored. At
the top in both is a dependent peninsula: Kamchatka in Asia, Scandinavia in Europe; each enclosing a sea: Okhotsk in the former case,
the Baltic in the latter. South of each, stretches an indented continental coast line, that of Amuria, Manchuria, and China in Asia; that
of Germany, the Low Countries, France, and Portugal in Europe.
To seaward of both lies an archipelago — that of Nippon in the
East, that of Britain in the West. Finally, each has a most significant
peninsula pointing to these island groups. In Asia we have Korea
pointing to Nippon and giving it much of its population and culture;
in Europe we have Brittany pointing to Britain and providing
throughout history a similar steppingstone to that country. In both
cases, moreover, the populations of the mainland, the peninsulas, and
the archipelagoes have always been distinct. Then again, another
parallel may be seen in the histories of the two areas. The southern
parts of the continental masses have always been areas of confusion,
strife, and cultural progress — China in the East, France, Spain, Italy,
and the other Mediterranean countries in the West — while in both
cases the northern hinterland has remained a vast bucolic amorphism
— Russia on the one hand, Outer Siberia on the other. As archaeological and anthropological researches proceed, we now come to
find that the past histories of the two areas appear also to have been
similar for much vaster stretches of time than we had previously supposed. In fact, the so-called prehistory of Far East Asia is strangely
similar to that of western Europe, and the time schedule is not
too far out either.

When the neolithic peoples of Scandinavia were pursuing whales
of all kinds in skin boats, or kayaks, about 6000 B.C. at one side of
Eurasia, a certain obscure people were apparently doing likewise
at the other end of that continent in similar latitudes, and specifically
on the island of Sakhalin. The former recorded their actions on

open rock faces, the latter in delicate lines on the bones of birds. The story is bizarre, to say the least, and happened this wise.

One Professor Shōgorō Tsuboi of Tokyo made a trip to the southern (then Japanese) portion of the island of Sakhalin in the early 1920s, in order to examine some mounds containing the remains of ancient human dwellings, at a point where a river named the Susuya debouches into the Aniwa Bay. In these mounds he found not only a considerable amount of crude pottery and stone and bone implements, but also some extremely curious artifacts made out of the hollow bones of birds. One of the largest of these, made from the leg bone of an eagle, was highly polished and had obviously been used like our "straws" for some such purpose as sucking eggs or other primeval equivalents of ice-cream sodas. Further, this was carefully incised, not with a simple design like other similar objects, but with a clear picture of two whales, each with a long-handled harpoon sticking out of its back from which a line wandered away on the one hand to a globular object and on the other to lens-shaped things crossed by seven and eight upright lines respectively.

The interpretation of this might well floor the amateur, but after one has perused the findings of the professional archaeologists who have studied the past cultures of that area and especially the history of boats employed by those people, both there and elsewhere, it becomes very obvious. The boats used by the ancients thereabouts were made of skins sewn together and stretched on a framework of withes like the present-day kayaks of the Eskimos. Secondly, bladders made from the stomachs of seals or other animals, or from sewn skins, and inflated with air were used by many primitive peoples — and notably by the Amerindians, who are both racially and culturally related to the early inhabitants of northeastern Asia — to keep the harpoon afloat or to retard the whales. These facts explain the details of this precious bird-bone tube, except for the little upright strokes incised over the boat figures. It has been suggested that these indicate the number of men employed in each boat, and this seems reasonable. Therefore, we have a record in this discovery of open-sea whaling by the ancient inhabitants of the island of Sakhalin during the Late Stone Age, or Neolithic Period, when pottery, at least, was in use. Nevertheless, this carries us back in time to a date that has been estimated as certainly more than 2000 and probably nearer 4000 B.C. The next obvious question is, therefore, who were these whalers who built small, half-sunken, round houses, connected by passages and dotted about the foreshore not only of Sakhalin but also of the Kuriles, Hokkaido, Kyushu, and other islands to the south, as well as on the mainland and notably on the coasts of Korea? The answer to this leads us into some strange channels, and finally throws us up on the beaches of Japan some five thousand years later.

Those strange people, popularly called the "Hairy Ainus," who are still to be found on the island of Hokkaido and on Sakhalin are apparently not, as was at one time supposed, the original inhabitants of the Nipponese archipelago. First, they are basically of Caucasian stock — that is to say, the same race as the early Europeans, or "white man" — and they arrived in far eastern Asia only comparatively recently, speaking from the anthropological point of view. Their arrival in Nippon was certainly prehistoric, but it was just as certainly not prior to the Neolithic Period, or Late Stone Age. Where they came from we do not know, but they brought with them a number of customs that may be traced back all across Eurasia to the west, including a "bear cult" that has some strange aspects, to say the least. From archaeological delvings and from certain direct evidence given by these Ainus themselves, they were not the first people in the Nipponese archipelago. They, their traditional fables, and the spades of the archaeologists, all tell the same story; namely, that the Ainus found in those islands a dwarf people, or certainly a race of smaller stature than themselves, who were very primitive, were copper-colored, used stone and bone implements, and who either dwelt in caves or built little cavelike round-houses, sometimes joined together like certain wasps' nests. These were sunk about three feet into the ground, and the walls were made of piled and fitted boulders. Above these, some form of domed roof must have been erected and then the whole covered with earth, peat, or some light substance. In these we see an almost exact parallel to the round-houses of the neolithic peoples of the fringe of western Europe. To clinch the similarity, moreover, Professor Shinji Nishimura found whale-vertebrae stools in these primitive mounds, and one of these was actually buried in the same mound in Sakhalin in which the bird-bone tube with whaling pictures had been found.

These people were midden-makers, shore-dwellers, and whale-chasers. But who were they?

The Ainus called them "Koro-pok-guru," or dwarfs, and later the Japanese called them "Tsuchi-Gumo," which means "earth spiders," because they were small of stature and lived in caves. Both the Ainus and the Japanese seem to have treated them abominably and to have deliberately set out to exterminate them. They appear originally to have inhabited the whole archipelago, and they seem to have been related to the indigenes of Kamchatka, to the Koryaks, and to the Chukchis of far northeast Asia. Perhaps they were co-ancestors of the Eskimos also, for they seem to have lived an existence that is typical of those people prior to the impact of modern civilization upon their culture. They lived in "igloos" of stone, earth, and possibly also of whales' bones rather than of ice, but they built skin boats, harpooned marine animals, were small of stature, sturdy, and copperish in color, and they were expert engravers of bone and ivory. They appear to have been Mongoloid rather than Caucasian, but they were very definitely "modern men" as opposed to submen.

The arrival of the Ainus on the far eastern coast of Asia wrought a great change. Being continentals, and therefore landsmen, they did not comprehend seamanship or the pursuit of the whale. They apparently had primitive boats, but they did not venture upon the sea. Nonetheless, they appear to have derived sea products from somewhere, and we can only suppose that these came from the despised Koro-pok-guru, some of whom they had left alone to follow their aqueous pursuits along the shores. Then, many hundreds and possibly thousands of years later, came the Japanese. The origin of these people is shrouded in mythological history but is from a purely anthropological point of view somewhat clearer.

The Mongoloid stock is separable into two major parts; on the one hand a northern group of continentals; on the other a southeastern aggregate. The latter, although mixed with all manner of aboriginal peoples and with a certain amount of immigrant Caucasic blood, are quite distinct, and include the inhabitants of Indonesia and the Philippines (other than those with Spanish blood, of course), the Indo-Chinese of all kinds, the Thais, and others. These peoples suddenly erupted, starting about 1000 B.C., and spread both southeast and northeast. They were a maritime lot and they apparently ricocheted up the Chinese coast, seizing all the offshore islands and finally jumping from north China to what is today called Japan.

The inhabitants of those islands have a venerable tradition about this final hop, which they date as of 660 B.C. precisely for purely political reasons but which was actually achieved over a thousand years later. In that year, they now contend, one Jimmo Tenno sailed east from the mainland and finally landed, three years later, in Nippon and established a beachhead. The alleged meanderings and conquests of this personage are not part of our story but, despite their patent lack of authenticity, may well constitute a fair shadow of the first chapter of Japanese history. Jimmo Tenno's real name was apparently Kami Yamato Ihare-Biko, and he set out from the island of Kyushu, but he may well have existed as a leader because somebody had to lead the first invasion of the archipelago by the Japanese, just as William the Conqueror led the Gallic Norse from Normandy to the shores of Britain sixteen hundred years later. What these first Japanese — and they apparently continued to come in waves — found in the islands of Nippon we cannot say, but there were certainly still a lot of Tsuchi-Gumo on Honshu and the southern islands and of Ainus on both of these and on Hokkaido. The Japanese exterminated all they could of both, and either assimilated the rest or drove them north to Hokkaido. Somewhere along the line, however, they acquired from these primitives a knowledge of whaling.

The primary interests of Japanese historians are, naturally, centered in fields other than that of whaling. Therefore, they have not paid any particular attention to this abstruse but essential industrial enterprise. Nonetheless, there is a continuous thread of whaling discernible throughout the history of this country from Stone Age times until the present day, and now that we know the earliest aborigines followed this practice, it becomes easier to understand how and why the people we know as the Japanese, even if they were not already a maritime race, came to adopt the custom and the tradition. Whaling, indeed, proceeded apparently uninterrupted for centuries all around the archipelago, even during a long period when the Japanese did not, or were not even allowed to, build any ships of any consequence.

The history of Nippon must be broken down — at least from our point of view — into five periods. First, there is the prehistoric, or pre-Japanese, which came to an end about 600 B.C. and initiated what may be called the Early Period. This lasted from 600 B.C. until 700 A.D. and is handed down to us more in myth than in solid record. After that, the record becomes properly historic, but the country remains obscure until 1600 A.D. when the Portuguese and Dutch contacted the empire. After this, there was a period of almost three hundred years during which the age-old traditions of the country were perfected and novel ideas were considered but not employed. After 1880 the country decided to join the comity of nations and leaped ahead into the modern world of mechanical enterprise. From the point of view of whaling this whole history can be divided into a prehistoric, a Japanese, and a modern period when the Norwegians arrived in their steam chasers. The industry was taken over in 1906 when the government banned foreigners from the business, and then a primarily Japanese period lasted until the Second World War. Since then, a most curious Americano-Nipponese effort has developed, but this is of no concern to us. We pick up the story now after the Japanese people have established themselves on the archipelago of Nippon.

Apparently, one of the staple diets of the aborigines had been whale meat, and the new occupants of the islands adopted and continued this practice. This we know because we find them whaling offshore very soon after they established themselves in this country. Jimmo Tenno, or whoever he was, obviously had ships, otherwise he could never have reached the islands or sailed from one of them to conquer other parts. However, in 81 B.C. we find the Emperor Sujin recording the fact that his maritime people, depending on seafoods, lacked sufficient ships. As a result he ordered ships to be built — and they were. Some scholars consider these to be the first real ships, as opposed to mere boats, to be built in Nippon, but this belief is decidedly doubtful. Nevertheless, there was obviously a big push in shipbuilding in the time of that emperor. Then, in 200 A.D. the Empress Jingu caused a really vast fleet to invade Korea. This is the first indication of a Japanese naval eruption. Apparently it was so impressive that the Koreans capitulated at once and offered all manner of tributes and other bribes to get these new pestilences off their necks. From then on the Koreans and Japanese kept sparring for centuries.

In 274 A.D. the Emperor Ojin had a boat built that measured a hundred feet. This created a most extraordinary sensation, the thing being regarded with awe throughout the country for a century, and when it finally became useless due to rot, its timbers were used to evaporate tons of sea water, the salt resulting from this operation being sent to all parts of the realm in memory of the wondrous object. This is a strange thing to contemplate among a maritime people at a time when even the dismal Romans were barging about the Mediterranean in enormous quinqueremes, and Dravidian ships carrying several hundred people had been in use almost three thousand years before, in the Indian Ocean. Nevertheless, the Japanese do not seem to have employed sail until about 1000 A.D. All their earlier ships were propelled by oars, and there was even a period in their history when no shipbuilding was allowed at all. This was designed to prevent nationals from leaving the country, which was made illegal by imperial decree.

Now, about this time a certain meticulous historian in China happened to record in detail items sent to his emperor by the tributary Su-Shen people of the north, and these included "bone armor." This simple statement means a lot more than it might indicate, for the armor was stated to have been made of *ku-tu-si*. This is not a Chinese word but is one of Khitan origin. The Khitans were Tungus who lived and still live to the north of Manchuria (see map on page 105). The Chinese colloquialized this word, first to *kutusi*, and then simply to *kutu*, and in this form it became the trade name for a very valuable product throughout Asia for thousands of years. It finally reached the Turks, who wrote it *hutū*, and this was transliterated by the Arabs as *chutww*, which must be just about the most improbable word ever written in Roman characters. It was regarded as a priceless gem, but what it really was proves a little disappointing and rather surprising; yet, it is quite important to our main theme. It was walrus ivory.

Without going into the details of this fabulous Chinese trade, we may record that two substances known respectively as *ku-tu-si* and *tu-na-si* were in great demand throughout Asia from at least 100 to 1500 A.D. The second was the ivory of the narwhal's "spear," as described in the preceding chapter. This was collected by some peoples, probably the Eskimos, Yakuts, Chukchis, and Koryaks of the north, and traded by them down the coast via the Kamchadales and the Tungus to the Koreans, and thus to the Chinese. An alternative route may have been overland directly from the Yakuts to the Tungus, and thence via Mongolia and Manchuria to China. In any case, these two forms of ivory were known in most ancient times, but it was apparently not till the present day that the Chinese really came to know from what animals they were derived. They used the narwhal ivory primarily as sword and dagger hilts, but they passed this material along to the rest of Asia in trade for all manner of goods, so that it finally reached eastern Europe and the Arab world, where it merged with a supply of identical material coming from the north of Europe initiated originally, as far as we know, by the Norse, as also described in the preceding chapter.

Thus, we see that during this otherwise undocumented period, there must have been a great deal of coastal whaling proceeding in the North Pacific. Most of this was probably prosecuted by the ancestors of the Eskimos or the descendants of those mound builders whom we met on the island of Sakhalin, but, at the same time, ambergris is first mentioned by the Chinese — specifically by Pen Ts'ao — as *lung sien hiang*, which means "dragon's saliva perfume." In fact, this writer states that this material is aromatic and is vomited out of the stomachs of large parties of sea dragons who congregate in the southern oceans at certain times of year. This is so near the truth that we can only surmise there was a full-fledged whaling industry in action somewhere off the coast of southern China in those times.

The bone armor referred to was apparently made of overlapping pieces of ivory derived from the tusks of walruses, and was almost impenetrable by any weapons of that time. Any who doubt the statement that this was walrus ivory are referred to the appropriate references to certain extensive works listed in the bibliography attached hereto. Apparently, the inhabitants of the great peninsular subcontinent north of China and Japan carried on a walrus-hunting and whaling enterprise for at least four thousand years, in direct accord with the traditions of the mound builders of Sakhalin. That this was so is also confirmed by certain activities in other parts of the Pacific which produced similar results. To these we must now turn for a moment.

The history of the vast Pacific Ocean is less known than that of any other part of the world. What is more, there are more contradictory theories about it than about any area, yet each theory is supported by a group of very real experts who have devoted their lives to the study of its history, and each theory appears to be backed up by great volumes of physical evidence. The controversy does not concern us, but certain of the theories do, and we must have some clear idea of the geography of the area before we can understand anything about its peoples or its history.

Of primary importance in this respect is to appreciate the fact that the Pacific is most clearly divided into two major portions — a northern, which extends from 30° N. to the Arctic Ocean at the Bering Strait, and thus includes the north temperate and boreal latitudes; and a southern, which reaches south from 30° N. to the Antarctic, and almost all of which is warm, containing as it does all the tropic latitudes of both hemispheres and the south temperate belt. The dividing line is the vast, blank, islandless region that extends right across the North Pacific from Samoa to California. We will dispose of the southern portion first and in very short order because, despite its very real fascination, it unfortunately cannot at present contribute anything really concrete to our story during this period of history.

There are those — notably Thor Heyerdahl of *Kon-tiki* fame — who maintain that there was emigration from South America to the archipelagoes of the South Pacific. There are others who deny this, and contend that all the people came in successive waves from southeast Asia via Indonesia, New Guinea, thence along the string of great islands — the Solomons, New Hebrides, Fiji, Tonga, Samoa, Tahiti — to the Marquesas, and finally to Hawaii. The first wave, they state, were the Melanesians, of whom the only remnants are the little Negritos, and the Papuans of New Guinea, both of Proto-Negroid type. Next came a race related to the Dravidians of southern India, who, as we have already seen, were great seamen and possibly the first true open-ocean sailors. They too have left fairly pure remnants, such as the Mentawi Islanders off the coast of Sumatra. These were the great voyagers who, when they passed onward into the Pacific, became known to us as the Polynesians. Next came a mixed Mongolo-Caucasian group derived from southeast Asia which we call the Indonesians, or Pre-Malays, who are still found in the form of the Dyaks of Borneo and the Battas of Sumatra. Finally came the true Malays.

Although there are many indications that both the Pre-Malays and the true Malays have followed the whale at various times, there are no reliable historical accounts of their efforts. Matters are unfortunately little better regarding the Polynesians, but we have definite evidence that these people carried on regular whaling industries at several points throughout the South Pacific, notably in the Fijis, in New Zealand, and possibly in Hawaii. Certain whale products are held in the highest esteem and are even revered in the Fijis, so that a sperm whale's tooth is still considered there the most valuable official present that can be offered to visiting dignitaries, and one was bestowed upon Queen Elizabeth of England when she visited those islands in 1953. Further, the early records of the Maoris mention their use of all manner of artifacts made from whale bone, whale's teeth, and even from baleen. Unfortunately, we have no proper record or account of these Polynesian efforts, especially during the early period which we are now investigating. Turning to the North Pacific, however, we encounter quite a different state of affairs and one of enormous interest to our main theme.

Due to the presence of a tremendous warm current called the *Kuro Siwo* which flows up the east coast of Asia from the hot tropical waters of Indonesia — just as the Gulf Stream does up the east coast of North America — a moderate climate extends to the southern islands of Japan and then swings out to the east and crosses the ocean to bathe the western shores of what is now Canada. However, as in the North Atlantic, a contrary cold current creeps down from the Arctic inside this *Kuro Siwo*, reaching to the northern shores of Japan, while a tenuous thread of cold water clings to the west coast of North America also. As will be seen from the end-paper map, whaling (as opposed to sperming) grounds all lie in these cold currents, and mostly where they are wedged, or thrust into corners, between land masses and hot currents. This is where the food of the whales is most abundant.

Now the wedges of cold water in the North Pacific have always been infested with whales of many kinds, and from earliest times the inhabitants of these shores, including those living on the American as well as the Asiatic side, have pursued them. Moreover, the practice continued uninterruptedly right up till the arrival of Europeans on the west coast of North America, for they found the Amerindians there whaling in a very special manner. This ancient and wholly independent operation provides us with a clear picture of Stone Age whaling such as must have been undertaken by the Koro-pok-guru of Sakhalin, the Kamchadales, Koryaks, Chukchis, and others in northeast Asia in neolithic and later prehistoric times. It answers many of the puzzling questions about this early labor, notably how primitive man devised strong enough equipment to take and handle whales. For instance, as described by eyewitnesses, the Makahs of the Cape Flattery region at the oceanic entrance to Puget Sound in what is now Washington State carried on the job as follows:

They had large stone or copper harpoons (the copper was probably entirely indigenous and obtained from inland tribes and not from white men, for there is much evidence that the Amerindians were just entering the Age of Copper when the Europeans arrived). The barbs on these harpoons were made of spikes of elk horn which were inserted into holes or grooves along the edges of the harpoon stem, like teeth in a dog's jaw, and then most cunningly bound in with a sort of tape made from the sinews of whales' tails. The whole was coated with a gum made from the sap of a spruce tree. A wonderfully strong and pliant line about thirty feet long was attached directly to this harpoon. This was also made of connected and braided whale sinews, and the whole length was then bound around with a thin twine made from shredded bark fibers which had been rolled into a compact strand using the palm of the hand against the inside of the thigh with a certain amount of rosin applied with the fingers of the left hand. Thread for hammocks is still made in this manner in many parts of Central and South America, the work being done by the women.

Copper harpoons had a tubular collar at the back for insertion of the harpoon shaft, but the stone heads were finished off behind in long, tapering spikes. These were inserted into holes in the front end of the shaft. The shaft was a most ingenious structure, made in two parts with a collar, or sleeve, of bark at the hinder end of the front part into which the tapering end of the back portion was inserted. The whole was eighteen feet long. The line from the harpoon was attached to a float made of sealskin, very neatly sewn up with the fur left inside, and completely watertight. This was blown up with air and was extremely buoyant, so that when about thirty floats were attached to even the largest whale, the animal simply could no longer sound. When a harpoon was driven into a whale and it took, the shaft was either pulled out or fell out and floated, to be picked up by the owner in his canoe. He then inserted it in another harpoon head and went after the quarry again. Finally, the floats were caught and joined together by stout ropes made from spruce roots roasted in hot ashes, then split into fibers, and finally twisted into long lines.

Lookouts were posted on shore at all times to watch for the whales, and when a school was sighted, the whole able-bodied male population went to sea in large bark or skin canoes, each carrying a specialist harpooner, a steersman, and six paddlers. When a whale had been grappled, it was lanced to death by any and all means possible, and then was towed to shore at the village beach. The whole community then attacked it with knives. The blubber was cut into blocks about two feet square for hauling above tide level, where it was then cut into smaller pieces by the women and rendered in large earthenware pots, the oil being skimmed off with large clam shells. The fibrous residue was then smoked. It was tough, but had a flavor not unlike that of bacon.

Here we see a living demonstration of prehistoric whaling techniques, and when we come to examine the tools and other devices employed, we suddenly find that the seeming impossibility of the business has been dissipated. I shall always remember the first time I cut a tree down with a stone axe made in neolithic times, but set into a modern ash haft in the manner devised by prehistoric people. To my amazement and that of a man with me who wielded an axe professionally made of the best modern steel, my seemingly blunt instrument could almost keep up with his powerful and rhythmical swings. What is more, it made an astonishingly clean cut.

Certain aspects of this primitive whaling are, however, even more significant — notably the number of men in each canoe, the immense harpoon shaft, and the comparatively short lines attached to the floats. These are exactly as depicted on the bird-bone tube found in Sakhalin and they point directly not only to that early Asiatic whaling but also to its later development by the Japanese.

Apart from some tradition, many myths, and the findings of archaeologists, there is no Japanese history prior to 700 A.D. At this point the story becomes clearer in a written record called the *Kojiki*, or *The Record of Ancient Matters*, which was written, under imperial decree, by a remarkable woman who had been trained to memorize all the ancient accounts that had till then been passed down by word of mouth. This was composed in 712 A.D. Then in 720 A.D. the *Nihongi*, or *Nihon Shoki*, the *Chronicles of Japan*, were completed. These works give us much information but, being composed in the then current frame of reference, are sorely lacking in the more intimate details of life in Nippon that we would so much like to know; also, they are not historically reliable up till the immediately preceding centuries.

From that time until the arrival of the Portuguese and Hollanders in the sixteenth century, there are contemporary records of ever-increasing reliability which provide historians with a wealth of general information, but which are unfortunately almost useless in regard to our speciality. Direct references to whaling are all but nonexistent, yet there are numerous indications that it was prosecuted continuously as a regular part of the fishing industry, which has always been of primary importance to this now almost wholly maritime people. What is more, when we do finally get actual specific accounts of the business, which are of almost modern date, like the *Yugyotoru Eshi*, or *Pictures of Whaling*, by Yamada Yosei, published in 1829, they invariably describe a procedure which, it is clearly given to be understood, is most ancient. That this must have been so is even more clearly indicated by the degree of specialization and formality with which whaling was conducted and the intricate procedures it employed.

Relying on these latter-day descriptions with their wonderfully busy illustrations of positively furious activities on both sea and land, we find that the Japanese were whaling with considerable success at the same time as, and in a very like manner to, the Basques of the Bay of Biscay, but that they developed some most novel ideas that are unique. First, having been slow to develop sail, they started whaling in large paddled or oar-propelled open boats that were double-ended and distinctly canoe-shaped. They were probably derived in the first instance from the Koro-pok-guru skin boats and both carried seven or eight men. What is more, the Japanese whalers maintained this tradition until the coming of the Yankee barques, and even later until the arrival of the first Norwegian steam whalers. They started building some merchant ships upon European lines in the early eighteenth century, and they had previously very studiously copied the Chinese junks, and both to good advantage, but they do not appear ever to have employed either of these for whaling except as sort of floating hostelries. There is absolutely not one iota of evidence that they ever used them to carry the oared whaling boats or to process the whales. This latter was invariably done on shore, to which the whales were towed.

If the pictures of their whaling are to be believed — and like all Japanese illustrative records these devote tremendous care to detail — the whale simply never had a chance, for these industrious and logical people did not rely on half a dozen little cockleshells as the Yankees and almost everybody else had done. Instead, they rushed upon the luckless beasts in positive armadas of fair-sized boats driven by as many as thirty or forty oarsmen. Moreover, the number of harpoons with the traditional bladder floats attached that they poked into the quarry apparently had no upper limit, so that the whole sea looks as if it were covered with a vast spider's web in many of the pictures. Then, just to make doubly sure, these ingenious people invented still another trap to ensnare the poor creatures. How they manipulated these is quite beyond our ken, though I have talked to an ancient one in person in Japan who had assisted in this function. He made it all sound very simple, but I still cannot see how they managed to entangle a full-sized sei or right whale in a net; however, that they did so, many foreign eyewitnesses can attest. The resultant mess, as depicted in the illustrations, is so appalling that it becomes an even more acute puzzle trying to fathom how they ever disentangled the brute after it was killed. If you have tried to get a small herring out of a raveled seine, you will know what I mean.

The corpse, buoyed up by the countless bladders if it was a rorqual — and this explains how the Japanese alone were able to take these animals at this early period, because rorquals sink when dead — was heaved right up on to the shore by a primitive slipway that led to the entrance of a large warehouselike building. Even in ancient times, it appears that every bit of the whale was used. Unlike the Europeans and others who made use of the whole animal in earliest times but then jettisoned an ever-increasing amount of it until they took only the blubber and baleen or, at one period, only the baleen but who have now been forced to return to the more economical practice of processing the entire corpse, the Japanese always got the utmost out of their prize. The pictures of the processes they employed are most enlightening on this score.

First, the blubber was stripped and carted into the building to be rendered in a series of large iron pots placed neatly against one wall, their fires fed by a troop of special laborers. The baleen, if it were a rorqual or right whale, went into a separate room where it was washed, *ironed*, and dried. The flesh was then neatly butchered, graded, and even, in some cases, packaged in split-bamboo cartons and rushed off to market by another group of laborers, distinguished by different clothing, who bore their loads suspended from either end of long poles. The bones and the residue that could not be eaten — which was astonishingly little, for almost all parts of the intestines were thoroughly scoured and cut into special delicacies for the table — were then hacked into small pieces and shipped to the farmers in large baskets. We can only assume that, from the first, this residue was used by them as manure, just as the Amerindians used little fishes to fertilize their corn crops at the time of planting. A wiser and more wholesome use of a product of the sea has never been devised by any people, and in its efficiency it not only parallels and equals, but even surpasses, the most modern phase of whaling, wherein almost the entire animal is used, for we still throw away the stomach and its contents, while the early Japanese appear to have made use even of these, either directly as food or via their employment as manure or fertilizer, and we nowadays also throw away the baleen.

The Japanese from earliest times seem to have been able to take all kinds of whales by using the ingenious prehistoric device of the inflated bladder, or float. Not only were black rights and sperms taken, but also all the rorquals and even the gray whale, which later was of some importance to the late Norsk-Nipponese industry on the coast of Korea, where Roy Chapman Andrews rediscovered this species, thought to have been totally extinct for a quarter of a century. One of the commonest species off the Japanese coasts and one which these whalers particularly favored was always the sei, the third greatest of the rorquals, otherwise known as the pollack whale by the British, Rudolphi's Rorqual, the *otta sotta*, by the Icelanders, and as the *iwashi-kujira* by the Japanese. The name "sei" comes from the Norwegian *seïevhal*, which was applied to them in olden times because they appeared along the coast coincident with the migrations of the *sei*, *seje*, or "coalfish." It is now known to science as *Balaenoptera borealis*.

This slender, streamlined species, with an exceedingly compressed tail and a pronounced dorsal fin, grows to a length of sixty feet and is probably the fastest swimmer of all whales, exceeding even the finner when cruising, and being able to get away from any except the killer in his final short dash. In color it is blue-black above and grayish on the flanks; the underside is white from the chin to the anus, narrowing about the flippers, which are tiny. The undersides of the tail and the flukes are never white. The pleats under the throat are variable in number, but never extend further aft than the region of the flippers. There are about 330 baleen plates per side, and their fringes are pure white. They are only about thirteen inches long. The blowholes lie in twin furrows, and the males have a beard of about 25 thick bristles on either side of the lower jaw.

They feed on perhaps the most remarkable of all foods for any animal their size. Although their Japanese name means the "sardine-whale," this seems to refer more to their shape than to their dietary preferences, for very few of those fish have ever been found in their stomachs. On the other hand, many have been found to eat the krill that form the usual staple diet of the mighty blue whale. In the North Atlantic, however, they appear to maintain life almost exclusively on a tiny crustaceous animal only about an eighth of an inch long known as *Calanus finmarchicus* which propels itself by rowing with a pair of immense, hairy antennae. Although this tiny thing lives in absolutely countless numbers in northern waters, it still seems almost impossible that it could provide enough sustenance for thousands of sixty-foot mammals.

The spout of the sei is cone-shaped and vertical, and is accompanied by a very distinct loud whistle as it is ejected. The sei is a great wanderer, and marked individuals have turned up in different oceans. It migrates annually, appearing off the coast of Norway in June and disappearing again in August, and off Japan in June and July. The young appear to be born at all times of the year in different areas, and mating is random. Seis are found all over the world from the Arctic to the Antarctic, and off almost all coasts, though their presence was not noticed, except in Japan, until modern whaling began.

Thus, we find that whaling was proceeding at both sides of the earth from the earliest times, that some people were matching the efforts of the Norse in this respect in far northeastern Asia, and that by the end of the first millennium of our era the Japanese had developed methods that were in advance of any to be found in Europe. However, it is to the whaling conducted in the latter continent that we must now return.

# 6
# Softly Comes the Dawn
## (*Basque*)

THE LITTLE SHALLOP with harpooner Jean Echeverrey
alert in the prow and Philippe Sansterre at the steering oar
draws slowly away from the towering side of the wallowing caravel. The ten sturdy men manning the oars pull hard in perfect unison born of half a lifetime of experience, so that the little open boat
gains momentum and cuts through the choppy waves. And from
various distances up to three miles away, and from various directions
in a rough half circle, six other little white boats also set out, and
move slowly towards a certain place upon the open bosom of the
ocean.

For once all is silence aboard the caravel except for the slow
roll of the loose gear below in rhythmic phase with the easy squeak-
ing of taut rigging pulled by swinging yardarms. Not one of the
whole company of fifty-odd souls remaining aboard speaks or even
moves. The mariners crowd the high bulwarks, their tousled heads
surmounted by an assortment of greasy caps, and their bearded
faces just appearing over the rail, while on the towering poop the

captain, with the master and *contremaître*, or second officer, stands grimly silent, peering out over the gray sea. Somewhat apart and perched upon the rail sits Martin Cormareche, the Breton, pilot not only of the caravel *Snt. Jean de Zaburu*, but of the whole fleet of seven vessels. Silence at such a moment is rare indeed, but this is an occasion that no man will ever forget. Each, even the youngest serving boy, knows that he is witnessing something that has never happened before and may never happen again.

Every now and then each man glances surreptitiously at the captain, hoping for some sign of his inner emotions upon his taut, hatchet-shaped face, but then they, of all men, should know that even in the greatest emergency the thoughts of François Sopite never betray themselves, for is he not *Eskualdunak* too, and what man of their ancient race would display emotion even when fighting? Yet, they would like a sign from him because he has himself explained to them so many times exactly what this experiment may mean to their families, to their town, and perhaps to all their *Etat*. But François Sopite stands silently upon the poop with his hands behind his back peering out from under his curious floppy black hat.

Meanwhile the shallops slowly converge upon the ocean, but for what reason or exactly how they know where to do this would be incomprehensible except to those men aboard the seven caravels. When they are but a few hundred feet apart, their oars are stilled and they bob up and down on the waves, while from time to time one of them sinks down into the immense unseen trough of the great Atlantic swell. The caravels creak and wallow, keeping their distance, every eye aboard them fixed on that place among the little shallops.

This great experiment has called for the unstinted cooperation of some four hundred men, and has taken months of wrangling and discussion to prepare. For once all the age-old rights and claims have been waived and it has been agreed that whatever man of whatever ship from whatever port making up the little fleet strikes first and whatever boat draws the kill shall not only renounce any personal claim to the prize but help in every way to bring it to the ship of Captain François Sopite, where certain things will be done or attempted. If the enterprise is successful, every man will benefit and all know this fact.

Then suddenly something breaks out of the waves right before the little shallops, and a twenty-foot plume of white vapor whistles skyward, curves over, and begins to drift away on the fresh breeze, vanishing almost immediately. At once all the boats fling themselves into action and labor furiously towards the leviathan. It sinks slowly below, rolling forward like a great lazy ship, quite unaware that it is the center of so much concentrated attention. When it has gone below, the shallops redouble their effort and rush to the spot where it appeared and on over the sea as if bent upon pursuing a wraith forever on the bosom of the infinite. They know their business, however, for suddenly right before them, and twice as close this time, the great black dome again breaks the waves and, whistling shrilly, lets out another tall, steamy jet. Then again it rolls lazily over, forward and away from the straining shallops. The process repeats itself twice more, but then the little boats are almost upon the huge form. And now comes the critical time for every man to strain his tired muscles to the utmost. The leather thongs lashed to oars and rowlocks "thwang," and the knife-edged prows of the boats literally cut the waves. Then, all at once, it happens.

Out of the murky chop once again rolls the immensity of shining blackness; once again the white mist comes wheezing out of it, but it never reaches its full height this time because the boats are right on top of it. Without a sound from any man, and without the pounding rhythm of the jerking oars faltering even for a moment, three brawny arms are raised high and three fifteen-foot staves with keen-barbed harpoon heads and trailing stout ropes arch out and thud into the mass. There is a moment of silence, and then two steersmen raise a shout. There is blood in the waves and two lines have gone taut and started whirring out between the stout pegs hammered into the forepieces of the shallops. Two harpoons have struck.

But there is no time for more than a single shout because the two boats lurch forward and almost go below. All is now confusion. Oars are swung inboard and shipped; men leap to avoid the whirling loops of the rope as it rushes out over the prow; and the steersmen wrestle desperately with their blades. The two boats rush away from the others, firmly attached to, and now towed by, the monster of the deep. The others hoist white cloths on oars as a signal and then lean-to manfully, trying to follow. There then ensues an anxious period of many minutes while the two shallops almost disappear towards the horizon, careening madly from side to side, sometimes one behind the other, sometimes rushing through the waters alongside.

Meanwhile the big ships unfurl their tremendous square sails and, by close-hauling them, get ponderously under way in pursuit. The whole fleet is now strung out for miles across the ocean, the two shallops far ahead, next the five others struggling to follow them, and far behind the seven caravels sweeping along in a somewhat disordered line. Then, the two shallops come to an abrupt halt, and a fountain of white spray arises between them. Far in the distance as they are, still those on the big ships see men leaping up and down and, for an instant, something enormous towering above them. Every inch of canvas is spread to the wind in eagerness to come up with the melee. Eventually the first of the big ships hauls abreast of the five straining shallops, and lines are thrown to them. One by one the little boats are taken in tow.

But the battle ahead ends as suddenly as it began, and again the two forward shallops go bounding over the waves at a speed with which even the big ships cannot compete. But now they are being towed by five instead of two lines, and the spume that passes their rushing hulls is constantly flecked with crimson blood. The chase goes on and on.

After the third battle and endless resetting of the sails aboard the caravels, the whole pageant has come almost half circle so that the big ships are now running before the wind. In no time at all the first of them bears down upon the struggle and, sweeping majestically by, only a few yards to larboard, drops the tow lines of the five other shallops, which instantly converge upon the raging pool of bloody foam. Now arms rise and fall with an almost constant rhythm, jabbing downwards with long, cruel, slender lances, and with each jab more blood jets into the sea. This is all very grim and satisfactory, but every man in the shallops knows that the really dangerous period in the struggle is yet to come. And come it does, with startling abruptness, but fortunately just then the caravel of Captain François Sopite heaves-to within hailing distance.

Suddenly the monster rears its cumbrous head above the waves, opens its cavernous mouth so that foam cascades from its wall of baleen plates, and without further ado leaps head downward and plunges straight into the deep. Without warning of any kind one of the shallops simply upends and disappears below, and it is some seconds before its dozen occupants bob to the surface. Another goes careening off to one side, water pouring over its gunwale, while two others are also upended and smoke sizzles from the forepieces where the lines run out at an uncalculable speed. But the presence of the big ship saves the day, and the floundering mariners swim towards it and are hauled out of the cold waters, one by one, chattering and cursing.

Meanwhile strange things are happening below. The great beast making its final plunge in a vain attempt to rid itself of the multiple lines and harpoons that now are attached firmly to its blubber, and crazed by a hundred deep wounds from the keen lances, finds its strength unequal to the pull from above, which includes a very bouyant wooden boat firmly attached to it by no less than three stout lines. Sounding to only a slight depth, it gives up the struggle and lets itself float slowly to the surface, and as soon as its head breaks through the waves the struggle is all but over. More keen blades lance into it from every side and with an audible gasp it opens its mouth and belches up gallons of blood; its great tail lashes twice and then all is still. As everyone relaxes, two of the caravels inch forward and the lines attached to the beast are drawn aboard. They close upon either side of the huge thing and hold it suspended between them.

François Sopite still stands quietly with his hands behind his back, his keen features and dark eyes fixed upon the prize, but the rest of the company raises a shout of triumph. There is a long pause while the wind moans in the rigging and the ships bump against the vast corpse between them. The first stage of the experiment is successfully completed. Now to see whether the great idea itself will work. The captain gives an order very quietly and men leap to work.

Down on the flat, cluttered deck in the belly of the caravel stands an odd structure, seemingly quite out of place on the high seas. It is a rectangular thing like a small house neatly built of bricks. On top of it are two large, round holes in which sit huge, hemispherical iron bowls; in its sides are four square holes from which smoke soon begins to curl. The whole erection stands upon a platform of carefully cemented bricks and stones, and over it is raised a wooden canopy not unlike a curving tent. This is the great gamble of François Sopite. With this he hopes to free the *Eskualdunak* forever from the nausea of rotting, oily flesh, the worthless battling with winds and tides to reach home when the ship is but half burthened, the bitter disappointment of a half-empty purse after months of arduous labor. His orders therefore are curt to a degree.

Immediately men go overboard and jump on to the great corpse that floats alongside. Then, with long blades rasped to a razor's edge and attached to long handles they set to work cutting into the fatty mass of blackness that protrudes from the waves. Great hooks are lowered from the big ship above on the ends of ropes passed through blocks high upon the rigging, and slowly long belts of blubber three feet wide and ten, twenty, thirty feet long are hoisted into the air as men cut and hack and the great corpse slowly revolves in the water. It is like peeling an enormous orange. At the same time hooks are inserted into the tip of the immense lower jaw, and when the animal is floating on its back, the cavernous mouth is opened and men go right inside to hack away the lips and loosen the hundreds of baleen plates, while others cut in behind the bulging white tongue so that it may be hoisted out with tackle and a heavy winch all in one piece.

And as the strips of blubber come aboard the ship, Captain François Sopite personally supervises their dissection into blocks about two feet square. Meanwhile a wood fire has been stoked within the brick house, and when the iron bowls sunk into its top are almost red hot, the blocks of blubber are tossed in to crackle and sizzle. They sink down in a growing pool of clear oil which is then ladled out into iron tanks standing in larger wooden tanks of water, so that it may cool. The residue left in the bowls is brought out with large tongs and looks like vast bits of pork crackling. It is tossed into the fire below, where it burns furiously, giving off an acrid smell. Soon, in fact, the fire is burning on this crackling alone while oil runs continuously from the cooling tanks into barrels, and the whole process is self-sustaining. The great experiment is a success, and while men chant and shout in the gathering darkness lit by the glare of the fire, Captain François Sopite stands on the poop deck smiling wryly. The men see this and grin too.

ALTHOUGH we have no actual written record of this event, we can safely reconstruct its details from a wide range of other sources, some of them eyewitness accounts of the same process at later dates. This particular instance, however, constituted one of the four most important events in the whole ten thousand years of known whaling history. What is more, it is the first truly historical event in this industry, because we have the name of the man who initiated it, and we know a considerable amount about him and his background. The great experiment of the Basque Captain François Sopite Zaburu, of St. Jean de Luz, as we now call the port, made at the end of the sixteenth century altered the whole course of whaling and, occurring when it did, contributed to the general expansion of Europe overseas in a way that has seldom, if ever, been fully appreciated. The other great discoveries that altered whaling practice were those of Captain Christopher Hussey of New England, who initiated sperming a century later, of Svend Foyn of Norway, who invented the harpoon gun in the middle of the nineteenth century, and, finally, of Captain Carl Anton Larsen, who built the first real factory ship in 1923.

This was the first occasion that we know of definitely when the products for which the whale has always been sought — oil and baleen — were extracted on the high seas, and by its successful conclusion it released the industry from one of its most cramping aspects. However, as is the case with so many great inventions, it was the outcome of necessity brought about by the march of much wider events — in this instance two in number. First, the only whales that could be hunted on the open sea at that time were certain species known in English as the right whales — simply because they were the *right* ones to hunt and this because they floated when dead. All others sank, and as the idea of the heavy ballista of the old Norse had been either lost or never adopted outside of Norway, hand harpooning from small boats was the only means of capture, and with these weapons only light lines could be employed which would not hold up a whale that sank when killed.

The right whale, found off the coasts of Europe migrates annually north in summer to far upper latitudes and south in winter when at one time it appears to have bred in considerable numbers off the coast of Spain and in the Bay of Biscay. The Basques had been hunting this whale for more than five centuries, as we shall see, and it is invariably stated that they had by this activity exterminated these whales off their shores and so had to hunt them in larger ships farther and farther afield, first to the coasts of Holland, then through the North Sea to Iceland and beyond. More careful investigation of the history of their whaling industry, however, reveals from actual records that no one of the dozen coastal communities actively engaged in this enterprise appears ever to have killed more than about half a dozen whales in any one year, and often none at all. In fact, the record of the town of Lequeito shows only 48 killed during the 145 years from 1517 to 1661, though this is admittedly after the time when the whales are said to have already disappeared. Some Spanish historians, however, state that right whales always visited their shores annually and there is considerable doubt that they ever became scarce or nonexistent in the Bay of Biscay and, if they did, whether this was due to the whaling activities of the Basques or to some natural causes such as changes in ocean currents or the temperature of the water.

Then again we may be putting the cart before the horse or rather, let us say, the other way round, the whale before the ship. It is quite possible that the development of shipbuilding among the Basques made it possible for them to follow the whale ever farther along its migration routes and to kill it on the high seas in greater numbers, rather than waiting ashore for it to come within rowing distance of land. And this brings us to the second cause of the almost inevitable invention which happened finally to be undertaken by François Sopite. This was the general expansion of western Europe overseas, that had begun with the great Portuguese explorers two centuries before.

As European colonies sprang up overseas, maritime enterprises of an oceanic rather than a coastal nature became increasingly important, and shipbuilding received a great stimulus. In this the Basques were in the lead, and once given the ships, they reached out over the North Atlantic ahead of all others. In fact, despite all the debate on the subject, they seem to have reached America ahead of Cabot and perhaps even Columbus. Whalers thus sailing thousands of miles from their home port simply had to develop some method of extracting the oil from their catches at sea in order to make their voyages profitable. The old method of loading up only the blubber and then freighting it back to the home port, there to be "tryed-out," or boiled down, for the extraction of the oil, had become quite uneconomic.

François Sopite's invention came, nevertheless, almost at the end of Basque whaling history, and in large part brought about its final extinction, as we shall see. It was an end product of continuous development by his ancient and extraordinary race which started so long ago that most of the few historians who have written on this subject begin by saying something to the effect that "it is not certain whether the Basques actually *invented* whaling." This we now know to be very far from the truth, for it had been going on in Scandinavia for at least nine thousand years, but it is still quite possible that the Basques had indeed been at the business themselves along their shores for just as long if not longer. Such an extraordinary statement calls for considerable clarification.

Nobody knows who the Basques are or where they came from. It has recently been discovered that they even have a predominantly different blood type from all the rest of humanity; this, in the estimation of some anthropologists, makes them a separate race. Affinities with them, their language, or their culture have been claimed by other peoples all over the earth, from the Caucasus to Ethiopia, and even to North and South America. There are even those who believe they are the remnants of the inhabitants of a series of large islands that once lay out in the Atlantic but sank due to earth movements and gave rise to the story of the lost continent of Atlantis. Current scientific opinion favors the theory that they are the descendants of the Iberians, who appeared with an obviously maritime culture in the peninsula to which they gave their name about ten thousand years ago and then spread far and wide over and around the Mediterranean basin. However, this does not help very much because we don't know where the Iberians came from either, though their culture suggests a slow development, over an immense period of time, from that of still earlier peoples in the same area — the so-called Azilians and others — while these in turn may have evolved from the palaeolithic Magdalenians and these from the still earlier Aurignacian culture of Cro-Magnon Man. Now, Cro-Magnon Man was the first true or modern man that we know of, and we certainly don't know where he came from. He just suddenly popped up in the midst of the primitive Neanderthal Apemen, complete with a culture, including magnificent art — that of the famous cave paintings — and a religion that must have taken untold ages to develop. What is more, Cro-Magnon Man first appeared on the extreme western fringes of Europe around the area where the Basques still live, and nothing like him or his culture before his arrival there has ever been found north, east, or south of that area. It does, in fact, look very much as if he came out of what is now the Atlantic, and thus from some land mass therein which has now sunk below its waters. However this may be, there is no possible doubt that the Basques have been dwelling somewhere around the limited area they now occupy on the northeast coast of Spain and the extreme southwest coast of France since the end of the Stone Age.

The Basque language tells us quite a lot about the history of its speakers. First, it is written quite differently from the way it is spoken; then, it has a perfectly ghastly syntax that requires thinking quite alien to our own. One French cleric writing three centuries ago recorded, "The Basques speak among themselves in a tongue that they say they understand but I frankly don't believe it." But its most interesting feature is its actual words, and especially their roots: for instance, the sound which is expressed in writing by the syllable *aitz*, which means a stone. We find that the word for a knife is *aitztto*, or "small stone," for a dart, *aitzkon*, or "stone point," a pick, *aitzkor*, or a "raised stone," while for scissors their word is *aitzttur*, which means "two small stones for tearing." From these samples alone it will be seen that this language quite obviously originated before the discovery of metal. It also has a number of enchanting side lights, such as that there are words for numerals from one to a hundred but none for a thousand, and words for dozens of various kinds of animals and plants but none for "animal" or "plant." The Basque word for God is *Jinkoa*, meaning "the Great One on High," from which we get "by jingo," originally "High Jinko." But there is one of their ancient Stone Age words that must interest us above all others, and this means "to grasp or to hold," namely *arpoi*, from which we get harpoon, via the Spanish *arpón*.[1]

Now, bone harpoons are found in palaeolithic cave sites of the Magdalenian period dated about 16,000 B.C. not only in Basque country but all around, and harpoons are troublesome and tedious things to make with only stone tools to work with. They were made for a specific and important purpose and not as toys or religious symbols, and were obviously used for fishing. Most of them are only about six inches long, but a few of more than double that size have been found and it would have to be an awfully large fish that required such a large weapon. Could these palaeolithic peoples of Spain, then, have been practicing offshore whaling eight thousand years *before* the Norwegian rock carvers were so engaged, or about eighteen thousand years ago? We have no evidence either in palaeolithic rock paintings or in artifacts or materials found by excavation that any whale products were used by the Magdalenians, but harpoons continued to be made in that area till the dawn of history.

The Romans mentioned tribes with a strange language in this area, but the first real record we have of the Basques occurs in a Latin document dated 980 A.D. which delimited the Diocese of Bayonne, though there are vague references in documents of the sixth century to their arrival north of the Pyrenees in what is now France. Enrique de Gandiá (see Bibliography) provides interesting evidence from ancient texts that the Basques used leather canoes for shore fishing as early as 700 A.D., but he believes Basque pirates using large galleys, which are known to have been built somewhere in Spain at that time, actually reached the Faeroe Islands in 875 A.D. From Latin sources we learn that whales were fished in the Bay of Biscay in the same year, but the word used is not the Latin *balaena*, *physeter*, or *orca*, but *crassus piscis*, or "fat fish," which may probably refer to the *porcus piscis*, or "pig fish," namely, the common porpoise. The earliest definite record of a proper whaling industry is embodied among privileges granted by King Sancho the Wise to the city of San Sebastian in 1150 A.D. The next is dated 1199 A.D. when one Jean Sans Terre gave to one Vital de Biel the tithe on two whales. But by this time the industry was fully organized among all the ports along the Basque coast.

[1] It has recently been pointed out that the Greek word for harpoon, arpoi, has not only a similar, but an identical stem.

In these early times it appears to have consisted only of offshore hunting in small boats with a harpooner, steersman, and ten oarsmen. Watchtowers were constructed all along the coast and these were continually manned during the fall and winter months when the whales came by on their annual migrations. When whales were sighted, bundles of damp straw or branches were lighted on the tower tops, and drums were beaten. The nearest village rushed for the boats, and when a whale was killed after the hazardous effort of hand-harpooning and lancing, it was towed ashore and carefully divided according to a complicated formula. The greatest delicacy, the tongue, often went to the Church, and the meat was eaten, while the oil and baleen were divided amongst the hunters. Quite a lot could be written on the whole procedure, but it would be only a repetition of facts that we have already explained and will often meet again in each case of offshore whaling.

The only whale hunted, as stated above, was the enormous Black Right Whale (*Balaena biscayensis*). This animal is world-wide in range outside tropical and warm temperate waters. There are apparently recognizable varieties in the North Atlantic, North Pacific, South Atlantic, and South Pacific. The Dutch call them *nordkaper* or *noortkaper;* Icelanders *sletbag* or *skeltbakr;* the Norse *slettebakkar;* the early French, the *sarde;* and the Basques, the *sarda*. In the North Atlantic they are found from the region of Bear Island in the extreme north in summer to an east-west line drawn from the Azores to Bermuda. They have been stranded in the Mediterranean. They normally travel singly or in pairs with or without young, but before the semiannual migrations they used to assemble in large schools called "gams." Although apparently never exceeding about sixty feet in length, they are of enormous girth and bulk with an utterly preposterous-looking head which accounts for a quarter of their total length. The lower jaw is huge and bowed outwards and upwards and, together with the enormous pendent "throat," is designed as a sort of tank into which the baleen may be lowered. This whole question of *baleen* is extremely hard to explain unless you have personally looked into a whale's mouth.

Baleen is a horny substance growing from the roof of the mouth and is, in fact, an exaggerated development of the ridges that we can feel on the roofs of our own mouths. These horny plates are triangular in shape with the hypotenuse facing inward and downward into the mouth, and this edge is frayed out into a fringe of hairs. The short sides of the plates are joined to the roof of the mouth along the curve of the upper jaws in a continuous series an inch or so apart, like the plates of a storage battery. They extend from the point of the upper jaw, where the two sets meet, to the back of the mouth on either side. Baleen is known chemically as keratin, and is thus the same material as our own fingernails. Baleen was used for a variety of things, from the plumes on knights' helmets, for which it was shredded and artificially colored, to the stays in women's corsets, hoops in skirts, springs for chairs, bristles for hairbrushes, and even the springs in the first typewriters. Today it still sometimes goes to the textile industry, being shredded and woven into certain fabrics to give them resilience. At one time it had the extraordinary value of $3500 per ton, and that at the rate of exchange prevailing in 1750.

Baleen whales feed by swimming through the water with their vast mouths open where a certain kind of small, shrimplike creature about an inch and a half long, known as krill (*Euphausia*), occurs in countless numbers. The water swirls around in the great lower jaw, and the krill become entangled in the hairs fringing the baleen sheets, which form a domed mat all over the roof of the mouth, because, it has been suggested, when the krill are frightened, they tend to surge upwards. When a mass is so entangled, the whale closes his mouth and presses his huge, bulging, flabby tongue upwards. All the krill are jammed against the baleen fringe while the water goes out between them, as in a sieve, and pours along outside the jaws to a special notch at the hind angle of the lips where it jets out into the sea. The krill are then scooped backwards by the tongue and swallowed. The right whales feed exclusively on krill.

Black right whales have comparatively small flippers and large tail flukes, but no dorsal fin. They are normally jet black in color, but one in about every five has some white patches, usually below. Their most distinctive feature is an excrescence about two feet in diameter on the tip of the snout. This is called the "bonnet," and consists of horny, disorganized skin in which parasitic worms bore and tunnel, and upon which all manner of barnacles grow and whale lice crawl. Its purpose is not known. When feeding, this whale usually stays below for about fifteen minutes, then surfaces to

breathe five or six times in rapid succession, rolling just below the
surface between each breath. It is a stupid, blundering beast that
appears to cause harm only by mistake and when in its death throes.
Its mouth contains up to 250 baleen plates, the longest averaging six
to seven feet; these are black in color. It yields an enormous quantity
of oil, and was therefore extremely valuable. Whether the Basques
exterminated it along these coasts or drove it away from them, its
total numbers were eventually so reduced that it was on the verge of
extinction by the beginning of the present century.

Basque offshore whaling is of great historical interest, first because it bridges the gap between the ancient industries, culminating
in that of the Norse, and the modern periods, and secondly because
it may itself be the outcome of a sixteen-thousand-year tradition.
But the Basques' high-sea whaling is of much greater importance.
Although again this was not their exclusive invention, in view of the
Phoenician activities of almost three thousand years before, it is
from their initiative in this field that all modern whaling practices
have stemmed.

Somewhere between the thirteenth and fourteenth centuries the
Basques took to following the whales upon the high seas in large
vessels. These may at first have been late types of galleys with both
sail and oars, but when this enterprise comes under the clearer light
of recorded history, we find that a type of ship known as the caravel
is their principal means of transport. This was originally about fifty
to sixty feet long, with a beam of up to thirty feet, and drew only
about seven feet; it had a high prow and bulwarks, and a towering
poop built up like a castle — this was, in fact, known as the *castillette*.
The exact shape of a caravel can hardly be described. It was grossly
top-heavy although filled with many tons of sand ballast on which
the galley fire was built and on which the "try-works" for boiling
the whale blubber were later constructed. However, since all this
was below the single main deck, it often resulted in the ship's catching fire. Caravels evolved throughout several centuries, ending up
with three-decker ships of 700 to 1000 tons, and having a complement of 250 men.

The caravel carried three masts; one placed centrally, and about
eighty feet tall, had a large squaresail with a smaller sail above, and a
"crow's-nest," often of elaborate design, on top, and usually a tre-

mendous pennant at the head. Far forward was a fifty-foot *triquiet*, or foremast, with one or two squaresails, and equally far aft a mizzen of some forty feet on which a variety of square, lateen, or fore-and-aft sails was rigged. There was also a tremendous bowsprit forty feet long bearing another sprit, known as a *civadière*, of up to twenty feet, below which a small sail could be set. Although clumsy to operate, caravels were practical ocean-going vessels. They were, however, so uncomfortable it seems hard to understand how even the toughest Basques could survive an extended cruise in one.

Not even the captain had a cabin or an appointed place to sleep. The company numbered about fifty, consisting of the pilot, who was almost invariably a Breton or Norman, first and second officers, carpenter, two cook-pursers, harpooners, steersmen, flensers, who specialized in cutting up the whales, mariners, and a number of apprentices. The food consisted of hung beef and biscuits which were invariably moldy, rotten, or filled with weevils. The fresh water was kept in barrels and went foul also, but large quantities of cider were carried for the outward voyage — as many as 3680 barrels were shipped from one small port alone in the year 1625. One shallop was carried inboard, but when the whaling became more extensive and small Basque fleets roved the seas together, up to five were carried on some ships, although only two per ship were used at a time. Navigation was aided by compass, astrolabe, and wood and metal quadrants, but time had to be kept by sand clocks.

Throughout the fourteenth, fifteenth, and sixteenth centuries, high-sea whaling was a Basque monopoly. All the Basques' coast ports, both on the Spanish and French sides, were engaged in the industry, and since Spain regarded them as foreigners, the Basques set up trade consulates in the various countries where they marketed whale products and, later, the dried codfish which eventually fed half of Europe. There are constant references to this international semidiplomatic activity with Denmark, Holland, and England. Matters did not always go smoothly either, and there is some very amusing reading to be found among old complaints, such as that of an Englishman named Mellowes who got the whole British Government in an uproar by wanting to sell rapeseed for soapmaking in competition with whaleoil. All kinds of monopolies and privileges were involved, and he seems to have won his case, but then to have gone

# The North Atlantic, as Seen by the Basques

The Basques viewed the North Atlantic from an angle that was different from that of the early Norse. They were in pursuit of one particular whale and one species of fish rather than engaged in a search for lands to settle or ravish. Thus, their expansion was predicated by the behavior of the animals they sought and, in the case of the whale, by their migratory habits. These happened to entail the passage of the animals from their breeding grounds in the Bay of Biscay through both the English Channel and the Irish Sea, and west of Ireland to the comparatively narrow passageway from the Atlantic to the Norse Sea between the Shetlands and Iceland.

Following the whales thither, the Basques fell in with the ancient Norse route to Greenland and the West, and this they followed, seeking codfish rather than whales as the latter turned to the right, or north, in their migration. Thus, the Basques got to the Labrador Basin and, doubtless on the advice of the Greenlanders, then turned left and went to work on the fabulous Grand Banks off Newfoundland where cod swarm in a profusion found nowhere else. They then returned home as fast as possible, and to do this they employed the prevailing Westerlies, as shown. Meanwhile, their whalers turned right, south of Iceland, following the black right whales, and thus came at an early date to Jan Mayen Land and thence to Spitsbergen, which they probably knew long before Barents first sighted the archipelago. At the same time the British and Hollanders arrived at the same point by sailing up the Scandinavian coast, primarily in search of a northeast passage to Russia and the East. The British soon gave up the effort, but the Dutch made this the gateway to a sea empire.

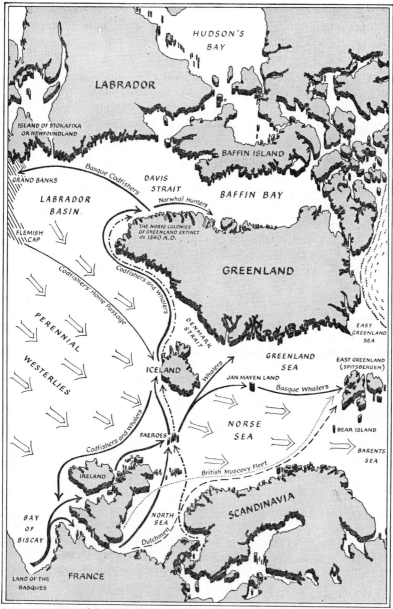

# Map 4   The North Atlantic, as Seen by the Basques

Polar Azimuthal
Equidistant Projection
Scale 1:29,000,000

⟵——  Basques          ⟵·······  British
⟵– – –  Dutch          ⟸  Westerly Winds
⟵·—·—·—  Ancient Route to Scandinavian Colonies

bankrupt. England signed regular trade and diplomatic treaties with the Basque communities as early as the twelfth century, and the two peoples seem to have always had a great regard for each other.

This widespread trade continued with the extensive navigations after whales, and the curiously ambiguous position of the Basques themselves, in the midst of continuous international rivalries, led them into some strange situations. Unfortunately, although the Basques were intensely and *racially* exclusive, they did not think of themselves *nationally*, and they made no attempt to record their history or activities until a later date. What is more, like the Phoenicians, they were somewhat secretive about their voyages and their discoveries. As a result, about a century ago furious arguments broke out among historians regarding the latter — debates that are still going on. The trouble seems to have been started by one Marc Lescarbot in 1609 in his *Histoire* in which he said he had seen a chart made by Guillaume Postel, who died in 1581, on which Newfoundland was shown, with a note that it "was visited and frequented by the Gauls earlier than 1600 years previously," namely at the beginning of the Christian Era. This is obviously absurd in view of the Norse discoveries, but everybody immediately began trying to reduce the date by leaving off either the initial or terminal unit, giving us 600 or 160 years respectively. Now, the first gives us the date of the Norse discovery of Vinland, 1000 A.D., and the latter the year 1420 A.D.

How the Basques became substituted for the Gauls is not clear, but various French writers filled with righteous national pride, and knowing of the extensive voyages of their Basques, claimed and set out to prove that they reached America before Columbus reached the West Indies, giving dates for such discovery from the end of the fourteenth century to about 1420. In the earliest colonial days of Canada, Basques are known to have visited the Grand Banks annually in search of codfish, which they cured at semipermanent settlements on Newfoundland, and they communicated with the Amerindians and the Eskimos farther north in a sort of pidgin-Basque-Indian jargon. Certain stone buildings in the New World are believed by some to have been Basque watchtowers; and gravestones with Basque inscriptions, but all of a later date, have been found in Newfoundland. However, the first voyages to Newfoundland that are definitely recorded in Basque archives are dated 1538 to 1540.

Historians as a whole take the view that there is no more truth in the assertion that the Basques visited the North American coast in the fourteenth century than there is in the old and quite baseless story that Columbus learned of the New World from a Basque captain whom he met in the Azores.

Nevertheless, there is absolute evidence that the Basques did reach Newfoundland and several more distant points long before that date. Even if there were not much evidence, it would still be obvious that they must have known about America because Scandinavian ships had been sailing regularly to and from Iceland since 1000 A.D., and up until about 1300 A.D. they were still occasionally going to Greenland. It was in 1362 A.D., you will remember, that King Magnus Ericson of Norway sent his ill-fated expedition into Hudson's Bay to look for the lost contingent of the Greenland colonies. Further, two maps by Andrea de Bianco, dated 1436 and 1448, or more than half a century before Columbus's arrival in the West Indies, show, far west of Iceland, a large island named Isla de Stokafixa — Isle of Stockfish, or Codfish — which is by its position definitely Newfoundland. Again, the *Carta Catalán de Mecia de Viladestes*, of 1413, now in the National Library of Paris, shows a whale and a caravel far northwest of Iceland. The Icelanders did not build caravels or, as far as we know from their records, follow the whale on the high seas. We don't know of any other Europeans who were so engaged in such ships at that time except the Basques. Moreover, the Basques reached Iceland before 1400 A.D. and the Icelanders certainly knew of Greenland and probably of Newfoundland and Vinland from their own history. Finally, Newfoundland continued to be called the Isla de Stokafixa on many maps until after 1500 A.D.

While the codfishers went to the Grand Banks, off Newfoundland, the whalers seem to have gone towards Greenland waters, where they met the other species of right whale — the Bowhead, or Arctic Right Whale, *(Balaena mysticetus)* — which they were definitely catching by 1500 A.D. What is more, they continued to hold their high-sea monopoly unchallenged for another century after that, culminating in François Sopite's great invention about 1600 A.D. But shortly thereafter a number of events occurred rapidly that initiated the Basques' decline, though there was still one Basque ship operating as late as 1725.

In 1596 a Dutch ship with the famous Barents as pilot, owned by J. Hendrick Heemskerke and J. Cornelius van Rijp, discovered the islands of Spitsbergen; a few years later a Basque whaler blown off his course happened to arrive there too, and found a surfeit of whales. The whaling fleets of his countrymen followed him there, but by this time both the Dutch and the English had organized companies to exploit whaling, and had hired Basque harpooners and flensers to teach them the trade. Also, they had learned of François Sopite's invention, and they began not only to rival, but to harry the Basque ships. Finally, British-French rivalries ended in the loss of Newfoundland by the latter to the former and Basque ships were excluded from the Grand Banks.

These events dealt a death blow to Basque whaling, and when the Basque ports themselves were laid waste in 1636, a change of objective appears to have taken place. Henceforth we have less and less whaling and more and more piracy, which in turn became more and more respectable, was called privateering, and often obtained official blessing. The Basques continued to fish for cod and also started the sardine industry in which they are still engaged. But after five hundred years, probably nearer a thousand, and perhaps several millennia, they fade from our picture, leaving others to follow the whale.

# Part Four

1600 A.D. TO 1700 A.D.

## *The Middle Period*

# 7
# Early Morn in the North
### (*British I*)

THE MORNING of the twenty-sixth of July, in the year 1613, broke dark and very threatening off the grim, rocky coast that lies south of the deep inlet known as Thomas Smyth's Bay in the arctic isles of Spitsbergen. Beyond the barren, lifeless jumble of rocks that reaches upwards to a line of low, craggy peaks, lies a great, low white dome of ice, bright against the deep gray sky, and an ominous clarity gives exceptional vision. But already, this day, the sea is flecked with white. These are never kindly lands, and conditions may become as terrible in midsummer as in the perpetual darkness of winter.

Captain Stanley Burkett, master of the *Martha Marguerite*, a sturdy vessel of only a hundred and fifty tons but deep of draught, out of Bristol, England, is most dissatisfied with the look of the weather. Unfortunately, although he is officially the master of the ship, decisions even as to navigation are not entirely his to make, for he has the company agent aboard, one Mr. Jonas Lodge, whose business acumen apparently is not matched by his knowledge of seamanship.

Captain Stanley Burkett squints at the black sky over the distant ice-field and feels a chill wind blow in his face; he peers along the rocky coast line ahead, with its numerous headlands and low prom-ontories often terminating in a line of half-submerged rocks, like giant teeth, and utters a quiet sigh reserved for himself. Then he turns on his heel and goes below in search of this agent fellow. When he leaves, the helmsman looks at the mate. Their eyes meet and hold for a long moment.

Below in the cramped cabin of the poop the captain finds Mr. Jonas Lodge poring over a large and detailed tabulation of figures, a dirty quill pen, practically without any plume left, in his hand. He is looking almost pleasant for once, and he even attempts a sour smile as the captain enters. The ship's Basque harpooners have killed a small whale from which twelve tons of oil have been extracted and stowed below; they have also killed five hundred walrus in Thomas Smyth's Bay, and the produce of these has prompted Mr. Lodge's immediate decision to return home. He is already computing the profits — the first to accrue to the floundering Muscovy Company from its whaling endeavors. When, therefore, Captain Burkett once again pleads to be allowed to seek a safe haven in some deep bay where he may ride out the storm which he knows is almost upon them, the agent dismisses him curtly with the admonition to avoid all delays at all costs.

Never before has Captain Burkett been placed in such a position as this — to be master of a ship and yet to have to take orders from a man who, although admittedly himself a mariner, has now shipped as watchdog for a lot of bloated court toadies and has no real rank aboard. Then and there the captain decides to do precisely what he is told and if anything should go wrong, to submit himself to the command of this Mr. Lodge. Thereupon he ascends the poop and, being a deep-water sailor, prepares to get as far away from the coast as possible by ordering a starboard helm and then setting a course directly out into what is believed to be the open Greenland Sea.

It would be hard to say which rose more quickly and furiously thereafter, the passions and tensions among the ship's company or the winds and the waves, but by nightfall the little ship was working in every timber and lunging headlong before an angry following sea under shortened canvas. A blizzard raged and the rigging soon gave signs of being unequal to its weight. Long before midnight sundry other catastrophes had occurred. Mr. Jonas Lodge, shouting that he too was a master mariner with many years' experience of northern seas, had struck the first mate, ostensibly for insubordination. The cargo in the after hold had shifted, causing an awkward list to port that could only be counteracted by coming partially about and trying to run across the wind. In maneuvering, the mizzen had blown clean out of the deck, carrying away some of the mainstays, and while effecting repairs in the total darkness, two men had been lost overboard as the ship drifted athwart the sea. But much worse was disclosed as soon as visibility returned.

To port and starboard and all ahead, ragged islands and a cruelly indented coast line appeared among a foaming line of storm-tossed sea. At the first cry from the lookout, who had had to be lashed to the samson-post to avoid being swept overboard, the captain himself flung the wheel hard over in an effort to come about and lay-to, facing the oncoming sea, but without a mizzen the stem-heavy *Martha Marguerite* would respond only just so far, and there, rolling like a log and to a dangerous angle on the leeside, she wallowed while the pure force of the wind drove her broadside towards the rocks, still only half seen in the first morning light. And so it was that Captain Stanley Burkett found himself faced with two alternatives: to founder either by default, because he could no longer make way against the storm, or by design. He chose the latter course and himself staggered forward, shouting commands to set all canvas the mainmast would carry.

If they must run ashore in a raging storm, still it was better to try to pick their own place to do so. Then again, nobody knew what land this was that seemed to have risen suddenly out of what ought to have been open sea, and there just might be a channel or a fjord leading into it which could be navigated even with a crippled ship at the mercy of the wind. And Captain Burkett was at first lucky, because in the gray murk he soon espied a break in the coast towards which he instantly gave directions to steer. This proved to be a wide channel into which the waves rolled in orderly procession. Deep water obviously led through the channel between the towering cliffs, and the battered ship drove rapidly towards this apparent haven. But, alas, the captain's luck did not hold, for when they rounded the headland, they found that the fjord opened up, and was filled with a madly churning mass of ice floes interspersed with small green icebergs all heaving up and down, crunching and grinding upon each other in one ghastly uproar. And into this wild melee the crippled *Martha Marguerite* drove relentlessly.

All aboard stared in horror and no man moved, for to every one of them it was instantly plain that disaster lay only a few minutes ahead. Although land rose almost within hailing distance to either side, and there was even a shelving beach far off, no man and no small boat could exist for more than an instant in the jaws of that great natural grinding machine. Nonetheless, Captain Burkett called for more sail and, rushing aft to the helm again, flung the wheel hard over in a last brave endeavor to beach the ship or jettison it upon the rocks before it reached the ice. But the cumbrous sails were so wet and the rigging so damaged that long ere the ship gained steerageway it was among the first ice floes. These rammed her hull from every side, sending great shudders through her from stem to stern. At first the great seas also broke over her, adding their weight to the battering of the ship so that timbers split and the deck opened up, and down below the barrels of priceless oil broke loose and tumbled against the weakened frame, making a ghastly hollow drumming from within. In a matter of minutes it was plain to all that the ship was breaking up.

Then the cook comes yelling from below that the ballast is awash and the forward hold flooded. Although the ship is not yet holed, the seams are opening and the ship is sinking. Captain Burkett struggles through the tangled mass of ropes that now clutter the deck where Jonas Lodge still stands at the poop rail glaring defiance at the raging sea and ice. Although just an agent now, he is still a mariner at heart, and he is not by any means a coward. He knows disaster when he sees it as well as any sailor and he looks Captain Burkett directly and manfully in the eye. Then, with something close to humility, he gives a quiet command. "Abandon ship as best you can, Mr. Burkett."

"And you, sir?" replies the latter.

"These are my orders, Mr. Burkett. Are you questioning my authority? Remember, sir, this is my ship although you be her master. Proceed without delay."

And so, some reluctantly and some in panic, the company prepare to abandon ship, clutching what possessions and food they can gather in the turmoil. They crowd the rail in her belly, awaiting the command of the captain with what fortitude they can muster.

Just at this moment, however, the battered ship crashes against an ice floe so large that, although heaving up and down like the rest, it does not tilt or plunge below the waves. At a single shouted command every man scrambles upon the rail and, dangling by loose ropes, awaits his chance to leap to the ice. Not all are successful, and with screams of horror, first one and then another slips and falls between the ship and the ice, to disappear instantly into the black waters below and be crushed to a pulp. Soon all survivors are huddled on the ice, the last to leap in safety being Captain Burkett, who stayed to plead with Jonas Lodge to follow the company, but that man remained adamant to his former seafaring tradition, and as the now half-sunken ship slowly drifts away among the churning ice blocks, they see him still standing upon the poop, his back to them and his shoulders hunched. Slowly ship and man fade behind the snowy murk and disappear together forever. For a day and a night the company huddle on the ice floe as great hunks are split away so that its size ever shrinks. As the raging of the elements subsides, however, the men find themselves in an even worse plight, abandoned almost without food and still in the middle of the channel.

But when the waters calm down sufficiently, Captain Burkett decides upon a desperate course. The Basques have brought their harpoons with them and he orders them to capture a small ice floe. When one is held alongside their raft, he has crude paddles made by tying lengths of canvas between two harpoons held apart at the end by the scabbards of jackknives, and then ordering his first mate to take as many men aboard this crude raft as it will carry, he sets them adrift with orders to try to paddle to the nearest shore or to wherever the ice is packing up and freezing together. It is a desperate move, but the only one left to them, and fearfully those remaining watch the wobbling thing pull slowly away over a channel of dark water. But almost immediately disaster even more terrible than anything that has yet occurred to them strikes unexpectedly.

When still only a few yards off, the little ice raft suddenly upends, and while the desperate men slowly slide into the icy waters, an enormous black and white head rushes up from the depths and opens a cavernous mouth with both jaws ringed by great yellow teeth; it lunges at the nearest man, dragging him under. Amid cries of horror the others slide below the water, only to appear immediately swimming for the big floe with the insanity of pure horror in their eyes. But the narrow space separating them from their companions and comparative safety is now suddenly filled with gigantic forms that rush at them, literally snapping them in two or hauling them bodily below. Only four of fifteen men who have set out are finally pulled out of the water to safety, while the ravenous monsters of the sea now rush at the big floe, trying to smash it from below or actually, it seems, to leap upon it. Utterly abandoned and lost, the men huddle around Captain Burkett in the middle of the ice to await their end, which is now inevitable, either from hunger, drowning, or the attacks of these beasts they know so well — the dreadful killers, the most terrible flesh-eating animals on earth.

IN THIS STORY the names and dates have been altered, but not too much, and this for a specific purpose. There was a ship named the *Mary Margaret*, with a Captain Steven Benet as her master and with a Mr. Thomas Edge aboard as company agent, that killed one small whale and five hundred walrus in Thomas Smyth's Bay in Spitsbergen in June, 1611, and which was then lost with all hands on the return voyage. The story is fully recorded, but we constructed a purely fictitious counterpart in order to bring to the fore a number of the basic inefficiencies that plagued the history of the Muscovy Company, which was England's first corporate effort to enter the whaling industry, and which was one of the most colossal failures in commercial history. Notable among these inefficiencies were inadequate ships, interference by the company in maritime affairs, lack of experience, and failure to even try to cooperate with other nations.

Despite the Dutch claim to having discovered Spitsbergen in 1596, there is no doubt that an Englishman named Hugh Willoughby at least sighted it in 1553 while on a planned voyage to "discover" a northeast route round the North Cape to Russia — itself a strangely redundant effort in view of the voyage of Ohthere over five hundred years before. However, it now appears from the study of ancient

climates that there may have been a very great extension of the
Arctic Ice-cap from about 1450 A.D. onwards, so that the old Norse
route might have been sealed and made impassable, requiring a voyage of investigation. Then, in 1557, another Englishman, also on a
voyage to Muscovy (Russia) reported, "About the Island of Zenam
we saw many whales, very monstrous, about our ships, some by estimation of 60 feet long, and being the engendering time they roared
and cried terrible."

It is believed that the Island of Zenam refers to Spitsbergen, although this was from the first and up until 1800 called "East Greenland" by the British. It may, however, have been Bear Island (see
map). In any case, this account stirred up considerable interest
among the directors of the newly founded great joint-stock company which had been chartered on the sixth of February, 1555, under
the title "Merchants Adventurers of England for the Discovery of
Lands, Territories, Isles, Dominions, and Seigniories, unknown and
not before that late Adventure or Enterprise by sea or navigation
commonly frequented," otherwise known as the "Muscovy Company." The directors decided to enter the whaling industry, but in
the way events have always taken place in England, it was 1576 before the Crown granted the company, which had by then been rein-
corporated as the "Fellowship of English Merchants for Discovery
of New Trades," the monopoly to kill whales and make train oil
(whale oil) for twenty years.

Although the Crown took so long to get into action, some British
whaling was, in the meantime, being prosecuted off the coast of
Norway and off Newfoundland. These were private enterprises
carrying on a tradition which, on closer research, turns out to have
been quite ancient. We have less concrete or recorded evidence on
the early British whaling history than on that of any other of the
dozen nations or peoples we shall meet by the end of our journey,
but it is still there, as is shown by a remarkable little interchange in
the *Chronica Majora* of Matthew Paris, published in 1240, consisting
of Anglo-Saxon chronicles of the period prior to the Norman conquest in 1066, and written in Latin. In this is some dialogue composed by one Aelfric, Abbot of Ensham, in the form of questions
and answers to teach his Saxon pupils Latin. It goes as follows, in
somewhat literal translation:

Q. What things are to be caught in the sea?
A. Marketable marine fishes are; dolphins and sturgeons, lobsters and crabs, mussels . . .
Q. Have you strength to capture any whales?
A. No.
Q. Why?
A. Because it is very dangerous to catch whales. It is only safe to go upon deep water in a ship and for me in as many ships as possible if to chase whales.
Q. And yet for all that, many people do capture whales and avoid danger?

This would indicate that whaling was well known in Anglo-Saxon England, and that it appears to have been carried on there, off the coasts at least.

The English were always great privateers, and from time to time they captured Basque ships loaded with whale products returning from Newfoundland. The *Mary Margaret* was probably the first British ship to be specially fitted out for whaling, and that was only in 1611, but fifty years before, British fishermen occasionally went to Newfoundland along with the Basque fleets. In 1578 there were 100 Basque codfishers and 30 whalers there, 50 Portuguese, 150 French and Breton, all after cod with very small ships, and 50 British ships. The earliest record of a British ship going specifially for whales to the Newfoundland area is that of the *Grace* of only 35 tons and with a crew of twelve out of Bristol in 1594. They collected only some baleen from two wrecked Basque ships. In the meantime, however, as we have seen already, the Muscovy Company had been formed in 1555, and reorganized in 1575, but still nothing concrete happened for another quarter of a century.

The British have only recently become noted for their invariable policy of "too little and too late," and it is not realized in some quarters that this is a most venerable tradition among them. After more than fifty years of debate the Muscovy Company finally sent out one little ship of 60 tons, under one Thomas Welden, to Bear Island, where it collected some walrus oil in 1604. Five years later a slightly larger vessel, the *Lionesse*, under an odd character named Jonas Poole, claimed Bear Island for Britain and then, since the walrus there were getting scarce, reported on "the multitude of whales that showed themselves on the coast of Greenland" (Spitsbergen, in this case.) By this time, however, the profits of the Muscovy Company were deplorable from the point of view of the capital invested, and the directors were finally goaded into a proper investigation of the possibilities of whaling.

Consequently, they re-equipped the *Lionesse* and fitted out the *Amitie*, giving the former to Thomas Edge and the latter to Jonas Poole. These two sailed on the ninth of March, 1610, and reached Spitsbergen, where they whaled in Deere Sound with some success, but instead of trying out the oil there or at sea, they brought home only the blubber and were heavily censured. The profits of the company dropped again. In 1611 the *Elizabeth*, a barque of 50 tons, and the *Mary Margaret* of 150 tons, with Thomas Edge shipping on the latter as agent, were dispatched and, as we have seen, were successful in fishing, but the latter ship was lost on the return journey. Thomas Edge left for us a fantastic story of the privations suffered by himself and his crew. This was found years later hidden in a cairn of stones on Spitsbergen. In 1612, four larger British ships accompanied by a Dutchman and a Spaniard, both piloted by Englishmen, took seventeen whales and the Muscovy Company paid a 90 per cent dividend.

The next year, encouraged by this success, five ships and a little pinnace with a crew of five made the two-thousand-mile passage in eighteen days' sailing, killed thirty whales, and bagged the proceeds of eight others from two Frenchmen taken as prizes. But this year there were eight Spanish, four French, two Dunkirk, four other English "interlopers," two Dutch, and a 700-ton Basque ship on hand. Numerous squabbles broke out, and one British captain records that "for pilfering and for some perempterorie, two of the Rochellers were dunked at our yards arme, the one on the one side, and the other on the other." From then on until 1625 the Muscovy Company sent an average of eleven ships per year to the Spitsbergen whale grounds, but the success varied widely from year to year and the whole company gradually declined.

Throughout, the British were up to their old tricks, first claiming everything and giving their ships' captains grandiose letters of patent and monopoly but with no arms to back them up, so that they could not enforce their claims and often lost their cargoes or even their ships. Then, they would send out a fleet of heavily armed ships and engage in wholesale privateering, only to lapse once again the next year and let unarmed fishermen brave the elements and the wrath of all the combined foreign fleets. However, despite all this inefficiency and the deplorable interorganizational squabbles between officialdom, shipowners, ships' captains, the directors of the company, and its shareholders, it was the determined actions of the Dutch that finally forced the British to give up. Having built a seasonal settlement with a fort in Spitsbergen, the Dutch took to convoying their whaling fleet with men-of-war, as we shall see. After 1625 the British quit, and out of a merchant fleet of 1400 ships only 18 remained in the whaling industry, and these mostly as part-time privateers.

This first British whaling period is a curious little incident, of, at the most, some quarter of a century's duration, in the immense sweep of millennia during which the art has been carried on, but it laid a very important foundation for much that came later. The British are as notoriously stubborn as they are ponderously slow, and their empire was built as much by the labor of others as by their own very real initiative. Having once seen the profits that could be made out of whaling, but having found out that they were totally incapable of extracting these for themselves, they went quietly to work to find out who else they could get to do the job for them. They made four separate attempts during the next three hundred years — the first three almost equally unsuccessful, although they acquired a lot of other worthwhile property along the way, purely as a side line — but finally they succeeded, and in no uncertain terms, in our present century by putting up the money to finance the Norwegians to catch and process the whales on a lot of otherwise useless British Antarctic islands, and finally collecting the profits on the sale of oil to other countries.

It is not because the English, neither at this time or later, pursued any one particular whale that we chose to describe them first in association with the wicked killer, an animal on which no special industry has ever been founded. This choice was deliberately, though perhaps rather maliciously, made because the habits of the latter in some respects mirror those of the former. Both are predominantly predacious in their whaling endeavor, and both, in the long run, are extremely adept at it. Both can and do subsist for the most part on other activities, the killer eating anything from small fish and even crabs to penguins and other sea birds, seals, including the huge sea elephant, and the walrus, and any other whale it can catch from porpoises to the mighty blue whale, which it will attack in packs and, if the quarry is wounded or weak, tear to pieces.

Male killers, which are almost twice the size of the females, have been recorded up to thirty feet in length; these animals are barrel-shaped and very bulky, and, with their speed, and very large jaws armed with huge knife-edged, recurved, interlocking teeth, they are the most terrible flesh-eating creatures on our planet, far surpassing even the great white shark in boldness and acumen. Everything in the sea flees from them, even the largest whales, which have been reported as uttering bellows of fear on such occasions. One killer was caught choking on a seal, and when opened up, was found to contain no fewer than fourteen others; from another, thirteen porpoises and fourteen seals were taken; and from still a third, only sixteen feet long itself, fourteen more seals. Killers will attack small boats, possibly under the impression that they are whales, and will batter ice floes from below to get at marooned men. They often try to pull dead whales away from whalers and used to be a great menace when cutting-in was done at sea by lunging up on to the corpses to grab at the flensers. They actually bite large hunks out of the bigger whales and then surface to chew the pieces.

The Killer (*Orcinus orca*), is universal in range from the Arctic to the Antarctic and is fairly common. There appears to be a distinct race in the Pacific that lacks the white spot on the side of the head, but there is, in any case, considerable variation in the color pattern. This is as shown in the illustration at the end of this book, the dark areas being jet black, and the light pure white. The flippers and the flukes of the tail are very large and the dorsal fin is exceptionally slender and tall, sometimes being more than six feet long, and turning over at the tip like a dog's ear. Killers travel in packs of from four to forty and often swim in close formation at a very rapid rate.

The English sometimes call them the "grampus" from the Old English *grapeys*, ex the Old French *grapois*, which was a contraction of the term *crassus piscis* applied to all the toothed whales, other than the *Physeter*, or sperm whale. The name grampus is now properly reserved for quite a different small whale, only ten to thirteen feet long that inhabits principally the North Atlantic, Mediterranean, and South Atlantic and which is also known as Risso's Dolphin (*Grampus griseus*). It is variously colored, yellow-brown to bluish-white with dark-brown patches, and is covered with odd-shaped light streaks as if someone had been cleaning a paintbrush on its back and flanks. These marks are thought to be scars of wounds left by large squid and octopus suckers or beaks, since this species feeds principally on these. There are seven pairs of teeth and these only in the front of the lower jaw. The head is rather small and blunt, the flippers very slender and shaped like sickles, the tail flukes small, and the dorsal fin tall, slender, and sharklike. The head is usually light, but the fin, flippers, and tail are always dark, often almost black.

Certain Roman writers say of the killer, to which they gave the name by which it is now known to science — *Orca* — that it is the *tyrannus balaenarum* or *formidabilissimus balaenarum hostis*, which needs no translation and certainly most adequately describes the brutes.

# 8

# Midmorning by the Ice
## (*Dutch*)

CAPTAIN PETER VETTEWINKEL had always accepted it as a God-given certainty that nobody born outside of Amsterdam, or at least outside the Kingdom of Orange, could be capable of doing anything efficiently. And with this absolute assumption it was frankly very hard to take issue when on a ship riding at anchor off the settlement of Smeerenburg, or Blubbertown, as the English called it, in Spitsbergen in the year 1625. In this desolate and otherwise quite useless spot something that could well be described as a thriving port producing almost pure profit had grown up solely through the ingenuity, foresight, and industry of people born in the particular area in western Europe specified, and under the direction of persons from his own home port of Amsterdam. This, of course, the gallant captain deemed wholly appropriate.

On the gently sloping shoulder of a gently curving bay, deep in a sound protected from all possible winds, and hard by a deep-water anchorage with firm sand bottom, Smeerenburg's low huts, warehouses, shops, camps, and dormitories nestled in neat rows and obvious solidity. On the crest of the shoulder, within ample shooting range of the farthest opposite side of the sound, rose a fairly stout fort adequately armed and manned; behind the center of the bay stood a small white church of imposing but dignified simplicity. It even had a bell. Most efficient of all, the sound was ice-free in the summer and lacked a glacier at its head, so that safe navigation was as far as possible assured at all times in that perilous group of islands.

Captain Peter Cornelius Vettewinkel leaned contentedly upon the rail of his rather large ship and viewed the scene in the brilliant evening sunlight. One particular whale of the four he had so luckily struck just when about to take advantage of an exceptionally favorable wind to run home empty-handed was now alongside the jetty, and the shore crew, supervised by the captain's own *speksnijer*, boatswain, and chief Basque harpooner, were already busily affixing the tail lines. As the sun would set only for a few minutes, and the light hardly fade at all throughout the whole night, there was no need to become excited, yet, complacent Hollander even though he was, Captain Vettewinkel could hardly wait for the quarry to be hauled up the slipway to see what it looked like.

Many times on quiet evenings during fine weather while in passage to or from the whaling grounds, when sail was properly set to a steady wind, the evening prayers had been disposed of, and pipes lit, Captain Vettewinkel had listened with much more interest than he had ever displayed to the information occasionally but so blandly given by his old Basque harpooners about whales in general. They had told how their forefathers, on reaching Newfoundland almost two centuries before, had thought that the *sardas*, or *noortkapers*, they found there were different from those that visited their own home shores. They had gone on to tell how one Tomás of Santander, whose father had been half Portuguese, had one year chosen a course far west of the normal whale run and north of Iceland and had taken a vast whale, undoubtedly a *sarda* because of its general shape and because it did not sink when killed, but nonetheless without any "bonnet" and of completely different aspect, as his whole crew had later testified. What is more, the whale had yielded a surfeit of fine oil. The captain had always listened most intently when his harpooners had told of later Basque captains who had also taken this whale, which they now called the *sardako baleak*, and more particularly when they had dropped any hint as to exactly where or when this feat had been accomplished.

Putting together in his mind a lot of facts thus gleaned, Captain Vettewinkel had long since decided to take his ship in search of these creatures, and he had, in fact, been feeling out the route when, quite by accident and much to the surprise even of his Basques, he had struck a lone one in those latitudes where the Greenland Sea joins the more arctic East Greenland Sea. Could it be because the ice was so late in retreating north this year? And if so, could it mean that the *sardako baleak* must be sought by the Ice-front? Captain Vettewinkel was not going to ask these questions of anybody, or do any other talking. First he wanted to see what he had got.

It would have been quite undignified and distinctly undiplomatic to have gone ashore to watch the mundane operations of hauling the whale up the slipway. Besides, there was quite enough excitement and talk about it already and a considerable crowd, composed of all the polyglot gangs left from crews of the hundred-odd vessels using the port. Also, the crews who lived ashore all summer had gathered by the jetty to give advice, both useless and useful. And while the captain watched excitedly but morosely from over the water, a ten-oared gig pulled out from behind the jetty, drove a spike into the whale's head, and, running out a short line, began to pull lustily to the accompaniment of a sea chantey. Slowly the vast bulk of the beast slewed around so that it drifted headfirst out into the sound, while the shore gang, holding a line, maneuvered the tail into position over the slipway, where it disappeared below the still water's edge.

Presently, four immense capstans—such as are used to haul the heaviest ships on to shallows for careening—set up on solid stone bases, each supplied with eight arms and each of these pushed by six men apiece start to turn in unison, their lines converging upon the tail of the whale. And slowly the great corpse begins to inch out of the still, dark waters up the great slipway. The boatswain and the cox of the shore gang are seen running about hither and yon, placing a little grease here or there, testing ropes, or shouting orders to the crew of the gig, whose duty it is to keep the head of the monster pointed directly in line with the slipway. The minutes pass while the great capstans scream and more and more interested Smeerenburg spectators gather around to watch.

But as the dead whale slowly moves up the slipway, both the crowd and the captain are increasingly overcome by a sense of disappointment verging on annoyance. This does not seem to be an *extraordinary* whale, even if it does not have a "bonnet" and does have white patches on its belly. The Basques, however, only look grimmer and more determined and some of them start throwing taunts and curses — or so it seems — in their own impossible language at the crowd, who call back and jeer. It is, in fact, only after almost two hours of hard labor, and not until the capstan gangs have been relieved twice, that a casual onlooker in a small skiff anchored near the end of the slipway calls out in Hollandsche, "*Maar, het, heeft een nek!*" (But, it has a neck!) and the crowd mills forward down the beach to peer.

And, by *Jinkoa*, it does at first sight appear to have a "neck," because the head is so great, the top of it bowed upwards into a pointed hump, and the lower jaws are so spread out that it looks as if the head of a veritable monster had grown on the body of an ordinary *noortkaper*, or black right whale. What is more, when the points of the jaws appear, it is plain for all to see that in place of a "bonnet" there are a number of stiff, white bristles sprinkled over the tip of the snout and the end of the lower jaw. There is much white about the flabby, bulging belly of this whale, and the whole lower jaw is pale, silvery gray. Then the chief Basque points out to the assembled crowd that the flippers are longer and wider at the base than those of any whale they have seen.

While those on shore mill around, preparing the corpse for cutting-in, stoking the try-works, or just idly probing the beast, the chief Basque and the boatswain row back to the ship and hail the captain, inviting him to come and inspect the whale. And almost without hesitation — and somewhat to their amusement — Captain Vettewinkel accedes to their request and climbs down into the skiff. Arrived at the jetty, he approaches the slipway with all the casualness he can muster and permits his harpooner to point out to him the points whereby the *sardako baleak* differs from the *sarda*. The captain is greatly impressed, especially by the first baleen plates, which are cut out four hours later, for they are twelve feet long.

In fact, he stays the rest of the night ashore, watching the blubber flensed from back and sides, the lower jaw cut out, and the baleen removed, and when he returns to his ship, he takes with him the first sheets of his *speksnijer's* tally. As he sits somberly in the back of the skiff, his mind is filled with financial computations and navigational problems, for it is obvious to him that these *sardako baleak* are worth an infinity of trouble from now on.

AND SO INDEED they were, as other Dutch whaling captains and finally the government of the Netherlands itself were also to discover. The *sardako baleak* of the Basques — now known to science as *Balaena mysticetus* and in English as the "Bowhead," Greenland, or Arctic Right Whale — is an immense creature, from forty-five to sixty feet in length, though an unusually large one seventy feet long was caught off Spitsbergen in 1900. It is commonly of the appearance described in our story above, but the amount of white on the body varies greatly and the whole animal may be piebald. The shape is as shown in the illustration in Appendix E, from which it will be noted that the body is greater in girth and the head much larger in proportion to the body than that of the black right whale. So also are the tail flukes and flippers, while the head is raised into a sort of conical crest, on top of which is the blowhole. There are 350 to 370 baleen plates on each side of the mouth; these are black and normally ten to thirteen feet long, but some of those of the seventy-foot specimen mentioned above were over fifteen feet long. An average specimen yields two thousand pounds and a large specimen as much as three thousand pounds of baleen, which at one time was worth four to five dollars a pound, or eight thousand to ten thousand dollars. Even at a comparatively late date it cost only this amount to fit out a whaling vessel for a whole season.

Today, this species is rare, but in the sixteenth century it appears to have existed in considerable numbers in the North Atlantic. These animals are essentially an arctic species, staying by the Ice-front where the krill and a small kind of swimming shellfish, a pteropod known as *Clio borealis,* on which they feed, are found in great abundance. They migrate with the Ice-front, being in latitudes 75° to 78° in summer — that is, in the East Greenland Sea in the

# The Greenland Seas, as Seen by the Dutch

With the decline in the number of black right whales, notably around Spitsbergen, due to the increased efficiency of whaling methods employed by the Dutchmen, new sources of raw material had to be sought. This led the Dutch first to the northwest and then southward. The reasons for this movement were twofold. First, a new species of whale, the arctic, Greenland, or bowhead, had been discovered by the Basques in the East Greenland Sea, and this animal ranged south round the coast of Greenland and into the Davis Strait and Baffin Bay. Second, at that time there was another practically unmolested population of black rights on the western side of the Atlantic that migrated up and down the New England coast and spent the summer in the Labrador Basin when its arctic cousin, the bowhead, was far north by the ice.

On passing Spitsbergen and turning left, the Dutch immediately came face to face with the Arctic Ice-front. The permanent Ice-raft lies athwart the East Greenland Sea, but pack ice blocks the western half of this, the Greenland Sea, and the Denmark Strait, and thence extends to Cape Farewell and up into Davis Strait. Drift ice ranges much farther south and east, as shown on this map by the fine dotted line. The southern limits of pack ice vary widely between winter and summer and their extent varies from year to year. Also, the over-all volume of pack ice seems to fluctuate over the decades and centuries. In winter it fills Baffin Bay and Davis Strait and often blocks most of the Labrador Basin, linking up with the ice of the Gulf of Saint Lawrence. South of Spitsbergen it may reach almost to Jan Mayen Land. Iceland, the southern tip of Greenland, and the coast of Norway are kept free only by the Gulf Stream, branches of which bathe these lands with their comparatively warm waters. Thus it was that this ocean river had much greater significance than winds or land conformity to the whalers of this period. It defined the limits of their operations, and, to almost as great an extent as did the Ice-front itself, it regulated their movements.

The most profitable whaling was prosecuted right at the Ice-front, so the whalers followed this to the north every spring and then retreated south again before its advance, in the fall. Thus, they finally reached north to Lancaster Sound and passed through this into the Gulf of Boothia among the Canadian Islands. Foxe Basin and Hudson's Bay did not prove to be profitable grounds because the whales went up Baffin Bay and then turned west.

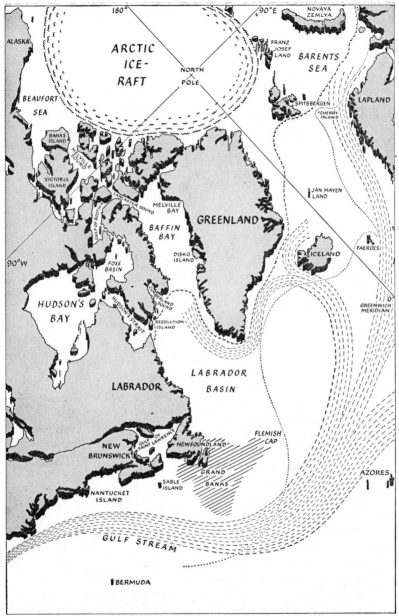

# Map 5 The Greenland Seas, as Seen by the Dutch

Polar Azimuthal Equidistant Projection
Scale 1:40,000,000

ᴗᴗᴗᴗᴗᴗ Mean Pack-Ice Front
.............. Limits of Drift Ice
☰☰☰☰☰ Gulf Stream

Atlantic, and in the upper reaches of Baffin Bay (see map). In winter they come south as far as latitude 65° N. between Iceland and Greenland and to 58° N. in Davis Strait. They have never been found east of Novaya Zemlya in the Kara Sea. The bowhead of the North Pacific is somewhat different and has been given the name of *Balaena sieboldii*. In summer it is in the Siberian, Wrangel, and Beaufort Seas (see map page 255), and in winter migrates through the Bering Strait to the Bering Sea and south through the Kuriles to the Sea of Okhotsk. It used to be very numerous in the latter sea, where the young, called "poggies," were born. The single calf is fourteen to sixteen feet long at birth and stays with its mother for a year.

The bowhead is an excessively timid animal and even slight sounds or a small bird alighting on its back will send it rushing off in a frenzy. It is one of the, if not *the*, slowest swimmers of all whales, wallowing along at about four and a half knots and being able to raise only nine knots even *in extremis*. When unalarmed and traveling, bowheads stay below for about ten minutes; when feeding, for about twenty minutes; but in either case they usually breach three or four times in quick succession before going below again. Wounded specimens have, however, stayed below for over an hour and a half. They are enormously powerful creatures and have been known to dive with such force in comparatively shallow water that they smashed their jaws on the bottom.

The arctic right whale was first discovered by the Basques sometime in the early sixteenth century, or still earlier, if we accept their presence off Greenland in the fourteenth and fifteenth centuries. Spitsbergen is at the border of the winter ice and so far within the Arctic Circle that navigation, whaling, or any other operations are impossible there except during a comparatively short summer season. Furthermore, as we have seen, Spitsbergen was reached only in the first decade of the seventeenth century. Thus, it was not until then that the arctic right whale could be hunted in its summer quarters in the East Greenland Sea.

The Hollanders built a small, permanent whaling depot for use in the summer months on Jan Mayen Island (see map) in 1617, but two years later they decided to move their main operations to Spitsbergen. They had always been competent seamen, but they also possessed other qualities with which neither the Basques nor any other peoples who had followed the whale previously — with the possible exception of the Phoenicians, of whose industry we know so little — seem to have been endowed. They were basically traders and businessmen and they had a strong constructive and mechanical bent, while they were then, as now, most methodical in all they did. Although it was never so stated in print, as far as I know, they were obviously appalled by the waste and uncertainty of whaling as carried on by the Basques and by the lack of a definite business policy as displayed by their only rivals, the British. They therefore set out to overcome these inefficiencies in every way possible. This they accomplished in three phases: first, by the establishment of semipermanent shore stations; second, by convoying their fleets with men-of-war; and third, by introducing two mechanical novelties and two important refinements to the industrial process as a whole. They did all of this within a decade, but it was more than two centuries later before their industrial improvements were universally adopted. As a result they took the lead in following the whale and held it for about two hundred years.

The Dutch idea of shore stations to which dead whales could be towed for processing probably stemmed from some very ancient practices that had been carried on along their own coasts, and to the north by the Frisians, and to the south by the Flemings, since the Dark Ages. In a work entitled *De la Translation et des Miracles de Saint Waast*, being a life of Saint Arnold, Bishop of Soisson in the eleventh century, it is mentioned that there was already such an offshore whaling industry on the Flanders coast in 875 A.D. That was at the height of the Norse viking raids, and considered in conjunction with the Norsemen's own whaling, the dialogue of Aelfric in Saxon England, and what we have seen of early Basque enterprise, it gives us an entirely new picture of the west European seaboard in the Dark Ages. It now appears that everybody from Finmark to Gibraltar was engaged in whaling, for the Danes had a porpoise fishery from earliest times, and there are references to the Portuguese marketing whale products in the ninth century. We will eventually discover that this did not apply to western Europe alone, but to all the oceanic coasts of the Northern Hemisphere.

When the Basques first built ships large enough to follow the whales north on their migrations, they immediately appeared off the coast of Holland. They may have arrived there as early as 900 A.D. and were certainly there by 1300 A.D. It is further recorded that Dutch pilot boats attended these Basque whalers and sometimes took their kills ashore for processing. Then again, the Hollanders were originally riverine-gulfine, as opposed to insular-peninsular, seamen and would naturally tend to prefer shore stations to open-sea operations; they were already most highly skilled port engineers because of the configuration of their own home coast, with its endless dikes and canals. The erection of a base overseas on even the most inhospitable shore presented no problems to them.

Just when they first began high-seas whaling is still obscure, but as early as 1614 we read of a *new* company being formed with a three-year charter to "Trade and Fish from the United Netherlands on or to the Coasts of the Lands between Nova Zemblya and Fretum Davidis, including Spitzbergen, Beer-en-Eiland, and Greenland." This would seem to indicate, first, that they already had a fleet with crews versed in the practice of whaling — though, as we know, employing Basque harpooners and flensers — and second, that they had considerable knowledge of North Atlantic and Arctic waters.

Their progress from 1612 till 1626, when they completed Smeerenberg, was, however, cautious in the extreme. In 1612 one Dutch ship with a British pilot visited Spitsbergen; the following year two came; and in 1614 none at all; but after the foundation of the new company in that year, fourteen ships went there, and this number rose steadily until it was twenty-three in 1618, fifty-two by 1621, and to what is described as great force in 1623 when the fleet included five-hundred-ton ships that brought timber and other materials to build the semipermanent or seasonal settlement, such as has already been described, at Smeerenburg. In 1625 the British more or less gave up, and the following year the Hollanders started going to the northwest ice in earnest because the black right whales were already becoming extremely scarce around Spitsbergen. However, Smeerenburg remained the Hollanders' summer depot for half a century, and they continued to use it even longer as a shore station for processing their catches.

The incident that initiated the second phase of Dutch dominance occurred in 1624. A privateer from the Port of Dunkirk, then nominally independent, seized a fully laden Dutch whaler on her return passage. Now, in 1615 the Danes had sent two warships to Spitsbergen to try to enforce their claim to the territory and its fisheries, and although the effort had failed, it impressed the Hollanders, who sent two of their own ships-of-the-realm in 1617. These did some surveying and protected the Dutch whalers against the bickerings of the crowd of other nationalities whaling there that year, so that the Dutch company enjoyed a profitable season. The idea was logical and proved worth the expense even in time of peace, so it was immediately adopted as a regular routine after the incident with the Dunkirk pirate.

The effects were threefold and profound. First, the Dutch whaling fleet felt free and safe to pursue its arduous but peaceful tasks in an orderly manner. Second, foreigners found it advisable to let them do so without molestation or pilfering; and third, it resulted in a somewhat unexpected development. Whalers of other nations and private "interlopers" sought this protection either by combining their efforts with the Dutch fleets or by offering their services to these as seamen or technicians, or even as shipowners with their vessels. And more prestige and profits accrued to the perspicacious Hollanders through this move than, perhaps, through any other.

The third phase of Dutch enterprise made its appearance in the early stages of the development of the Spitsbergen trade, and so little is made of it in contemporary Dutch accounts — though it is commented upon with some amazement by all other nationalities — that it would seem to have been the outcome of a fairly venerable tradition devised elsewhere rather than a series of novel inventions of that date. Its four principal and several subsidiary aspects may be lumped together under the title of industrial improvements.

The two most important of these were the practice of towing whales when killed to a permanent or semipermanent shore station for processing and the employment there on the shore of slipways up which the whales could be pulled by winches for flensing and trying out. The idea of towing the whales to a base would probably be almost second nature to most Hollanders because of their age-old competence in towing first inland, then estuarine, and finally sea-going barges. A sixty-foot whale with the flukes of its tail cut off, so that it would not revolve and snap the towline by twisting, would present them with no problem at all. Then, their skill in shipbuilding and the hauling up of heavy boats on their shallow coasts had given them much experience with slipways, tackle, and heavy shore winches. Hauling a ship of three hundred tons burthen over a mudbank presents infinitely greater problems than pulling a whale of only seventy tons dead weight up a gentle, greased incline. This procedure, moreover, reduced the risk of losses of all kinds compared to the task of cutting-in and trying-out a whale on the open North Atlantic, a body of water that is hardly ever still. This aspect weighed very heavily with the Hollanders.

Although the Hollanders clung to these sensible and efficient methods whenever possible, they were often forced by circumstances to get along without them after they took to going to the Ice-front for the bowhead. Land was often too far off, or the nearest coast was too icebound or rocky. The curious fact is, however, that nobody else seems to have adopted the idea until the Norwegians in the latter half of the nineteenth century found methods of killing the rorquals and keeping them afloat by pumping air into them. Even the New Englanders in the later stages of their offshore whaling persisted in cutting-in at sea and freighting the blubber to port.

An even greater augmentation of the profits of whaling, however, was brought about by the Hollanders through better methods of refining the oil and the partial use of flesh and other parts of the whale as well as the blubber. The latter was a foreshadowing of the great, modern industry, where the whole beast is pressure cooked and comes out as half a dozen grades of oil and a predictable number of sacks of chicken feed and high-grade fertilizer. It was the Hollanders also who apparently first introduced the practice of double boiling and grading the oil at the station, or as soon as possible on arrival ashore, and then marketing the various grades at different and sometimes enhanced prices. When, moreover, there was a lack of blubber to keep the try-works going, they experimented with the rendering of those other parts of the whale that seemed to contain most oil, notably the intestines with their contained matter, the tongues, and scraps. Then, there is evidence — though admittedly not as precise as we would like — that it was the Hollanders who also discovered the high glycerin content in the skins of whales and collected it by a primitive fractionation of the refuse and washings from the flensing slipways. Finally, the Hollanders seem somehow to have always, throughout history, obtained a better price for their baleen than anybody else, but perhaps this was due as much to business acumen as to careful trade practices.

After the discovery of the arctic right whale by the Hollanders, as depicted in our story, a great change took place in the whole industry, primarily because the fleet moved farther and farther north and west in pursuit of the quarry. Nevertheless, other factors played an important part in the subsequent history of whaling as a whole. The first change came in 1634 when the French challenged the Hollanders over Spitsbergen and forbade French Basques to serve on their ships. The Hollanders immediately employed Frisians from the west German islands, who seem to have been just as competent. Their industry, however, continued to grow lustily until 1640 when the Hanseatic League entered the trade and founded a "whale house" in Hamburg. From then on the Germans were a constant source of competition and petty annoyance, culminating in 1709 when the Hollanders combined with the British and French in an endeavor to drive the Hanseatic League and its great commercial houses out of the trade. However, we still find 80 German whalers in Greenland waters twelve years later, competing with 250 Hollanders and 20 Basques.

Dutch whaling passed through sundry other vicissitudes during the important period of its dominance from 1626 to 1726. First, in 1642 the great Noordsche Company lost its monopoly over the trade, but this only stimulated increased private enterprise and in 1645 it became free for all, resulting in such a rapid expansion that prices fell drastically and the products began to be marketed abroad to avoid a two per cent landing tax in the Netherlands. This twist was stopped by law in 1652 on the outbreak of the first Dutch-British war, which lasted for three years. Then in 1658 the Hollanders allied themselves with the Danes against Sweden, and the Dutch whalers started registering with and working for foreigners to avoid bellicose complications, but this too was forbidden in 1661. The second Dutch-British war of 1665–1667 crippled the whole industry, and after its termination even rapeseed oil, in place of whale oil, had to be bought from the British. However, the clever move of throwing the Greenland whale fisheries open to all in 1672 led to most satisfactory results during the third Dutch-British war in 1672–1674 and thereafter for ten years, which was the peak of Dutch whaling.

The history of Dutch whaling after that is one of continued success for another hundred and fifty years, or until 1799 when the fleet was virtually destroyed, though even after that they still carried on at a reduced tempo but without loss of profits until the Norwegians with their entirely new methods and following new whales — the rorquals — began to take over in the North Atlantic. This is an amazing record and one that is neither widely recognized, even in the Netherlands, nor sufficiently appreciated elsewhere. Nevertheless, it must be remembered that the Hollanders fished exclusively in the North Atlantic, entering Davis Strait in 1718 and thence pushing on to Baffin Island. Further, their industry was founded almost solely on right whales and, with few exceptions, they clung to this enterprise for almost a century after other nations had learned the art of sperming and had followed these whales to the ultimate ends of the earth. As the number of right whales declined in the North Atlantic, so did the Dutch industry, but it took two centuries to virtually exterminate them, and during this time the Hollanders accrued herefrom vast wealth.

During the period 1675–1721 alone they employed a total of 5886 ships and took 32,907 whales, which, at an average value of $2500 each, brought them a gross of $82,267,500, which in that day and age represented a positively enormous sum of money. Regarded from an over-all point of view, and despite the fact that the modern Norwegian industry has more capital invested, takes more whales, markets more products, and makes greater nominal profits in a single year than the Hollanders did in a hundred, we may safely say that the Hollanders have been the most generally successful of all whalers. Year in and year out for almost two centuries they made handsome profits despite monopolies, wars, fluctuating prices, and the normal hazards of the business, and they exploited only one comparatively small area at the expense of only two steadily declining species of whales.

It is an amazing history but, withal, one singularly lacking in glamour. Dutch ships were as well-found as their owners' businesses, and although many foundered, the majority simply kept on catching whales by the time-honored methods of searching them out in large ships and chasing them with hand harpoons in shallops. The Hollanders then extracted the valuable products by the best methods they could devise, freighted them to where they were needed, and sold them at the best prices they could get. And although conditions on their whalers were generally as deplorable as those on the ships of any other nation before and since, they did make some effort to maintain the health of their crews.

The average Dutch whaler was of about 350 tons burthen, 112 feet long, and of some 28 feet beam. They had steeply raked bowsprits and three masts, and the towering medieval poop was early done away with. The main well-deck was kept fairly clear and the forecastle, although above decks, was still below the rail and often partially sunk. The after poop was, however, one stage above the well, and since all Dutch ships are shaped somewhat like one of their wooden shoes and have a tremendous sheer, the navigator was raised considerably above the forepiece. Standard squaresail rig of the barque was gradually developed, but the Dutch whalers were early addicted to sundry, odd, fore-and-aft sails, for close and rapid maneuvering after their shallops when in pursuit of whales or because they had to duck in and out of narrow bays, fjords, and sounds, where unexpected mountain winds added to sailing hazards, or among ice floes, where the open lanes bear no relationship to any winds. Strangely too, the Dutch, although of riverine-gulfine origin, and often having home ports behind shallow bars, delighted in a deep draft. Hulks of the great whaling period that have recently been dug up in the silt lands of newly drained parts of the Zuider Zee have amazed marine architects by their bulging form and apparently tremendous draft. How they ever got into the places where they have been found, unless the whole land has since risen, is somewhat of a mystery.

In later days, of course, the Dutch, like everybody else, turned to ships with ugly horizontal lines and upright spars, such as are depicted in early prints but which were nonetheless most efficient and often speedy sea boats. The most practical, moreover, were those that were ugliest of all, according to the ideas of a born sailor, and which immediately preceded the full-rigged ship and the true clipper. In prints they look like children's drawings with unadorned horizontal rails, clipper bows, cut-off stems, and masts that curve slightly forward like saplings bending before a wind.

Life aboard the Dutch whalers was not what we today would call comfortable; in fact, it would be singularly unpleasant, if not impossible, for our pampered generation. Breakfast, consisting of coarse groats with rancid butter, was available at four o'clock and not thereafter. One or two other meals followed during the day according to work on hand; these were made up of an unending succession of gray or yellow peas, pickled meat or dried codfish, with old, maggot-infested bread that looked like peat and had to be washed before it was eaten. Water was still carried in barrels, often those used previously for whale oil, and it invariably went putrid.

However, here again the Dutch showed remarkable foresight, for they forced their crews to eat fresh whale meat whenever available, and organized hunts for, or obtained by barter, all the ducks, geese, and other edible birds they could. They also landed regularly on islands where sea birds nested; there they collected thousands of eggs. Finally, in Spitsbergen they employed apprentices to collect stores of a plant they called "Greenland salad," which they found prevented scurvy among their crews.

## 9

# Forenoon on New Seas

### (American I)

"WHATEVER you may say, Mr. Goodbody, I vow you these savages are unwitting. Nay, more than that, sir; they do not have brains, but rather the senses of beasts."

"I do not agree with you, Master Pomferoy. They are good men and true, and there be many among them who are also good Christians, pious and God-fearing."

Master Joshua Pomferoy's only answer, a loud snort, was drowned in a sudden gust of cruelly penetrating wind. Mr. Goodbody regarded him in silence, watching in mild interest while a drop of water gathered at the tip of his long, slender, pointed, red nose and was whisked into oblivion by the next gust of wind. Then the bigger man began to orate again. It was his favorite pastime now that he had relinquished command of his ship and had become so successful a farmer that he no longer needed even to work his land.

"The senses of beasts, I say to you, sir. Forsooth, what human, even a Dutch loon, would make to sea in a cockleshell like that on open water when the wind blows from this quarter. It is sheer madness. Look at that old heathen, Makatoqua!" he added, pointing scornfully. "He would launch his leaky canoe upon the weather side of the jetty."

And it was true, for the old Indian headman, aided only by one small boy, was shoving his rickety canoe down the rocky beach straight into the foaming breakers. Meanwhile, all other able-bodied Indian men and boys had also come running down from the settlement, and likewise made haste to launch their canoes. Master Pomferoy continued to deplore their actions and to ridicule their lack of wisdom in tones that defied the elements, until another voice broke in. It was Goodman Masterson.

Now, Ned Masterson was a God-fearing man, as everyone could attest. He was also an able seaman, having been born to the fishing trade in the old country, and when he spoke of things maritime, all would respect his word, although he was but a goodman and illiterate. And what he now said caused even Joshua Pomferoy to stop talking and listen.

"Be we men or landlubbers?" he called out suddenly. "By the ghost of Saint David, I would try my luck with the Indians, for whatever thou sayest, Master Pomferoy, they be both men and fine boatsmen. Begging your wishes, gentlemen, would there be aught among ye goodmen present who would launch the oaken gig with me and ply an oar in aid of Makatoqua? It is my belief that, abiding by the will of the Almighty, we still have a mite to learn from our heathen brethren. Methinks also that this fishery may, betimes, bring us goodly profit to boot."

The entire group turned to gaze upon Goodman Masterson, and quickly recovering from their surprise, one by one, led by old Étienne Quimpéry, the Breton sailor, the men stepped forward, each raising his hand and saying simply, "Aye." It took eight men to man the oars of the gig and in addition there was space for a helmsman and three others in the little open vessel. Seven men had stepped forward when Joshua Pomferoy let out a bellow.

"Odds balls and barrels," he boomed. "No man in this community is taking the helm of that gig whilst I stand upon the shore like a craven sheepherder. Fetch you Will Harvey from his forges and tell him to bring with him his hardest filing tools. Bring ye also

all manner of boat hooks and any long kitchen irons, and let us be-
gone. We waste time talking."

And so it was that a dozen determined colonists piled into the
small gig, armed with a crude assortment of iron spikes, hatchets,
axes, and other paraphernalia, while Master Joshua Pomferoy seized
the helm, and Ned Masterson and old Étienne Quimpéry shoved
off from the lee side of the little jetty. The sea, even here at the bottom of the inlet, was choppy, and waves splashed over the bulging
bow of the gig as the eight oarsmen struggled to fall into the age-
old staccato rhythm of the west European seaman's pull. Ned
Masterson acted as stroke upon the after thwart, and croaked out
a steady pulling rhythm — *kerrrr-yuk, kerrrr-yuk* . . .

The next half hour passed uneventfully while the eight sturdy
white men jabbed steadily and rhythmically at the bouncing gray
waters with their short, heavy sculls, and the little, tubby, deep-
draft, clinker-built gig wallowed down the channel, hugging the
lee shore. By this time the Indian canoes could be seen clearly, bobbing about on the much greater waves that drove in from the open
Atlantic beyond. They had arranged themselves in two groups, one
to the north, the other to the south side of the narrow entrance to
the inlet. Other Indians could also be seen on the bluffs above, running about and pointing in sign language to their leader below. By
these signs even the white men knew that the objects of all the
excitement were not only near at hand, but were also behaving in
the manner most desired by the Indians. It was now plain to all that
they were heading straight down the center of the channel.

Old Makatoqua could be seen half standing in his rocking canoe,
shielding his eyes with one hand while gesticulating with the other.
He was in the lee of the north cape, in company with a dozen other
canoes, each manned by two of his brother Indians. The rest of the
fleet, some three dozen strong, was floundering about in the rougher
water half a mile across the sound on the exposed windward side.
In between, there was a considerable foamy disturbance caused by
something as yet unseen by those afloat except Joshua Pomferoy,
and by the Indians on the cliffs above. A small school of whales
was moving leisurely into the sound in pursuit of food, as their
ancestors had been wont to do for millions of years during their
slow winter migration down the coast.

Joshua Pomferoy's whole soul was now concentrated upon reaching Makatoqua's side before the two canoe fleets joined up and started back into the sound behind the whales, for with their superior speed they would get away from the gig and he would be left like a pregnant sheep on a hillside, while the rest of the flock trooped into the fold. But it was the chief who came to him. Seeing the approach of the white men, he dropped to the belly of his canoe and with deft strokes of his long paddle came bounding straight across the waves to the gig. When he drew near, he raised his hand in welcome and called out in his high-pitched sing-song voice a greeting in his own language which, if the colonist had only known, was reserved for very special occasions. Then, turning to the small boy, he gave certain instructions, for he had never quite mastered the language of the foreigners, and as they drifted by, the boy stood up and, cupping his hands, called out:

"Sires, be you hence to see or to command? So asks my great father."

Joshua Pomferoy replied immediately, likewise cupping his hands and giving forth with the full power of his tremendous lungs. "We be present to help, tell your father." At which the small boy fell to earnest conversation with the old chief, who was obviously bewildered by this strange statement.

Finally the boy rose again and called out, "Would the masters kill the *bedagi?*"

"We would *help* kill the great fish," Joshua Pomferoy called back, and the process of interpretation was repeated in the chief's canoe.

"Would the masters have killing sticks?" the boy called back.

The colonists looked at each other and then at Master Pomferoy. This was, indeed, a sorry state of affairs, for they would have to admit that all they had were axes and boat hooks and three kitchen irons sharpened by smith Harvey and lashed to poles. But Master Pomferoy was not to be deprived of his initiative, especially before a heathen.

"Egad!" he yelled back. "Tell the chief we have all that be needed. We follow him and we strike when he strikes." Then, turning to the men in the boat, he shouted, "Pull for the fairway, men;

we'll be a-fishing afore the heathen." And all men bent to their oars once more.

Then suddenly it happened. An enormous, black, shiny dome rose out of the gray waters not two canoe lengths ahead of the gig. Immediately, a tremendous racket broke out, for the Indians had brought with them all manner of wooden drums and any metal pots or other objects that they had acquired from the white men with which they could make noise. Upon all of these they now started beating with the greatest vigor while uttering piercing screams and shouts and banging on the water with their paddles. So great was the din that it transcended even the moaning of the wind and the lashing of the waves and was carried down the inlet all the way to those assembled on shore at the head of the bay. The colonists in the gig caught the fever and also started a prodigious uproar. The result was electric and unexpected.

The vast leisurely bulk that had broken through the surface of the waves immediately rose into a high dome and half a dozen other similar shapes of various sizes came rushing up from the depths. The canoes of the Indians skimmed forward, breaking right through the waves and riding upon their dancing crests as if they were men upon the backs of galloping horses. Then an Indian arose in the prow of each canoe and, steadying himself by some means unknown, raised a long, heavy shaft to his shoulder. Each shaft bore at its fore end an eighteen-inch harpoon either of polished bone or fire-hardened wood, set with recurved stone teeth, chipped to a sharpness and slenderness that would defy even a knife grinder's art. To these harpoon heads, long, sinuous lines of twisted and well-greased fiber were attached. These snaked away into the bellies of the canoes where they were attached to four-foot lengths of light logs or to inflated bladders made of deer or dog skin neatly sewn and carefully sealed with a compound of rosin and other plant saps.

The great dark bulks rose from the waters, curved slowly over, and started sliding gently down into the depths again. Their motion appeared leisurely, yet only a few seconds passed and then they were gone. However, as the last of them did so, the light craft of the Indians darted forward and converged upon the largest before more than two thirds of its back had disappeared. Then, all together, the five most stalwart of the Indians raised their harpoons and struck directly down into the shining black back. So terrific was their rush forward that two of the canoes rode right up on to the back of the whale and tipped sideways, throwing their occupants into the sea, while a third actually scudded clean over the whale's back and went bouncing away over the waves beyond.

With a fountain of gray-green water something lashed up out of the sea, and a wave burst upon the surface like a blowing geyser. Canoes lurched outward, and amid shrieks and cries more men were suddenly bounced into the sea. The Indians on shore yelled; the colonists in the gig shouted; and the sea went mad all around in a pother of blinding foam. Then the great, black tail came down upon the water not four feet from the canoe of old Makatoqua, who, accompanied by his small grandson, was seen to bound half a dozen feet from the surface of the water with his canoe and all the paraphernalia that it contained.

But even in the resulting confusion there remained a thread of purpose, for other canoes appeared immediately upon the scene, while those who floundered in the water started rocking their swamped craft back and forth to empty them, and presently leaped back into the canoes' bellies to finish bailing them out. The old chief's head also appeared above the spray, as he shouted exhortations in his own tongue to the others. The sea was by now covered with bobbing deerskin bladders, and through this tangled mass the gig plowed. Joshua Pomferoy was yelling at the top of his voice.

The next thing he witnessed, however, was one of his goodmen disappearing overboard. The whale had turned and, dragging half a dozen floats attached to resilient ropes along with it, had swept by the gig and fouled one of the oars. Then another line fouled the tiller, and before the colonists knew what was about, the whole gig veered around and they were off towards the open sea at a good six knots. But the white men had now caught the spirit of the hunt and they were quick to action. Seizing their crude implements, they crowded forward, and as the immense, shiny back of the leviathan once more showed above the surface, they jabbed at it with all their might and with every pointed device that they had to hand. Even old Étienne Quimpéry took a swipe with an axe, which, in his enthusiasm, he nearly followed into the water.

No one in the gig was ever able to give any clear account of what actually happened thereafter during the remaining seven hours of daylight. Those on shore agreed that the boat covered at least fifteen miles about the inlet, mostly out near the narrows. Every canoe was said to have been capsized at least twice more, but it was noted by both the colonists on shore and the Indians that the gig did not founder. And it was the gig that at last came alongside the great bulk of the whale just about sundown, and it was from it that Makatoqua and three young tribesmen drove their longest lances and smith Harvey's sharpest iron into the base of the great animal's neck — if such it could be called. Thereafter, nothing much happened because the huge bulk of the beast slowly sank just below the surface and remained still, while blood flooded the whole harbor and formed a scum on the stones of the beach. The gig came drifting inshore, the men resting on their oars in utter exhaustion, while the canoes of the Indians scudded away one by one into the dusk, and the whole community ashore gathered on the jetty. A strange silence fell upon everybody, so that even when the gig slid alongside, and Joshua Pomferoy climbed ashore, nobody spoke.

Meanwhile, old Makatoqua had landed at the settlement, and now came walking along the stony beach, accompanied by a group of other Indians. Arrived at the jetty, one of their number raised his hand in greeting, and stepped forward to address the white men.

"Makatoqua say," he began, "man make great fire to this side" — and he indicated the settlement — "so that all men may see to pull the *bedagi* to beach."

Then he turned about and, accompanied by his brethren, started back along the foreshore. And it was only after they had gone that the settlers raised a great, spontaneous shout of satisfaction and excitement. Then one and all started running after the Indians to lend a hand.

In the earliest days of the settlement of our eastern seaboard, scenes such as this occurred everywhere along the coast wherever white colonists took up residence near an Amerindian community. To read this today may be rather startling because we have been deliberately conditioned for so long to think of the indigenous people of the North American continent as either running about in dense forests with bows and arrows, or whooping it up on the vast buffalo plains of the West. Only recently have we started to re-appraise our ideas of the red man, Amerindian, or "Indian," as he has so inaccurately been called, but this is proving to be a hard task in view of the malicious propaganda that has been disseminated regarding these people for nigh on two centuries.

The red man, before the coming of the Europeans, was probably better integrated with his environment than any other group of human beings known during historic times. He was, nonetheless, at the time of his discovery, still living in the Stone Age and, however fine his individual qualities or those of his race may have been, he simply could not survive the impact of the expanding west European culture with its two thousand years of experience of the Iron Age. Though there are said to be more "Indians" in North America today than there were at the time the *Mayflower* sailed, we must face the very obvious fact that the red man has "gone under" and has been, and still is being, absorbed into our own much vaster and technically more complex culture at an ever-increasing tempo.

Nevertheless, the red man's culture, though primitive, was also an ancient one, and it had achieved much more than the early chroniclers admit or would give us to suppose. The indigenous North American was not just a stupid savage, any more than was his Central or South American cousin. It is still not appreciated that the Aztecs of Mexico and the Incas of the Andes, though lacking such basic things as the wheel and, in the latter case, even writing, had nonetheless developed cultures that were in some respects far in advance of that of the Spanish Europeans who conquered and destroyed their civilizations. For instance, they gave us almost all our most valuable plant products — potatoes, tobacco, rubber, tomatoes, corn, cacao hence chocolate, quinine, cocaine, and dozens of beans and other vegetables. In fact, had their conquerors not been fired with a vicious and proselytizing religious mania, and had they not owned horses, and been able to grow beards, both of which greatly awed the natives, they never would have taken over those empires. The North Americans, while altogether less well organized than the Aztecs and Incas, still possessed a great wealth of traditional knowledge and many unique skills. These were mostly ignored by the European colonists, but some of them were quietly taken over. Due credit for their development, however, has seldom been given to the red man. The single most important of these skills, which was thus acquired by the European colonists, was that of offshore whaling.

There are those, and serious-minded historians among them, who try to deny this fact, but fortunately the original records are still extant for all of us to see, and everywhere you search around our coasts you will find some picture such as that given above in the early fishing records. Later on in our pursuit of the whale, we will see that the same thing also occurred on the west coast, in Canada, and in Alaska. The truth is that both the Eskimos and the Amerindians all around the edge of the North American continent were skilled fishermen, and all of them had regularly for thousands of years been killing whales when they approached the coast. It is, perhaps, our own native pride that causes us to recoil from the idea that our worthy ancestors learned what was later to become one of our most important industrial arts from various heathen peoples still living in the Stone Age, but there can be no denying the fact that they did so. The proof, moreover, is overwhelming.

More has probably been written on the so-called "discovery" of America than on almost any other historical incident, but there is a curious gap in all our history books following this famous event and extending to the emergence of English-speaking America. This covers a period of exactly one hundred years, from 1500 to 1600 A.D. Likewise, there is still totally insufficient popular understanding of the following century — namely, 1600 to 1700 A.D. — during which time the true foundations of what is now the United States were actually laid.

Cristoforo Colombo, as everybody knows, first sighted the West Indies in 1492, almost exactly five hundred years after the Norse first sighted Greenland. It is odd to realize that there were still Europeans living in America when he did so, for the last Norse Greenlander did not die till fifty years later. After 1500 A.D., however, Europe concentrated on tropical America. Apart from the voyages of John Cabot in 1497, Corte Real, about 1500, and Jacques Cartier up the St. Lawrence in 1534 and 1542, nothing really happened in North America until the landing of the Huguenots in Carolina in 1562. The British made abortive attempts at colonization in Newfoundland in 1583 under Sir Humphrey Gilbert, and at Roanoke in 1584 under Sir Walter Raleigh, but the century had turned before the first lasting settlement was planted in Virginia in 1607. The *Mayflower* did not reach Cape Cod until 1620. Thus it was a full century after Europe became aware of the Western Hemisphere before true colonization of the northern land mass began.

During this time the Basques were still in the ascendancy in European whaling. As we have seen, their energy was ebbing and they no longer had a monopoly of the trade, but they were still active. Their ships came regularly and in fair numbers to the Newfoundland fishing banks and to the Labrador Sea for both codfish and whales up until the end of the seventeenth century. However, they always remained in those frigid northern seas, and they did not play any part in the invasion of the North American continent. During the sixteenth century no other Europeans were whaling on the high seas, and it was not until the end of the seventeenth century that, as we have seen, the British and the Hollanders had learned the business. Thus, when the gates to the Western world were opened by the establishment of the colony of Virginia — which, it must not be forgotten, included the whole seaboard from Maine to Florida — and English-speaking settlers started pouring into the country, although there were many sailors and some fishermen among them, there were no whalers.

However, one and all among the first immigrants fully appreciated the value of a stranded whale because their lamps had to burn oil and all oils were in those days both scarce and costly. Thus it is that we find reference to whales in the very first records; one of the principal aspects of the charter given to those aboard the *Mayflower* granted its company "all royal *fishes, whales, balan, sturgeons and other fishes.*" The immigrants, moreover, almost chose Cape Cod as the location of their initial settlement because, among other things, "large whales of the best kind for oil and bone came daily alongside and played about the ship."

The colonists, however, knew nothing of how to go about catching these whales simply because, even if they were not inland farmers or artisans, none of them had ever done so on the shores of their homelands. No wonder they looked in amazement upon these activities of the Amerindians wherever they found them along the coast, for, using only flimsy canoes, these natives went boldly out to sea in all weather, killed the largest whales with stone- and bone-pointed harpoons, towed them ashore by hand or paddle power, and then used every part of them for food, lighting, medicine, and even, in the case of the larger species, their bones for building purposes. The colonists were quick to see the very real value of this enterprise, and they appear to have started lending a hand almost immediately after they landed.

Details of early history are obscure, but the first records of almost every settlement from the Bay of Fundy to the mouth of the Hudson River mention stalwart colonial fishermen aided by local Amerindian crews rowing about inshore waters in open boats in pursuit of whales. This activity continued and expanded during the next hundred years — that is, from 1620 to 1720 — entirely on its own initiative and quite uninfluenced by any similar activities in Europe. It thus developed its own techniques, which were curiously similar to those of the early days of the Basque industry and, before that, of the neolithic peoples of Scandinavia and the Western Isles. The colonists could learn nothing about whaling from the English simply because, apart from the brief and dismally unsuccessful attempt under the Muscovy Company, those people knew nothing of the business at that time, and had no whaling fleet. They learned nothing from the Hollanders because they in turn were busy during that period learning deep-sea whaling in the Arctic from the Basques. Moreover, the Hollanders have always been a reticent folk, and they were then being doubly cagey due to the wars with the British and the grandiose and ever-increasing profits which they were discovering to be forthcoming from the whaling business. The American colonists learned to go a-whaling from the Amerindians, and they learned it the hard way. However, they added some very novel features of their own to the business that changed the whole history of whaling.

We are dealing here only with the first period of American whaling, and although this concerns the whole northeastern coast line, it must inevitably end up on that unique island known to its original

Amerindian inhabitants as "Nanticut" — meaning the faraway land — or Nantucket, because it was there that a chance incident occurred which changed not only the whole history of whaling, but also the entire history of the world, influencing almost everything that has happened in the affairs of men up to the present day.

When that story unfolds we will see the incredible results that can stem from the action of a single man, but this must be reserved for later. In the meantime, a description of what occurred on Nantucket between 1660 and 1712 will serve to explain what took place all along the coast from the Bay of Fundy to Long Island Sound and on the outer side of Long Island, for everywhere the steps taken were similar. Only in point of time were there slight differences, so that we read of the first white settlers on Nantucket Island sending for one Ichabod Paddock from Cape Cod to teach them how to go whaling, which demonstrates that the business was organized in the latter place earlier than in the former.

The history of Nantucket, though almost too often told, is still delightful and unique. It begins, for the white man, that is, in 1602 when the mariner Bartholomew Gosnold explored the isles south of Cape Cod. Sometime thereafter the island was included in a charter to the Earl of Stirling, whose American agent sold it in 1641 for forty pounds to a Mr. Thomas Mayhew of Watertown, Massachusetts. It was inhabited by a subgroup of the Algonquins, who customarily went a-whaling and who, to say the least, disapproved strongly of all foreigners and of white men in particular. In this they anticipated the attitude of the present-day white inhabitants, who regard all persons other than the descendants of the first settlers, and particularly summer tourists, as "off-islanders." Nobody seems to have bothered to challenge the attitude of these Amerindians until 1658 when some refugees from Puritan religious intolerance in Salisbury, Massachusetts, landed upon the island's shores. There is a record that the Amerindians treated them with favor on account of this persecution, and thus the colonization of the island started in an atmosphere of internal tolerance combined with a pronounced xenophobia. The first comers were Thomas Macy and family and a friend named Edward Starbuck. One of the least results of this expedition is the famous Macy's department store in New York today, originally founded on the island by one of Thomas

Macy's descendants. The greatest is the present-day existence of a world-wide American economic empire.

Macy sent Starbuck back to the mainland a year later to co-opt other permanent settlers, and nine of them came over. These together bought nine tenths of the island, including all its Amerindian inhabitants, from Mayhew and divided it up equitably. Then each took a partner, and so founded the body known to and enormously venerated by all present-day islanders and historians as The Twenty Purchasers. They cleared land, planted crops, and built log cabins with thatched roofs. The Amerindians continued to fish for, and land, whales, but the colonists took no part in these operations until a right whale happened to wander into the enclosed natural harbor and bumbled around there for three days trying to find its way back to the open sea. Some of the islanders fashioned a crude harpoon, gave chase, and managed to kill and land the beast. This made a great impression on the whole community, but since the settlers were not seamen, and had only a few small rowboats, nothing happened regarding whales for some time. Nonetheless, parties used to gather on high places for recreation, according to the records, and from there they watched schools of whales passing their coasts, with the red men pursuing them in canoes. As a result, the elders finally decided to do something about this obvious waste of valuable raw material, and in 1690 they sent for Ichabod Paddock.

This man seems to have been most energetic, for he not only stimulated the building of boats, but he also set up a series of watch towers on the southern coast of the island, along which the whales most frequently passed. These consisted of huts and a sort of crow's-nest on a tall tower and were manned by the islanders on a cooperative and voluntary basis. When whales were sighted, all able-bodied male colonists and red men piled into large rowboats and went after them. They appear to have been successful immediately.

The procedure from then on seems to have been similar to the native practice on the mainland, except that rowboats were used instead of canoes, and the harpoons were made of iron instead of stone. It is not known whether log or skin floats were used on the island, but in any case the whales hunted were black right whales, which do not sink when killed. The really amazing thing to contemplate — and apparently it has not been considered by any historian —

is that these men in small, open rowboats somehow managed to tow hundred-ton whales to shore through the terrific tides, rips, and currents that run along the south coast of the island. How they did so is now almost incomprehensible, but that they did accomplish the feat time and time again is undeniable.

They also maneuvered their catches through the pounding surf that characterizes this island. The blubber was stripped from the corpse while it lay among the breakers, and was then hauled ashore by giant capstans known as "crabs." Somehow, these enterprising people also devised methods of turning the giant bodies over so that they could be stripped of their blubber from all sides. In this, we are told, they were ably assisted by the red men, who received in lieu of wages all the unwanted parts of the corpse plus cast-off clothing and rum.

The details of processing whales remained the same throughout the ages until the present century, so that they need not be described in this instance. The blubber was "tryed out," or rendered, in large pots, and the oil cleaned through cloth filters. The baleen was cleaned, trimmed, softened in hot water, and sold to manufacturers of various objects — notably ladies' stays — and the meat and bones were abandoned or given to the Indians.

On Nantucket, however, the whole procedure was devised upon novel principles that had most important consequences. The Nantucketers instituted an important innovation in the industry that had far-reaching effects, and, strangely, this was of a purely social nature.

Whatever whaling had been carried on in Europe since the haphazard, roistering, and individualistic days of the Norsemen had always been a rather grimly capitalistic affair with undertones of slavery. Even the Basques went to sea under the stern and watchful eye of a master who either owned the ship or represented its builders and the providers of its gear and supplies. Seamen and officers alike worked for masters and were paid set wages, albeit usually with some form of bonus. The British and Dutch dispensed with all such nonsense, and any dereliction of duty on one of their whalers resulted in a flogging at least, and death at worst. Even ships' captains, as we have seen, were sometimes subservient to company supercargoes or agents. The Nantucketers, on other hand, were something quite new in the field. They not only owned their lands and most else besides communally, but they also worked together on an almost ideally cooperative system, each man contributing what he could by his skills and labors to the common good. Their early whaling effort was organized along these lines, in which even the red men participated. It was a joint enterprise, initiated by cooperative labor, and entirely without subscribed capital. When successful, it resulted in an equitable distribution of all the proceeds. What is more, the portion received by every man was commensurate with what he had put into the job.

The ownership of the boats did not last for long upon this joint community system, and an arrangement of partnerships grew up, but the basic principle of part shares in any one company's profits persisted and gave rise to what was to become universally known as the "lay" system. By this, every man, from cabin boy to captain, and the widow ashore to the cooper aboard, received a share in the profits in proportion to his or her investment in money or labor. Thus, every man aboard the whaling ships was working for himself and to his own profit. The result was a veritable blossoming of free enterprise in a field that is thankless, to say the least, dangerous at all times, and at that time much less profitable than ordinary trading or slave trading.

The offshore whaling on the mainland had by 1700 already become a truly capitalistic enterprise with the white men employed on set salaries, with or without a bonus, and the red men employed for a set quota of rum, whale oil, or trade goods. However, there were still wide variations in the practice then because offshore whalers ran into many frustrating, bureaucratic obstacles erected by the British Government. There are records of most sorry and protracted bickerings between the colonist, who wished to indulge this enterprise, and the Crown, who wished either to prohibit it or to tax it for its own benefit. These disputes sometimes reached the highest courts of appeal in England. In time, however, the Nantucket practice of "lays" spread throughout the industry, and it finally spread also to the codfishery and to other related enterprises.

Despite the partially seasonal nature of this business, it appears to have been regarded so highly that strict laws governing some of its aspects were enacted in various areas, notably in New York to

cover the activities on Long Island. In addition to these formal regu-
lations, a wealth of strictly enforced custom also grew up. For instance, no food or drink was allowed aboard the boats while they
were at sea, on the grounds that the men required their every fac-
ulty during the chase.

The Indians were paid in clothing, powder and shot, liquor, and
sometimes in whale oil. In fact, whale oil was used as currency and
there are records of debts being settled in this medium, and even of
ministers and schoolteachers being paid their salaries in oil, which
was valued at from one pound ten shillings to two pounds per barrel. The Indians usually refused to cooperate unless they were
promised at least some liquor, and they often also requested certain
parts of the whale. There are records of their handing over title
to their lands in exchange for a few trade goods and a guarantee
that they might have the tail flukes and flippers of all whales landed,
together with permission to make what use they liked of whatever
was left of the corpse after the colonists had taken what they desired.

At the same time strict laws were enacted to protect the Indians
engaged in whaling. New York State passed legislation in 1708
which completely protected all Indians with whaling contracts from
being arrested or hindered in any other way while engaged in this
work. An earlier ordinance stipulated, "Whosoever hires an Indian
to go a-whaling shall not give him above one trucking cloath coat
for each whale he and his company shall kill, or half the blubber
without the whalebone." In most places the red man was highly regarded as a whaler, and was paid handsome wages for his help.

When a whale was landed in the early days, the whole community
helped in cutting it up. Later, however, the job fell to the crew
who had killed it, and this usually took them about a week, working night and day. The corpse was floated inshore to the beach,
and first the lips were stripped off so that the baleen could be extracted. Next, the head was cut off, and then strips of the blubber
were peeled from the body from neck to tail with block and tackle.
The body was turned over at high tides. The blubber then had to
be cut into small strips to go into the try kettles, which were large
iron pots of about 250 gallons' capacity. These were set on stone or
brick structures under which a fire was started with wood. The

residue of the blubber after the oil had been rendered from it formed a sort of monstrous crackling which burned furiously, and there was always enough of it to keep the fire going once the kettle had been filled. However, the oil kettle had to be kept at a certain temperature, which was ascertained by spitting into the oil, for if it got too hot, the introduction of new blubber would cause it to boil over.

Although the Indians ate the meat of whales with much relish, the white men seem to have spurned it even in times of severe food shortage. More curious still is the fact that, although the Indians rendered the meat, bones, liver, and intestines, together with the food matter contained therein, and thus obtained considerable quantities of oil for their own use, no others seem ever to have considered doing this regularly to all parts of all whales. Even the thrifty Hollanders never discovered the obvious fact that there is valuable oil in all parts of a whale, though there are records of their having collected glycerin from the washings of the platforms at their early shore stations in Spitsbergen. In time they might have learned of the oil value of the rest of the whale if they had continued these shore stations, but they took to high-sea whaling by the Arctic Ice where any such practice was obviously impractical.

The whales that the early colonists, and the Amerindians before them, pursued were the same black right whales which first tempted the Basques offshore. This species migrates south in the fall along the eastern American seaboard just as it does down the Western Euopean coast. During these migrations the vast, lazy beasts troll along and enter bays and inlets in pursuit of their small, agile food. In spring they move rather more rapidly northward again to their cool, summer-water quarters, often traveling far offshore. Thus it was that the Amerindians set regular watches from November to April for their passing, but only kept a casual lookout during the rest of the year, and then mostly for distressed fin whales or rorquals that might be washed ashore. In those days this occurred much more often than now because these animals existed in much greater abundance in the North Atlantic prior to the Norse whaling revival in the late twentieth century, which will be described later.

The offshore whaling of the Amerindians was not, however, restricted to the slaughter of the right whales, nor to the processing of chance stranded rorquals. It was in every sense more catholic. The Amerindian needed oil just as much as did the early colonist. Moreover, he was aware of the existence of an almost unlimited supply of oils in the sea, and he had since time immemorial devised methods of obtaining them. The mighty black right whales provided only one source, and a very unreliable one at that. If the red man relied on these whales alone and a school did not come by the bay where he lived in any one year, or if he and his comrades were unlucky in their capture of a specimen, his whole community might go hungry throughout a long and rigorous winter. These great whales came only twice a year, but there were little whales in the river mouths, gulfs, and inlets all year round. These were the porpoises, dolphins, and other smaller species, and upon these the Amerindians founded several regular industries centuries before the white man came to the Western Hemisphere. And the amazing thing is that the red men kept up these enterprises until they themselves disappeared from the industry and the white man took over the occupation.

There is still a "little-whale" enterprise in the St. Lawrence, and there were, until recently, others in the Bay of Fundy and at Cape Hatteras. These were based upon completely different animals, but they had much in common and in practice. The industry still pursued in Canada is not greatly different from a similar one that was carried on for centuries in the Bay of Fundy by the Passamaquoddys up until a time within the memory of living men. Simply stated, the procedure was this: men went out from shore in canoes or small rowboats whenever small cetaceans were sighted and either harpooned them or, later, shot them with rifles or smooth-bored guns, then gaffed them and towed them ashore. Latterly, the fishermen of Cape Hatteras found that they could net their quarry in large seines, and thus gave up the more hazardous practice of harpooning. This so-called porpoise industry — though the animals involved were never specifically porpoises — is common to the seashores of the entire world, as we have already seen and shall continue to see as our tale unfolds.

About Cape Hatteras the industry eventually developed a highly novel aspect, for here a species of dolphin was regularly taken in seine nets. The net was about a thousand feet long and made of extra-heavy, tarred twine. It was set some fifty yards to seaward of the surf, parallel to the flat, sandy shore, and a rowboat was stationed at either end. Dolphins of a species known as *Tursiops truncatus* crowd by Cape Hatteras in huge schools from late fall to early spring, following certain fish just beyond the surf. When a school passed thus to the landward of the net, the boats quickly carried the end lines ashore and then returned to station themselves outside the net to prevent the dolphins from jumping out to freedom. It took upwards of an hour to haul the great net to shore, but as many as a hundred animals could be taken at a single haul. This industry continued into the present century, principally because of a very special kind of oil that can be extracted from the lower jaws of the *Tursiops*.

This oil is taken from the back end of the lower jaw on either side and, when refined, was once valued as high as twenty dollars a gallon. It is extremely light and perfectly suited for oiling small watches and other delicate instruments. Secondly, the hides of these animals make very fine leather, and the blubber yields other oil of high grade.

The animals concerned are popularly known as Bottle-nosed Dolphins, and are apparently of world-wide range. The commonest species, which is that caught off Hatteras, is found all over the North Atlantic, and has been reported from the Mediterranean, the Black and Baltic seas, and from the Pacific as far south as New Zealand. There is a very similar species with the delightful name of *Tursiops abusalam*, found only in the Red Sea, and another from the Indian Ocean. All are about ten feet long, and they are fish-eaters, consuming not only enormous quantities of this food, but equally enormous individual fish. They will eat up to a hundred pounds in a day, and in captivity they will eat dead as well as live food. They mate between January and April, and they migrate north in summer.

The most notable feature of these dolphins is that they can turn their heads around almost like land animals and quite unlike any other whale that lives in the sea. Most whales have fixed, rigid necks, but the *Tursiops* can not only turn its head down to an angle of forty-five degrees, but it can also turn it to either side or raise it almost straight up. It has eyelids that are every bit as mobile as ours; these often give it a very bizarre expression. It also has a habit of winking. In color, the common species is shiny black with a white streak below, and its lower jaw protrudes beyond its upper beak. It is believed that bottle-nosed dolphins also formed the bulk of the quarry hunted in the Bay of Fundy by the Passamaquoddy Indians. However, records state that any kind of porpoise, dolphin, or other small whale was taken in that area, and thus a constant supply of meat, oil, and leather was harvested throughout the year.

The other porpoise industry was of quite a different and much more specialized nature. This was, and in fact still is, centered about the St. Lawrence inlet, and has likewise been taken over by the white man, though Indians may yet from time to time take part in the modern enterprise, using motorboats and small harpoon guns. The Eskimos also maintain a similar seasonal fishery in Alaska about the Mackenzie delta.

This small but highly remunerative industry is founded solely upon the Beluga, or White Whale (*Delphinapterus leucas*), which is known to the French Canadians as the *marsouin blanc*. The principal value of the animal, which can grow to almost twenty feet in length, is contained in its hide, which constitutes most of the "porpoise hide" of commerce, and which still commands a high price. From it also may be extracted oil of an exceptionally good grade which has always been in demand. For this reason it was regularly hunted at Spitsbergen — where it was known as the *sewria* in the early days — and in Greenland by the Norse. Then, the Eskimos and, later still, the Danes have hunted it in the latter area. In 1670 a small ship arrived in Yarmouth, England, directly from Greenland with "about 24 tons of oil made from whitefish."

Belugas were hunted in the St. Lawrence with harpoons thrown from canoes, but in Greenland they were sometimes netted, as they are very gregarious and travel about in large companies containing individuals of all ages. The Eskimos have always been most eager in their pursuit of this animal because they consider its blubber, both when cooked after being dried and, more especially, when fresh and eaten raw, to be the greatest delicacy. This they call *muk-tuk*, and it is traditionally prepared by them in the form of long ribbons of diamond-shaped pieces each about eight inches across.

The beluga is one of the most remarkable of all whales in several respects. Its only close relative is the narwhal, but it has no horn like that animal, and, instead, only ten small teeth in the fore part of the lower jaw. When young, it is very dark gray or black, but as it grows, the hide becomes mottled with gray on dirty yellow, then turns all yellow, and finally, absolutely pure, pristine, glistening white, of a purity otherwise seen only on fresh arctic snowfields. Belugas are circumpolar in distribution, but seldom if ever leave freezing water, though they regularly ascend rivers to great distances in pursuit of salmon. They enter the St. Lawrence in spring, and go as far inland as Quebec. They ascend the Yukon as far as six hundred miles beyond salt water. Their food consists of fish, squid and cuttlefish, and a certain amount of other shellfish, for which they are known to dive to incredible depths. They have no dorsal fin at all, and the flippers are small and placed far forward, while the tail is also small. They have distinct necks, but cannot move the head to any appreciable extent. Most amazing of all, however, is their voice.

It is now known that all whales, and especially porpoises and some dolphins, keep up a tremendous racket under water, lowing like cows, moaning, whistling, and making chuckling sounds. Although they have no external ears and auditory exits that will, even in the largest species, only just allow the insertion of a pencil, all whales appear to have very keen hearing both under water and in the air. Belugas have an enormous vocabulary of different sounds, which gives rise to their popular name among seamen of "sea canaries." They twitter, whistle, scream, gurgle, chuckle, hoot, and make strange popping and puffing noises. Also, when blowing, they let off a loud "phutt."

The Amerindian was not a seaman, but he was a skilled fisherman, as is the Eskimo. He had made use of practically every form of sea life he could catch or gather, and he had developed more distinct whaling industries than any other race, millennia before the coming of the Europeans to his country. What he lacked in technical knowledge and tools, such as metal weapons and clinker-built boats with oars, he fully made up for in skill, bravery, and endurance. But the latter were never quite enough to free him from a virtual slavery to his environment. It was the white man who first put the Amerindian's whaling efforts on a profitable basis, and it was a white man who finally stumbled upon a discovery that carried American whaling — and with it Anglo-Saxon culture and power — all over the globe. That man's name was Captain Christopher Hussey of Nantucket, and the date of his discovery was 1712.

# Part Five

1700 A.D. TO 1875 A.D.

## The Late Period

# High Noon on the High Seas

## (*American II*)

BRING HER head to the wind, Mr. Pritchard," a gruff voice roared from the darkness forward, and was instantly whisked away by the howling wind.

"Aye, aye, sir," came a reply from the boatswain back aft.

For a few moments nothing seemed to happen in the pitch darkness that enshrouded the tiny, open vessel, while the wind howled in the scant rigging aloft, and the waves came in ceaseless batteries against the low rail, sending jets of spray that felt like fair-sized gravel across the thwarts. Then the boatswain's voice broke through the uproar of the sea and the blackness of the night once more.

"Standing by the sheet, sir."

"Break out oars forward!" yelled the mate. Then, turning aft again and cupping his hands to his mouth, he deliberately counted ten before shouting with all his might, "Hard a'lee, Mr. Garvey!"

The little vessel answered immediately as if she had been seized by her keel in some gargantuan grip, and spray came flying down the length of her, smacking against the sails and drenching her belly.

But after the first wild plunge her antics abruptly changed from the tortured banging and wriggling of the past five hours, when she had fought across the wind, to a steady pitching. The canvas started an hysterical flapping aloft.

"Foresail away!" yelled Mate Pritchard above the roaring din. "Steady on the pull, men; keep her nose to the wind, Mr. Garvey." Then, turning forward, he again cupped his hands and, filling his lungs to the utmost, bellowed against the storm, "All square, sir."

There were four sturdy men on the forward oars — the Indian Amasak of Wauwinet, the Macy boys, and Michel Audant, the West Indian — the double-reefed mainsail was now close-hauled, and the little vessel had the lines of a porpoise so that once she was head to wind, even in a storm such as blew that night, she rode easily and the oarsmen hardly had to pull at all to keep her steady. No man aboard spoke a word, only Michel Audant grunted loudly and rhythmically as he pulled on his oar, while the rowlocks of the other three creaked and banged in perfect unison with his. The elements howled on.

This was the fourth time during the night they had come up into the wind. Each time they had pitched thus, up and down over the endless, foam-crested waves for what had seemed to every man to be an eternity. On no occasion had anyone spoken so much as a whispered word to another. So absolutely black was the night that none could see even his closest companion, and all awaited the next command, fearful of missing its import, for while the precedence of commands was maintained even in this extremity, every man aboard wanted to hear the command himself from the master. They knew Captain Hussey and they knew that it was ultimately on him alone that they must depend to be saved.

But this time, those aft who were not manning the oars and who were thus free to crouch facing forward began to call out to each other because, slowly and unmistakably, the shrouds were becoming visible as blacker lines against the blackness of the sky. Dawn at last was sweeping gently up beyond the horizon, lighting the darkness ahead of it with that blueness that is just not black. It was Isaiah Garvey, standing to the tiller, who first dimly saw the silhouette of Captain Hussey rocking against the paling sky in the extreme fore-peak of the boat.

"Aye, the day be a-coming," he called to the men. "Let us praise Him for this deliverance, for so be it."

And there were several among the company who fell quietly to praying, for they were deeply religious folk, and although brought up to the perils of the sea and fully cognizant of the skill of their captain, they knew full well that their survival this night was certainly a near miracle. It was not so much the storm, which instead of dying with the sun had increased in fury, but the position they had been in as night had fallen. There had been three preceding days of thick, low scud as dense as any fog which had precluded any possibility of fixing their position. Although they should have been well clear of any land, they might just as well have been within a mile of some rocky shore. In fact, they were lost and every man aboard knew it.

The coming of the dawn gave them at least half an advantage and their spirits began to revive along with the increasing light. Also, the wind began to drop appreciably.

Captain Christopher Hussey's bearlike figure could now be seen in full detail as he stood in the bow, his legs braced against the gunwales, pitching to the towering seas so that he looked more like a figurehead on a ship than a man wedged into the narrow end of a thirty-foot open sloop. He was soaked with spray and from his tremendous vigil his eyes under their shaggy brows were red and rimmed with salt, but he was as alert as he had ever been throughout the past twenty-four hours, and he peered this way and that, watching the swell around him, the sky above, and the horizon whenever he could see it. And nothing happened nor did anyone speak again for a full half hour while the sky brightened to the intense electric blue of a northern dawn.

Boatswain Garvey stood by the tiller, his deep-sunken eyes also scanning the horizon all around. He had ideas of his own as to their position, though he would never have made any suggestion on the subject to Captain Hussey. From the set of a current which was running strongly athwart the wind from the northeast, as estimated from the position of the rising sun, he felt that they must be much closer to land than they had been the day before, and therefore he concentrated most of his attention abaft, and it was thus that he first saw something that led to a most extraordinary series of events.

He had been gazing intently astern, waiting for the little vessel to rise over a wave so that he might scan the horizon, when suddenly and absolutely without warning something enormous, jet black, and glistening broke out of the side of a wave, heading straight for the boat. Hardly able to believe his eyes, Boatswain Garvey nonetheless reached behind him and grabbed the first man his wildly gesticulating hand encountered. This happened to be a twelve-year-old lad named Jake Horsefield. Seizing him firmly, Boatswain Garvey pulled him to the stern rail, and hissing an admonition to be silent into his ear, he pointed.

"See you what I see?" he whispered, and when Jake nodded emphatically, he shouted into his ear, "Get you forward with all speed, Jake, and tell the captain a whale be upon us. Make thou haste!"

The boy scrambled off through the wildly pitching vessel, but so excited was he that he quite forgot prescribed behavior and kept calling to the rest of the crew as he passed, "Whale off! Whale off!" so that by the time he reached the bow the whole company was in an uproar. Thus the most surprised man abroad in the end was Captain Christopher Hussey, but when he finally got the gist of Jake's panting message, he leaped into action.

Seizing the harping-irons which always lay ready forward, he gave frantic signaled commands to Mate Pritchard and Boatswain Garvey. The other men had already broken out oars, and all now waited, resting upon their stretchers, with eyes concentrated upon Boatswain Garvey.

Now, Isaiah Garvey was a man of considerable experience in the taking of whales, having pursued the profession off the mainland shore as well as from the first days on Nantucket, and he knew well the habits of the beasts — how when cruising undisturbed they will rise to blow gently three times in succession and then sound for a longer period to swim along with their great mouths open, gathering their huge quantities of tiny food. Therefore he felt confident that this whale, even if a lone bull, would do likewise and almost immediately come up again, perhaps right under the boat. But he was quite wrong, because in the half-light and the confusion of his first surprise, he had failed to observe properly even what he could see of this whale. So he was as much taken by surprise as anybody when a towering pillar of blackness rose rather slowly out of the waves only a few feet to larboard and remained poised there for what seemed to be minutes on end. The most amazing part of all was that this thing was quite square on top.

Despite the surprise of all aboard, those at the oars immediately maneuvered the boat around as soon as this apparition appeared, so that when it reached its greatest height, it towered directly ahead of Captain Hussey's poised harpoon. Without further ado the captain cast the iron with all his very considerable strength, but altogether without skill, for he didn't really know which part of the animal faced towards him. And luck was with him, for the iron sank almost to the haft into tough blubber and flesh and came to a grinding stop between bones. Contrary to all precedent, however, nothing seemed to happen. Captain Hussey transferred the second harpoon to his right hand, raised and cast it also. This too took, almost on top of the other. But again nothing happened, so that the boat actually rammed the beast and the men had time to ship their oars and break out the lances. Then suddenly, the whole vessel keeled over to within a degree of turning turtle, and the whale came out, almost clear of the water, before turning sideways and then diving head first straight downward.

The lines sang out so fast that smoke was soon pouring from them. Men leaped to pour water on them, and to splice other lines to them. Then, just as suddenly as it had all begun, it stopped. Both lines went slack abruptly.

"He's coming up!" cried Captain Hussey. "Take over, Mr. Pritchard. Back her off, Mr. Garvey. We're fast to a devil; no whale ever sounded thus in these waters. Be ready with the lances, Mr. Pritchard," he yelled as he passed the mate scrambling forward while he made his way aft to take the tiller. Everything was happening the wrong way round and nobody knew what to expect.

And the whale did come up — straight up — not twenty feet from the boat and continued right on out into the air above, where it seemed to pause for a long moment before falling backwards into the sea to send up a veritable volcano of creamy spume. Once again the little vessel almost turned turtle, but all men were already pulling mightily on the oars, and almost before the leviathan had disappeared, they were plunging into the trough caused by its great going down. Then began one of the most titanic struggles that can ever have taken place at sea.

Eleven exhausted men, lost on the open ocean in a tiny, open boat, armed only with puny hand lances, pitted their skill against almost a hundred tons of compact muscle, bone, and sinew stronger than steel and imbued with a natural ferocity second only to that of an enraged tiger, for Captain Hussey, although he still did not know it, was fast to a very large, bull sperm whale. Perhaps it was just as well that the men did not know what they were tackling in the dim half-light of dawn, for they might never have rowed in so boldly and actually stabbed directly downward upon the whale's arching back with their lances. As a result, it died before it could even gather breath for a second perpendicular dive.

It was all over so quickly that none of the company really realized what they had done, and certainly nobody had had time to consider what they might still have to do. What is more, nobody had thought to so much as glance at the horizon. It was Isaiah Garvey who first bethought himself of their predicament, and while the rest of the company were affixing lines to the tail of the whale, and hacking off its immense ten-foot flukes, he climbed the mast and scanned the horizon. Immediately, he let out a howl.

"Captain Hussey! Captain Hussey! It be Sankaty Head abeam." And he pointed off to starboard. Every face below was turned upward instantly and all activity ceased.

Captain Hussey himself seized the main rig and hauled himself aloft, then he too stared long at the thin, dark line on the far horizon. Finally he remarked almost casually, "Egad, Mr. Garvey, by the race that lies between and the set of the tide I would warrant you that be Sankaty." And dropping back to the deck, he started giving forth with a battery of commands.

Soon half a dozen stout lines were attached to the tail of the great whale and, passing over the stern of the sloop, were made fast to cleats and thwarts throughout the length of the vessel. This to distribute the strain. Then the sails were set, the vessel turned before the wind, and all hands manned the oars.

"Forsooth, Mr. Pritchard, we will pull this fish to the harbor by nightfall if the wind holds from this quarter and we bide fairly by the tides," Captain Hussey remarked; then turning to the boatswain, he added, "Break open the keg, Mr. Garvey. Half a cup, with a full cup of water, to each man. Just let us pull steady." Then the captain himself set the stroke and, an inch at a time, the strange procession began to move.

AND TOW a full-grown sperm whale through rip tides and across a wicked current they did. This is an historical fact. Unfortunately we do not have any other details of this extraordinary performance which, though a minor incident in itself, actually changed the whole history of the world, as we shall see. All that the records state is that "when lost in an open boat, one Captain Christopher Hussey of Nantucket struck and killed a Sperm Whale which when tryed-out proved to be extremely valuable." Before examining the true significance of this simple little record, however, we should say a word about this business of towing whales with rowboats.

While I was endeavoring to reconstruct Captain Hussey's epic above, an old friend of mine happened to visit me. Although now the holder of an American master's certificate, he was born a Dane and obtained his early experience and training on a 2000-ton sailing vessel without any auxiliary power. When I mentioned the enormity of such tasks performed by these men of not so long ago, he proceeded to recount to me how he as a youth, with only twelve others, manning two small rowboats, had towed this 2000-ton steel barque for two miles out of a land-locked harbor via a narrow channel in the face of trade-wind driven rollers. In this age of almost universal use of artificial power, it is hard to realize that, provided there were no adverse winds, tides, currents, or even air drifts, one could theoretically, and given time, dock the *Queen Elizabeth* using only a single thread of cotton. The only requirement would be to maintain a constant steady strain on the thread, and eventually the greatest thing afloat would move towards the point of pull.

Turning to another aspect of this towing business, it should be explained that experienced and healthy seamen can pull an oar for up to eight hours at a stretch with only brief rests, and I myself once fell asleep at an oar and did not, I was told, lose the stroke. The practice in olden days, when engaged on a long pull, was for three men at a time to take a fifteen-minute rest in rotation. The Nantucketers were, as we have seen, very experienced oarsmen, and by the year 1712, when this incident occurred, they had had twenty years in which to learn how to maneuver dead whales ashore through the currents that swirl round their little island.

However, the significance of Captain Christopher Hussey's performance lies neither in the boldness of his endeavor nor in the gargantuan effort of his crew. It is entirely due to the nature of the beast that he killed. Whether he did this by design or, as we have conjectured above with what we hope is legitimate literary license, at least partly by mistake does not detract from the fact that this was the first shot "fired" in a new industry, or, rather, one that had been extinct for three thousand years. No whalers, since the Phoenicians operated in the eastern Mediterranean at the time of Tiglath-Pileser of Assyria, had attempted to capture these tough, deep-sea creatures. All the western Europeans had contented themselves with harassing the comparatively stupid, slow-moving right whales which spend most of the year along coasts or ice fronts. It took a Nantucketer, and one lost in an open boat at that, to break with the old and establish a new tradition. What was so important about this whale?

The Sperm Whale (*Physeter catodon*) is the largest of the Toothed Whales, or *Odontoceti*. There is some doubt as to whether the toothed and the toothless, or baleen, whales should be included in the same group of animals; they are so unlike in so many significant points of their anatomy. The sperm whales are likewise very distinct from the rest of the toothed whales — the ziphioids, narwhals, belugas, killers, dolphins, and porpoises. There are only two sperm whales, the second being a rare little creature of rather remarkable appearance known as the Pigmy Sperm Whale (*Kogia breviceps*) which grows to a length of only about twelve feet, and has an underslung jaw like that of a shark. This little animal has never been observed at sea, and even stranded specimens are rare. It feeds on cuttlefish and squids, and has fourteen slender, recurved teeth on each side of the lower jaw. A form found in the Indian Ocean, to which the name *Kogia simus* has been given, has a distinctly upturned snout and two additional teeth in the upper jaw, but only nine teeth on each side of the lower. It is black above and light gray below, and the narrow mouth is bright pink. There is a small hydrostatic tank in the head, an organ which will be explained a little further on.

The origin of the scientific name *Kogia* has puzzled many since it was first bestowed on the creature in 1846 by the British zoologist Dr. John Gray. The best explanation is that it derives from the name of a corpulent and crochety old Turkish gentleman, one Cogia Effendi, who not only observed whales in the Mediterranean, but also, by reason of his grotesque profile and unbelievably stuffy demeanor, gave rise to our popular term "an old codger."

The great sperm whale is certainly the most unique form of animal life that we know of on this planet. The more it is studied, the more amazing it proves to be. Its habits are as weird as its anatomy, but we unfortunately know altogether too little about the former. Unlike the other large whales, it is a tropical and warm-water animal, only straying into polar seas on rare occasions, and then apparently by mistake, but it migrates just as regularly as the baleen whales. These migrations, however, seem to constitute two distinct interlocking processes. One is a sudden seasonal movement, by the females only, to the southern limits of the south temperate seas, followed by a slow return northward during which they meet and intermingle with the males and younger animals, which, in the meantime, have completed a semicircular sweep around the oceans traveling in a clockwise direction. This is the more peculiar since the major ocean currents follow a counterclockwise course in the southern oceans. The explanation for this procedure, it has been suggested, is the behavior of the food of the sperms. This food is primarily open-ocean, deep-water cephalopods — that is to say, squids, including the giant *Architeuthis*, which may grow to a length of twenty feet, have thirty-foot tentacles, and weigh up to fifteen tons — which either drift with certain deeper ocean currents, or themselves migrate because of seasonal changes in the salinity or temperature of the water, or because their food in turn migrates for these or still other purposes.

We are only now beginning to learn about the complex pattern of currents and countercurrents which flow at different depths and in all manner of contrary directions under the world's great oceans, and it will be a long time before we have mapped, let alone explained, the reason for them all. The sperm whales know them, and therefore just where their food is going to be concentrated at any particular time of the year, and here too they assemble. This becomes of great significance, as we shall see.

Sperm whales travel about in small parties which sometimes join up to form schools, or "gams," of considerable size. At these times they are very gregarious and show a strong tendency to keep together even in face of danger. When in small parties, on the other hand, they usually seek safety by scattering and sounding. The sperm is possibly the greatest diver on earth, descending to greater depths than any other surface-living sea creature and, certainly, any other air-breather of which we know. Their normal practice is to cruise along, blowing regularly in brief jets, then to dive straight down and remain below for from fifteen to forty minutes, though individuals have been known to remain below for an hour and a half. That they really dive deep rather than just staying below the surface like baleen whales is, moreover, proved by a remarkable case that occurred in 1932.

The submarine cable between Panama City and Guayaquil, Ecuador, failed, and a repair ship located a break about halfway between the two points at a depth of thirty-five hundred feet. When the broken ends of the cable were brought to the surface, a sperm whale was found entangled in one of the loose ends with a coil of the cable looped around its body. The depth at which the cable lay indicated a dive of more than half a mile straight down on the part of the whale. At that time and, in fact, until quite recently, it was a great puzzle to scientists how any air-breathing creature could be subjected to such incredible pressure as exists at that depth without the nitrogen in its blood "boiling," resulting in a fatal case of what divers call the "bends." At one time it was thought that the explanation lay in the fact that the sperm whale's blood contained a vast population of beneficial parasites, including what are called nitrogenous bacteria. These microscopic organisms breathe nitrogen, but they excrete oxygen. It was thought they were so numerous that they were able to take up all the free nitrogen squeezed out of the mammal's blood by the pressure and that, at the same time, they would serve to replenish the oxygen supply for their vast host. This explanation is now denied and it is believed that a much simpler mechanism explains the sperm whale's ability to make deep dives.

Whales start off by having much less nitrogen in their lungs than do land animals. When they dive, almost all the gas is forced out of the lungs by the increasing water pressure; all that is left is held in the corpuscles of the blood. This reduces the amount of nitrogen that can be released into the blood stream. At the same time, it has been found that whales do a much better job of oxygenating their blood when they do come up for air, renewing ninety per cent of it as opposed to some twenty per cent in ourselves. Finally, the rate of their heartbeat drops abruptly as soon as they make their dives. These characteristics combined are amply sufficient to overcome the "bends," but even then sperms probably have to return from deep dives in easy stages just like a human diver.

The sperm whale is in other ways also a sort of supersubmarine. The most characteristic feature of the species is the enormous square head which constitutes almost a third of the entire body. A fifty-eight-foot stranded bull that I once dissected had an eighteen-foot skull. The greater part of this vast head, however, is composed of an enormous fleshy tank. This is covered with straplike muscles running in all directions, and with a thick layer of blubber, like the rest of the animal, but it is hollow and normally filled with up to a ton of light oil. At the bottom is a deep layer of spongy tissue impregnated with an exceedingly light viscous wax called spermaceti. It was from this that the animal received its English name, as the early whalers thought this was the animal's supply of the male sperm. This mistaken notion persisted until the present century when more prosaic but nonetheless remarkable findings of physicists gained general acceptance. These are simply that the whole complex structure is nothing but what is called a hydrostatic organ — a kind of adjustable ballast just like the buoyancy tanks of submarines, or the swim bladders of fishes. Exactly how the animal accomplishes the necessary changes in density to make the device work has not as yet — at least to this writer's satisfaction — been explained.

Quite apart from this tank, the head of the sperm whale is altogether unique. First of all, it is completely asymmetrical and this to an extent that surpasses any other backboned animal, certain owls which have one ear pointing forward and the other backward not excluded. If you stand in a sperm whale's skull and look forward, you will see that the bones on one side of the upper jaw are quite different from those on the other. This asymmetry, moreover, is carried out to the surface, so that there is only one S-shaped blowhole pointing forward and on the left side of the snout. As a result, the spout of the sperm is very distinctive, being a rather feeble forward-curving jet.

The general conformity of the rest of the animal is more easily appreciated in an illustration than by verbal description (see Appendix E). Instead of a dorsal fin there is a series of low bumps along the latter half of the back, and the flippers are rather small but very wide and blunt. They contain the usual five mammalian digits, but the finger bones of all are multiplied. The tail is remarkable, being deep-notched in the middle and the flukes having large flaps on their inner hind edges, one lying over the other. The skin, which is jet black in life, is not much thicker than a sheet of carbon paper and is very susceptible to abrasions, whereby some very peculiar facts have been brought to light and then, we regret to state, scrupulously ignored.

As mentioned before, the principal food of the sperms is squid, though they are also known to take cuttles, octopus, spiny lobsters, and even some larger fish such as sharks. The largest squid known, the great *Architeuthis*, also described previously, has, like all of the octopus group, suckers on the inside of its eight tentacles and on the pads at the end of its two long feeler-arms. These suckers contain bony rings bearing teeth and looking like little coronets. The largest rings from the largest squids have a diameter of about four inches, yet scars left by such suckers on the skin of captured sperm whales have measured over eighteen inches in diameter. It took several centuries for zoologists to accept the existence of the kraken, as the Norse fishermen had always called the *Architeuthis*, and its size still seems somewhat shocking. The mere suggestion that there might be forms almost five times greater in the depths of the oceans is regarded as so outrageous as to be altogether taboo. Judging by the size of certain sharks' teeth that have been found in a fossilized condition, however, even this would appear by no means to be the limit of size to which marine creatures can grow.

The sperm whale has between twenty and thirty huge, peglike teeth embedded in a band of gristle which is in turn set in a trough running the length of each side of the lower jaw only. These teeth close into holes in similar bands of immensely tough, horny tissue lining the upper jaws and palate. The jaw is long and narrow and the whole apparatus is perfectly devised for seizing, holding, and chopping up large, slender, slippery things like giant squid. Lower jaws damaged in youth have been known to grow into corkscrewlike deformities, apparently without impairing the health or growth of the animals. The diameter of the throat is also amply sufficient to swallow a fair-sized shark, or even a man.

A bull sperm of sixty feet is considered large today, but there is a belief that sperms grew to a greater length in bygone times when they were less molested. This belief is quite incompatible with two assertions. First, there was a period of some fifty years, extending from the beginning of this century until 1951, when this species was hardly hunted at all. Second, it is asserted that the sperm whale has an exceedingly short life span, maybe even as short as ten years. Both of these cannot be true, and it is probable that the average length of the males is about sixty feet, while exceptional specimens reach seventy-five or even eighty feet today as they have always done, though they are seldom encountered, for the simple reason that they are not extensively hunted any more. Roy Chapman Andrews took a fourteen-foot-eight-inch unborn baby from a thirty-two-foot mother. The young are suckled for six months, the mother floating at the surface and the baby taking her nipple in the corner of his mouth, and are over twenty feet long when weaned. They appear to be fully adult at three and become sexually mature at four years. What happens after this is not wholly known, though specimens branded when full grown have been captured up to twenty-two years later. Young appear to be born at any time of the year.

Sperm whales, and especially lone bulls, are not animals to be trifled with. Normally they are fairly shy, but they will rush to protect wounded females or young, and have often been known to attack boats. On occasion they have attacked ships, and one sank a 400-ton steamer by charging it amidships and staving it in so that it sank in a few minutes. Even when not being deliberately aggressive they are more dangerous than the baleen whales, with the notable exception of the gray whale, which we shall meet later. Their habit of standing on their heads with their tails in the air before sounding and their considerable agility make them dangerous to small, open boats. All whalers agree that they are tougher to kill and take longer to succumb than other species. Also, of course, they are deep-sea rovers, and although normally slow cruisers proceeding at a steady four knots, they can put on spurts of up to twenty knots and sustain a steady sixteen for long distances. Their strange tails form a highly efficient pair of sculls which work with a double, semirotary action, making figure-of-eight motions around the fore and aft axis, which, combined, amount almost to the completely rotary action of a two-bladed screw propeller.

Such, then, was the animal that the Nantucketer, Captain Christopher Hussey, first took in the year 1712, though it must be presumed that he knew practically nothing of the nature of the beast and, it would seem, almost as little about its economic value. In fact, we here encounter something of a mystery in the history of whaling, for all extant records affirm that the great value of this first sperm whale was immediately appreciated. There is no explanation as to how anybody knew of its value, so we are presented with the curious paradox of something new being well recognized. If it was recognized, it must have been known before, and if it was known before, we may well ask why nothing had been done about it for some hundred years. At first glance there would seem to be no real problem involved, but the more you think about it and, certainly, the further you delve into what old records still exist, the more mysterious the whole business becomes. After considerable research I have been forced, albeit rather reluctantly, to the conclusion that once again the intelligence came from the Amerindians.

The sperm whale is admittedly an open-ocean or deep-water species, and the colonists had only just started making offshore voyages of more than a few days' duration by the year 1712, so they would have had little opportunity to encounter the animal. Further, at that time there were no other peoples engaged in sperming. On the other hand, sperm whales are washed ashore dead almost as often as baleen whales, so there may have been some general knowledge of the beast along the coast. However, the immediate appreciation and apparent considerable knowledge of the wide variety of economically worthwhile products that could be derived from the animal predispose a certain intimacy with the species. It is the supposed medicinal properties of the spermaceti that are specially mentioned, and this is definitely stated to be in accord with Indian beliefs.

The products of the sperm whale are indeed varied and valuable. First, the oil from their blubber is of a finer quality than that of any other species, and whale oils are today still rated in the following order:

Sperm Oil — from the blubber of sperms
Number 1 Oil — from the blubber of rorquals
Number 2 Oil — from the second boiling of rorqual blubber
Number 3 Oil — from meat, bones, and third pressing of rorqual blubber
Number 4 Oil — from blood, bones, scraps, and sperm meat

What is more, the average sperm yields more oil (65 to 80 barrels) than even the mighty blue whale of equal bulk (50 to 70 barrels). Second, the spermaceti, which is really a very light wax — a neutral, almost tasteless, fatty substance which is a liquid between thirty-eight and forty-seven degrees centigrade — is not only suitable for the manufacture of candles, for which it was mostly used in olden days, but also forms the basis of some of the finest machine oils known for very delicate instruments. Third, the teeth are fine-grained ivory and were previously put to many uses. The skin is high in glycerin content. Finally, it is from sperm whales that the exceedingly valuable ambergris is obtained.

Ambergris is an altogether bizarre thing. It has been known for thousands of years and has been used for an enormous variety of purposes. The ancient Egyptians seem to have known of it and used it in their temples, possibly as an incense. The Arabs first called it *anbar*, a word which turns up in the Coptic Bible to denote the "great fish" which swallowed Jonah. However, the same word also means "amber" in Arabic. Ambergris, or gray amber, is a light, inflammable, fatty substance, ashy gray in color, but when cut through, it shows a sort of marbling. It has a pleasant aroma, especially when heated, and this is due to the presence of a bacterium with the delightful name of *Spirillum recti physeteris*. Ambergris is formed in the large intestines of sperm whales, apparently as the result of ulceration caused therein by irritations set up by the horny beaks and bony rings from the suckers of the squids the whales eat. Sperms are notorious sufferers from colic, and when they are basking on the surface on very still days, the rumblings of their stomachs, punctuated by monumental belches, may be heard for a considerable distance. That they should suffer from peptic ulcers and thereby provide us with one of the four most valuable fixatives for our highest-priced perfumes is somehow strangely grotesque. Ambergris once fetched a price of $400 per ounce; its price at the time of writing was still $8.

Exactly how valuable this first sperm whale was to the Nantucketers is not, as far as can be ascertained, anywhere recorded, but Captain Hussey's little effort seems to have created more than just a stir. We find the whole island going deliberately and wittingly into the sperming business. As a matter of fact, the right whales had by that date declined almost to a point of extinction along the inshore waters of the New England coast, and several of the ports, with Nantucket in the lead, had begun to build larger boats and to take longer voyages farther offshore in pursuit of those whales that migrated north and south far out by the inner edge of the Gulf Stream. These vessels varied in size between fifteen and forty feet, and were rigged as sloops. Many were just glorified rowboats, without decking and setting only a single lateen sail. Others carried a gaff-rigged mainsail and a standing jib. The largest appear to have carried a jib from a short bowsprit, a staysail, and a mainsail, and they were decked, but had a large, open cockpit, while a wheel replaced a tiller. The first ocean-going sloop was built in Nantucket in 1694. At the time of Captain Hussey's epic, there were still only five out of the island, the larger fitted out for five- to seven-week cruises at sea.

The build-up of the ocean-going fleet began in earnest the very next year, though offshore whaling continued with small, open boats, so that a total of eighty-six whales was still taken by this means by twenty-eight boats in 1726. Meantime the larger sloops had increased in number to twenty-five, and in 1730 this fleet sold a total of £3200 worth of oil, a sum that would represent about $150,000 today. What is more, this bold little fleet had by then reached not only Greenland, but the north coast of Brazil. The sloops were of thirty to fifty tons, and in the year 1730 the first schooner of seventy tons was launched. The practice was for the whalers to fit out during winter, then go south in the spring — first to the Carolina coast, thence via the Bahamas either into the Gulf and the Caribbean or down the outside of the West Indies, then east to the Azores, from there to the Cape Verdes and the west coast of Africa. Later the voyages were extended back across the Atlantic to the Brazilian coast and even south to the Falklands. At first, however, the fleet returned to Nantucket in July, refitted, and then sailed again for the Grand Banks to the north.

While the Nantucketers were thus engaged, the mainland ports were building fleets with equal industry. Provincetown specialized in the northern fishery and by 1737 she had a dozen hundred-ton vessels trespassing upon the Dutch sea domains in Davis Strait, where they sought the arctic right whales, which were still plentiful by the ice fronts. New Bedford already had nearly a century of offshore whaling behind it, Joseph Russell, the founder of the port, having started the business in 1652, but it was 1755 before she sent four sloops to the high seas. By 1775, incidentally, she had a fleet of eighty large vessels engaged in whaling. One by one other ports got into the business, all the way from Maine to Williamsburg in Virginia. But all was not plain sailing, even in this first great phase of American whaling and seamanship.

The British were — as usual, one might almost say — at war with the French and the Spanish, and privateers of both nations appeared off the American coasts. The colonists seem to have given as good as they had to take at the hands of these semiofficial sea rovers, but they prudently decided to avoid the northern fishery and to concentrate on the southern, although the Grand Banks were still visited. In 1748 the British fell prone to a sort of monstrous economic hiccups which prompted them, first, to offer a twenty-shilling bounty for whaling in the Davis Strait, then, almost immediately (1755), to place an embargo on any fishing by the colonists on the Grand Banks, and, five years later, suddenly to throw the St. Lawrence and Belle Isle grounds open to them. Next, they clamped a heavy duty on all whale products but at the same time banned the colonists from selling such products in any country other than Britain.

Despite these irksome maneuvers, the colonists, led by the New Englanders and with Nantucket in the forefront, forged steadily ahead in the business, so that by 1774 the American ocean-going whaling fleet numbered three hundred and sixty bottoms, three hundred of them out of Massachusetts. And their owners were very prosperous, for all oil commanded a high price, and sperm oil as much as £40 per ton, while baleen was at a premium. Meanwhile,

# The Central Atlantic, as Seen by the Nantucketers

The eastern seaboard of North America runs more nearly west to east than north to south, and it hangs far out over the "top" of the Atlantic oceans if we look at a map directed at the North Pole. Nantucket Island thus faces due south and directly toward the great island of Hispaniola, with Bermuda slightly to the left. Straight ahead and not far offshore, the Gulf Stream runs from right to left in a concentrated flow.

Sperm whales are warm-water and tropical animals, and since it was in their pursuit that the Nantucketers first earnestly went to sea, they naturally set straight out to the south from their shores. This led them, by easy and progressive stages, first to the ocean off the Carolinian coasts, thence right into the Caribbean, half left to the northern coast of South America, and, skirting this, to the narrow neck between the North and South Atlantics. The hop from there to the west coast of Africa was predicated by following the whales, but was complicated by the southeast trade winds which tended always to force them back up north towards Europe. Moreover, it was by taking this easy course homeward that they stumbled upon the great Canary Islands, Morocco, Western Islands, and Western Grounds, and this explains why the two last were so called by them for, on this home passage, they saw the Atlantic from the same point of view as a European going west.

The Nantucketers also turned half right when they got into the South Atlantic and fished off Brazil, but the hunting was never good there and southeast trade winds kept blowing them back. The Carroll Ground off West Africa was so fertile a field that many ships made the hard run there first in the season and then used the trades to return home in a westerly direction via the famous Twelve-Forty Ground.

For identification of Central Atlantic whaling grounds, shown on the accompanying map by diagonal shading, see endpaper maps.

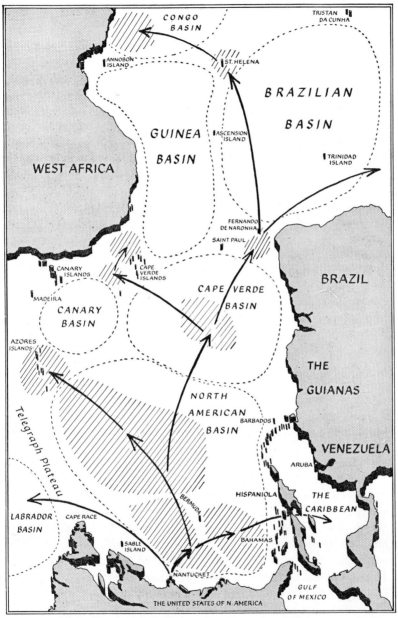

## Map 6 The Central Atlantic, as Seen by the Nantucketers
Miller Modified Mercator Projection       Scale 1:48,000,000

the sperm hunters had reached the Guinea coast by 1763 and in 1767 a fleet of fifty whalers actually made an experimental trip to the Antarctic, a story which, it is to be hoped, will one day be told in full. Then came the War of Independence, as it is called in British history books, or, as it is otherwise known, the Revolution.

Despite the tremendous historical significance of this affair and the heritage of recrimination that it bequeathed to all subsequent generations of English-speaking people, it was really neither a revolution nor a war in the strict sense, but it was certainly more nearly the latter than the former. It was a family quarrel and it retained undertones of gentlemanliness that amounted almost to chivalry. For instance, in what other war did the belligerents agree to allow a party of the one part to carry on his business unmolested, and even permit him to trade with a party of the second part? This, nevertheless, was the strange arrangement that was reached regarding Nantucket.

When the trouble first started, however, the British singled out the whaling fleet for special attention and swooped upon it on the high seas. Being unarmed and in many cases even unaware of the outbreak of hostilities, the whalers succumbed, and their vessels were either carried off as prizes, sunk, or burned. Nantucket suffered most severely, and as her entire economy was by that time dependent upon whaling, the plight of the island became desperate. The Nantucketers appealed as Quakers to the Society of Friends on both sides, and their desperate plea was recognized. In 1781 the British issued them a permit for twenty-four whalers to proceed to the fishing, and two years later Congress granted them the right to clear thirty-five ships. Nevertheless, by the end of hostilities the business was completely ruined and only three old ships were left on the island.

Meanwhile, the mainland ports had fared little better, and the colonial whaling industry was prostrate. Nor did the end of hostilities bring an end to the whalers' woes, for Britain clamped a prohibitive duty on whale oil, thus virtually closing the only overseas outlet and making it necessary to market the whole of the proceeds of the enterprise in the new republic, which offered a very limited demand. Prices dropped precipitately, and had it not been for the Nantucketers, driven by dire necessity, the whole industry might well have died away. They, however, started to build ships again, and in the meantime pressed smaller boats into service. They also agitated the

Commonwealth of Massachusetts into offering a bounty to ships registered in their state. This move, however, backfired badly, since it caused a still further drop in prices. Nevertheless, the number of ocean-going whalers registered in Massachusetts had again risen to one hundred by 1788, and thereafter there was a steady increase until 1806.

The new ships were larger and barque-rigged, and they fitted out for voyages of one, two, or three years. They went farther afield and they concentrated on the sperm whale. In 1791 the first American whalers rounded Cape Horn and entered the South Pacific, where they encountered a thriving whaling tradition maintained by the Chilean Spanish. But then a serious decline set in, occasioned for the most part by the general international economic strangulation which was being applied to the young republic, but also in some measure to the simple physical conformation of Nantucket's harbor.

Nantucket is a low, sandy island, shaped like a quarter moon, surrounded by reefs and sand bars, and containing a considerable but shallow inland lagoon on the landward side. There is one narrow channel leading into this lagoon, and the port and harbor are just inside this channel. While this made an ideal anchorage for small vessels, it became very troublesome to larger ships because a shallow bar lay across the entrance to the harbor and the sand kept filling in the channel. The Nantucketers tried in every way to overcome the difficulty. They unloaded cargo into lighters outside the bar; they built breakwaters; later they even built huge "camels" with which to float the laden ships over the bar; but all measures failed and they had to resort to unloading and refitting their vessels on Martha's Vineyard. They appealed to Congress for help in dredging a proper channel, but it was over a century before Congress got around to doing anything, and by then it was too late.

The Nantucketers had really begun to feel the economic pinch when the final blow fell. The senseless, mismanaged, but nonetheless, from a maritime point of view, deadly War of 1812 broke out, and within a matter of months the whole whaling fleet was virtually dissipated. Not only did Britain wreak havoc upon them; Congress commandeered ships as transports and for other warlike purposes. And so, after almost endless vicissitudes, the second phase of American whaling came to rather a dismal end.

## II

# Midday North and South

### (*British II*)

COLIN COLLINS sank slowly to the soft greensward at the top of the low bluff overlooking the river. The sun was setting in a blaze of flaming glory that tinted the shiny greenery overhanging the water with an orange sheen. Blue smoke drifted in gentle shreds from the snug cottages of the settlers below the bluff. Everything was so utterly peaceful that the young man began to cry. He sat silent and alone, experiencing emotions he had never known before, while the tears gathered of themselves in the corners of his eyes and rolled slowly down his cheeks to fall splashing on his dirty, bare feet.

Not only was this behavior new to the young man; it was altogether out of character for one who had been sold into bondage by his own mother almost before he could take care of himself, had been imprisoned before he was twelve for stealing his own food, had been apprenticed to a criminal who was hanged by the roadside for robbery on the King's Highway, and had then been jailed again at the age of fourteen for running away from his defunct master's squalid home. It was even more preposterous for one who had suffered passage in a slave ship to the West Indies in his teens, had been confined in a Spanish dungeon in Cuba for escaping from a labor gang in the Jamaican cane fields, and had then been pressed into the service of the Spanish Crown on a vessel whose crew promptly mutinied and took to piracy. Young men who had experienced such things and had then been captured by their original persecutors and shipped to still another continent in a convict ship did not know how to cry — at least, they usually did not, in the year of grace 1825. Thus the sight was somewhat surprising to one Captain Sean McNamara, master of the whaler *Shannon,* when he topped the bluff and came upon the young man.

The captain stopped in dumfounded amazement because he had believed until then that only his people gave way to their emotions in such an obvious manner. He shifted his pipe to the extreme corner of his mouth and refrained from puffing upon it. What, he turned over in his agile mind, could possibly have so affected the lad? Everything seemed to be outstandingly serene, and although the youth was unshod, it was summer and he seemed otherwise to be adequately clothed and fed. Sean McNamara had just about come to the conclusion that some precious girl must be the cause of this outrage when the young man suddenly turned and their eyes met. At that moment it would have been hard to say which of the two had the greatest desire to flee. Instead, they remained staring fixedly at each other in abashed silence. Finally Sean McNamara's pipe fell out of his slack jaw.

Colin Collins immediately sprang to his feet and, turning away, hastily ran the sleeve of his shirt over his eyes before making ready to take off. In that movement, however, the captain espied a glaring brand mark on the youth's right forearm, and his eyes opened in further amazement. Even before retrieving his pipe, he called out:

"Be not afeard, me lad, the King's men are not about these parts as yet. Ye be among friends here."

It was not so much the words spoken as the soft kindliness of their tone that arrested the young man from his impending headlong flight. No one had spoken to him thus before at any time in his life. There was something in the speech that complemented both his own strange mood and the glory of this new world. Although he did not comprehend the fact then, it spoke of freedom, which was something Colin had never known nor understood, but for which he had always sub-consciously yearned. He turned slowly to face the man, for almost the first time in his life pulling back his shoulders not to brace them against a whip but to steady his soul in the face of something new and strange.

"Forgive me, sir," was all he said.

Sean McNamara retrieved his pipe from the grass and then con-templated the lad from a distance.

"Have you papers?" he asked. But without waiting for an answer, he hurriedly continued, "Not that any are needed here. We are free folk in Launceston, for what it may be worth, and while we abide by the governor's law, we have need of strong lads. Did you come by the sloop or by land?" he added.

"By the sloop, sir," Colin replied simply.

Captain McNamara gulped visibly. He regarded the river and his eyes came to rest meditatively upon the small buoy to which the government sloop had been moored until a few hours before. He blinked and shook his head.

"And how, the Saints be praised, did ye come to be let ashore, may I ask?"

Colin Collins's eyes fell; then he looked up and stared the captain in the eye.

"Six harpoons and a noggin of the supercargo's rum to the harbor master," he replied. "Then I swam," he added.

The captain burst out laughing. "So, Will Jackson is learning a bit of good sense at last!" he chuckled. "Maybe I'll get me a crew yet, though I warrant he'll cleave to them harpoon heads. Tell me, were they good irons or jail-made?"

"I made them myself," answered Colin, "and they were the very finest irons, hard-barbed, the Spanish way. I am a smith by trade, sir."

"The devil ye be," Captain McNamara snorted. "I suppose that thieving, so-called harbor master, Jackson, thought to grab you for his forge on some official book-writing. Now you listen to me, me lad. Just show that forearm once in the town and you'll be right back aboard the first government ship that clears this port. Tell me," he added quickly, "be you indentured or runaway?"

"Both," replied Colin. "Indentured to Mr. Bartholemew of Derwent, and runaway from . . . from . . ."

"Never mind that," cut in Captain McNamara. "Just come along with me before some conniving blasphemer happens by. We're anchored up the river a piece and must be aboard before dark."

And so saying he strode off along the bluff not even bothering to look around. Colin Collins fell in behind him without saying a word. For the first time in his life he felt like a free man, and the truth was that for the first time he was.

And in so mundane a manner was half a continent opened to the world, a large part of the British Empire established, and a number of people in distant lands made famous, for Colin Collins was just what Captain McNamara most needed to complete the crew of his whaler, depleted by desertions on tropical islets, by deaths from disease and accidents, and by the seemingly everlasting depredations of officialdom, who appeared to claim any able-bodied man professing any trade. The captain needed three men, but a single one who was strong, had been to sea, and was a smith by trade would make up for the lack of any two brutish hands who had to be watched every minute.

Once he had this prize aboard, he weighed anchor and set about hiding the youth from the prying eyes of Harbor Master Jackson. The captain's intimate knowledge of his ship and a bottle of brandy achieved this end in short order, and the *Shannon* was soon slipping down the river to the open sea on the gentle current, aided by all canvas that might catch a breath of the land breeze. A week later she was lumbering under full sail along the uncharted barren coast of South Australia, a land that was later to be named after the young Victoria who was to ascend the throne of England.

Meanwhile, Colin Collins labored away on deck under an awning abaft the try-works with long tongs and an assortment of hammers both great and small, fashioning harpoons, lances, and all manner of irons. The *Shannon* had been at sea for two years and, apart from her officers, had changed crews more than once. Although her belly had been thrice stuffed with trade goods and twice with casks of good, clean whale oil, she was now empty not only of cargo but also, for the most part, of equipment. Captain McNamara had all hands at work serving rigging, sailmaking, splicing lines, assembling staves for the cooper, or doing anything of which they were capable to make up the deficiencies in essential equipment. His new smithy gave him a feeling of renewed confidence and of great things to come. And come they did within a very few days.

As the ship rounded a barren headland, the captain's eyes fell upon an unknown coast of apparently endless extent — dry, sear, and golden yellow. At first it looked as straight and dull as a man-made wall, but closer inspection through a spyglass disclosed a number of inlets cutting into the tall face of the land at almost regular intervals. In one of these a great commotion was proceeding. At first the captain thought this was a rip caused by some mighty river debouching into the sea; then he thought there might be some major native naval engagement in progress; but as the absurdity of both ideas dawned upon him, he slowly lowered the glass and, turning, blinked at his first mate. Then he reacted like a released spring and began yelling.

His outburst brought all heads around, and although the captain only spluttered and roared and said nothing coherent, every man knew just what was afoot. Without another word the entire crew leaped to prearranged stations, every man grabbing up whatever he needed in the mad rush as he went. In no time at all the boats were swung outboard and their crews took their places in each. The helmsman reacted without command and canvas flapped aloft for only a few moments before the fair breeze took hold, the deck literally rose beneath their feet, and the *Shannon* started in a rush towards the foaming inlet.

While yet a mile from the entrance all aboard could see a seething mass of vast shapes cavorting in the shoreward rollers: whales in such quantity and of such size as no man in the company had ever before seen. And they were the right whales, disporting themselves in a crazy sea dance designed both to rid themselves of parasites and, in the case of the males, to impress the females. They were so utterly engaged in their own monstrous behavior that they did not even notice the great bulk of the *Shannon* as she slipped towards them. Nor did they pay the slightest attention when five small, white boats began to bounce over the waves among them, and they failed to register any signal of danger when Colin Collins's keen, barbed harpoons were driven into the sides of their companions from a range of only a few feet.

The slaughter was consequently quite monumental, for no sooner had one whale been struck than it was lanced to death and left to float just beneath the rollers while another was attacked. There were seven hours of daylight for the chase and the boats never got farther than a mile from the *Shannon*. Seventeen whales were struck, sixteen of them fast, and fifteen killed. Everybody took turns in the boats, even the captain, the cook, the supercargo, and the smithy, Colin Collins. And it was he who struck three whales, an altogether unique experience for any man throughout the centuries on the very first day he had ever been in a whaleboat or hefted a harpoon.

But then they were his own harpoons, fashioned by his own hand and tempered with a loving care that expressed more than just good craftsmanship. Into them he had wrought something of his new-found glory, for this onetime bondsman, slave, and convict had found a new world in the green land of Tasmania and a new life in the pursuit of the oldest bonanza on earth, the whale.

THERE was nothing particularly remarkable about the slaughter of a lot of whales wholly taken up with some parody of what is now called sexual play in the lonely confines of a south Australian inlet, but in the year 1828 the outcome reached far beyond the immediate success of a chance whaling venture by an Irish captain out of the little colonial settlement of Launceston in the new colony of Tasmania. It was just such an everyday incident that started a systematic exploration of the entire southern coast of a vast new continent and, in its way, changed the whole history of the world. Young men such as Colin Collins, long since forgotten and never chronicled, made this possible, despite the iniquities of slavery, the vile practices of bondage and apprenticeship, the enormities of indentured labor, imprisonment for political originality, religious persecution, and all the other foul injustices to which citizens were subjected in the early nineteenth century. On the simple hard work of such as he, combined with the new-found freedom of others who colonized the southern continent, a vast industry was founded, and a great nation grew.

Just what such people, ejected from their homelands often for no cause at all, accomplished has not as yet been properly appreciated. And the part played by the whale in their efforts has been almost totally ignored.

When the British decided to make another attempt at whaling after their dismal failure under the Muscovy Company in the first quarter of the seventeenth century, they were immediately beset by all kinds of problems that were never encounterd by any others who engaged in this industry. One of the worst was the practice of press ganging, which, in the aggregate, probably caused more losses than all the foundering of ships, the interferences of officialdom, and the bungling of financiers put together. But despite these and all manner of other tribulations, whaling out of British ports continued uninterruptedly from this second start until the end of the nineteenth century, albeit with great fluctuations.

This interlude in whaling history is hard to define and most difficult to comprehend unless two points are made abundantly clear. The first is the somewhat confusing fact that it began only a few years after the Yankee deep-sea whaling, but then outlasted the American effort, thus bridging three whole phases of the latter and the two intervening interludes of almost complete cessation caused by the War of Independence and the War of 1812. Secondly, although this phase of British whaling has almost always been treated historically as an entity, and also appears thus in the official statistics and other records, it was, in point of fact, composed of two quite separate and almost wholly unrelated activities. One was conducted in the Arctic, had to contend with the novel phenomenon of ice, and was relatively unremunerative; the other was tropical and encountered entirely other challenges, but was considerably profitable. The former eventually triumphed, but then succumbed to a child of its own initiative; the latter just died on the stem and became extinct.

The new start was actually made in 1725 and was to a great extent prompted by reports of the Nantucketers' new successes leading from Captain Hussey's discovery. A number of prominent London financiers, backed to the hilt by certain moneyed landowners, had, in 1711, maneuvered the Crown into chartering a monumental enterprise called the South Sea Company which they stated would liquidate the national debt. Armed with their charter, the organizers raised an enormous sum by private and public subscription through promotional methods that would do credit to New York's Madison Avenue today. The published material is still extant in the old archives, and makes astonishing reading. Most of it is devoted to highly colorful descriptions of the wealth of certain lands distant from Europe, which, the documents imply, awaited only enterprising Englishmen with sufficient capital to exploit. The British public thought the whole thing a splendid idea and rushed to buy shares.

Among the original promoters, however, were some very shrewd merchants and shipowners who managed quietly to divert enough of the money, raised by public subscription, to the building of no fewer than twenty-four ships specifically for whaling. These came off the stocks with unusual speed and were promptly commissioned in and about 1725. Since there had been no British whalers for almost a century, skilled crews had to be imported from abroad — in this case from Holstein — and be paid exorbitant wages. Twelve ships sailed the first year, twenty-four the second, and twenty-five the third, though this number was quickly reduced by losses to twenty-one.

This fleet never once averaged even one whale killed per ship per season over eight years, and this accumulated an enormous debit balance for the company, despite the fact that the directors had in the meantime negotiated the passage of an Act of Parliament exempting all its vessels from all duties on all products taken on the high seas and imported in its bottoms. In all, these whalers lost 177,780 pounds sterling during the first eight years, which in those days represented a perfectly colossal sum. The most ridiculous aspect of the whole affair, as seen in retrospect, is that this much-vaunted South Sea Company's fleet went exclusively to the Greenland, or northern, seas, in the Arctic.

It was manifest even to the directors of the company that they could not present the stockholders with such a picture of failure year after year. Foreign whalers calculated that six bad years could be recouped in one good year, but after a seventh unprofitable season they advocated getting out of the business and cutting their losses. These gentlemen were, however, already in too deeply. Since the company's other enterprises had fared no better, the directors got to work on the government again and persuaded it to grant a bounty to the whale fisheries. And they got an Act passed that year too. Nevertheless, only two British ships sailed for the whaling grounds that season, and both were privately owned.

This bounty was in the form of twenty shillings per ton on all ships over two hundred tons fitted out in Britain. Despite this governmental generosity on the part of officials entrusted with the disbursement of public funds derived from taxes and excise, British whaling stubbornly continued to languish. In fact, it practically collapsed, so that even four years later only four British-registered ships indulged the extravagance of such voyages. One of these took seven whales, the others none.

Nor did Britons show any more enthusiasm for the business when the bounty was raised to thirty shillings a ton in 1740. Their best effort then was to fit out five ships, two of which were immediately lost to privateers in the then current war with Spain, while two others never even reached the whaling grounds but went off on piratical exploits of their own. It was not until the bounty was again raised to forty shillings in 1750 that certain independent merchants of London and some other ports began to take an interest in the possibilities of the business. This was the bounty that applied also to whalers built in the colonies, which so encouraged the New Englanders, but which was then promptly nullified, in their case, by contrary restrictions.

By 1760, however, matters showed a decided statistical improvement, at least in the number of ships, but the proceeds from the little fleet of thirty-five vessels, mostly privately owned and out of London, Hull, and Whitby, were still, in the aggregate, on the debit side. Only one vessel actually showed a profit, and this was a Scottish whaler out of Dundee. The Scots had entered the trade in 1750, and although they never had a large fleet and each port and even each owner in each port remained ruggedly independent about the whole business, they made a much better job of the endeavor, showed a considerably greater profit over the years, and remained much longer in the field. The reasons for this will be discussed later when we come to the specific part they played in the over-all history of whaling.

The most essential feature of English whaling enterprise — as distinct from the Scottish — was, however, that the entrepreneurs never truly comprehended the operation and never recognized it as something quite different from common fisheries. To the English it was always a purely business venture, and, as such, it finally paid off handsomely, but never specifically in whale products. Calculable returns actually included a world-wide empire, wealth and leisure to devote to the pursuit of science and technology, and a series of devastating wars. Had it not been for whaling, there would have been a great deal less red on British maps at the beginning of this century.

This was, of course, not foreseen by the directors of the South Sea Company, and still less by Parliament and the Crown, but there were a few individuals of considerable perspicacity connected with the business who had a very real appreciation of the over-all trend of history, and who were thus fully alert to the inherent possibilities. These men were the merchants resident in the great ports of England, who were not themselves seamen but shipowners, and most of whom were primarily engaged in importing. They knew only too well the value of the whale products that were purchased from the Dutch and other foreigners, and the enormous volume of this one-way trade distressed them mightily. They also knew much better than any London financiers or politicians the worth of a deep-sea whaling fleet both in peace and in war, and they were hearing daily of new trade routes being opened up by the American colonists in their pursuit of the sperm whale. Further, they also knew the inherent weaknesses of the giant joint-stock companies chartered by the Crown and backed by the government.

These cautious men waited a long time, but they eventually started building ships on their own, and they persuaded other citizens of their townships to subscribe funds for fitting them out. Among these enterprising merchants one family, that has traded for centuries under the name of Sam Enderby & Company of London, stands out most prominently. We shall hear a great deal of this firm later for, although they were comparative latecomers in the whaling business, they devoted most of their attention to what was called the southern fishery. The general policy adopted by these merchants, with regard to both whaling and officialdom, was essentially the same as that instituted by those merchants of London who had taken stock in the South Sea Company about the middle of the century.

All earlier efforts had been directed primarily towards the northern, or Arctic, fishery, which is to say to those sea-countries opened up by the Hollanders between Spitsbergen and Greenland and in the

Davis Strait and Baffin Bay to the west of Greenland. This fishery
was concentrated upon the arctic right whale, or "bowhead," and
what black right whales still remained. The products sought were both
oil and baleen, called "whalebone" or, often, even more mislead-
ingly, "fins," and both commanded a very fine price. The Hollanders had long before established the methods of hunting these whales
and they had been enormously successful in trying them out at sea,
the practice which had originally been devised by the Basques. In
fact, the Hollanders learned it from those people when the supply of
black right whales began to run out within towing distance of their
Spitsbergen shore stations.

When we speak of the "Dutch" as opposed to "Hollanders," or use
the word as an adjective, it must be understood that we are using the
title in the purist sense, for although Hollanders are Dutchmen to the
rest of the world, not all "Dutchmen" are Hollanders by any means.
And so it was with the so-called "Dutch" whale fleet. Most of the
vessels were built, based, and owned in Holland, but almost every
port from Flanders to Jutland was engaged in the trade, with Frisians, Holsteiners, Danes and Jutlanders, and many inland Germans
employed upon the vessels as seamen. All these North-Sea-men had
very close ties with their East Anglian fishermen counterparts, despite the fact that their respective countries were often at war, so it
was natural that the merchants of Hull, Whitby, and even London
should turn to them for skilled help in managing their new fleet of
whalers. The British and the Hollanders were, as a matter of fact,
more often at war than at peace throughout the preliminary period
of construction during the middle part of the eighteenth century, so
that we find a preponderance of Frisians and Holsteiners in the early
English whalers. And it was from them that the English seamen
learned about whaling — and they learned both well and fast, so that
they won praise even from the surly Hollanders for their skillful
seamanship and patient labor. But what they learned was not enough,
for it was in this period that the whalers encountered for the first
time a new problem — ice.

The truth of the matter was that nobody really understood the
Arctic Ice in those days and it was two centuries later before a
true concept of it was pieced together by modern scientific investigations. In the eighteenth century, however, it lay like a vast

barrier to navigation all across the northwest, one, moreover, that we might suppose would have been insurmountable or impassable by the clumsy, lumbering sailing vessels of that age. But the North-Sea-men of those days were exceptionally rugged individuals and unexcelled mariners, and they were driven by a strange urge which was neither avarice nor mere love of adventure for its own sake nor the result of fear nor a desire to escape the turmoil of Europe, but some curious compound of all these motives. They pursued the whale right into the ice and thereby suffered the most ghastly privations and disasters, as we shall see later on. At this point, however, we must turn aside, to follow the British in their pursuit of whales to quite other climes and into quite another area, and to observe one of the oddest phases of the whole history of whaling.

As we said above, British whaling was first deliberately revived under official governmental auspices with the express intention of exploiting the "South Seas." Not only did the whole effort fail miserably; nobody made even the slightest attempt to go to any sea south of the equator during the first fifty years. It was not until the great mercantile houses entered the field about 1775 that any real attempt was made to reach southern seas and even then the first successes resulted from pure chance. The lucrative trade with India and the Far East was closed to these traders by the all-powerful, Crown-chartered, government-sponsored monopoly known as the East India Company, but a vast watery empire lay to the south of their domains, waiting to be exploited. This was open to all and there were those who were earnestly contemplating its possibilities, though apparently British officialdom could see only one use for it then; this was as a dumping ground for unwanted citizenry who were costing money to keep in jails, had transgressed certain established social injunctions, such as the bonds of slavery or apprenticeship, or were politically obstreperous. By making their ships available for the transport and dumping of these unfortunates, the merchants gained not only legitimate but officially praiseworthy entrance to the South Pacific, and this they did for the most part from the west by going east round the Cape of Good Hope and across the Indian Ocean. However, this is not to say that they had not already made some attempt to exploit that ocean, and for whales, to boot.

The first tentative foray to the south was made by a few British whalers in 1775 who spent a season in the South Atlantic and sailed into higher latitudes. The results were not economically a success, but the next year a special bounty promulgated for the so-called "southern fishery" prompted further effort. Added encouragement was derived from an Act restricting American whaling, resultant upon the revolt of the colonists. The outcome was still uneconomic, and the effort languished, though a few ships persisted almost every year for more than a decade and gradually extended their voyages to the southern tip of South America. Then, two notable events took place at opposite sides of the Pacific Ocean.

Australia had been discovered by Captain Jansz in 1606, and New Zealand by Cook in 1769. Nothing had been done about either and it was not till 1786 that the first shipload of so-called "convicts" was dumped at the famous Botany Bay in Queensland on the latter. The same year, the first small fleet of South Sea whalers out of London made a determined attempt to fish the other side of the Pacific by sailing directly to and around Cape Horn. Both enterprises were noticeable for their inefficient conduct and virtual failure, but both stimulated further and more concerted effort.

Constantly prodded by the independent merchants and by the erstwhile directors of and the remaining investors in the ill-begotten South Sea Company, which had by then exploded in the famous "bubble," the government set about systematically emptying the jails and bundling their inmates off to Australia, on the one hand, while they released naval personnel and tonnage, on the other, to survey the southeast area of the Pacific via the Horn. In 1792, H.M.S. *Rattler* went to that area and conducted a survey that carried her north to the equator up the west coast of South America to the great sperming grounds; but, although she attempted whaling, she met with no success in this field. These enterprises initiated the first period of successful British whaling, for the northern fishery in the Greenland seas was being beset by an ever-mounting number of difficulties and obstructions. Worst of these were certain concomitants of the almost endless wars in which the British were involved throughout the latter half of the eighteenth century.

With the usual and always surprising lack of over-all planning for which the British have become famous, the iniquitous method of recruiting mariners known as "press ganging" was not only encouraged by the government but even officially organized. What is more, the Navy constantly harassed the whalers, as well as ordinary merchant-men, despite several edicts, issued from time to time, excluding them from being thus involuntarily impressed into Their Majesties' serv-ices. In some cases there were even pitched battles between returning whalers and naval patrol craft, one of which resulted in a popular revolt. While the government officially recognized the value of the whaling fleet and of whale products, especially during the war with the Hollanders, who had a virtual monopoly on these essential raw materials, it still persisted in this senseless persecution of the men who manned the whalers. And a seaman grabbed by an armed guard from a tavern in his home town only a few days after returning from a hazardous two-year voyage through the Arctic Ice and forced against his will to fight an enemy whom he had perhaps regarded only as a friendly rival up till a month previously did not make a reliable naval rating. Nor did the captains of whalers, thus robbed of their skilled crews, make reliable masters even if given guns and called armed merchantmen. All too many of both came to the conclusion that another semiofficially sanctioned practice was a lesser evil. This was privateering.

Privateering was the second bugbear of British whaling. Piracy was always dear to the hearts of the English, and when it could be regarded as a patriotic duty, it became quite respectable. Almost everybody indulged the pleasure, and as Britain's enemies changed so rapidly and news traveled so slowly, it was almost impossible to state just where privateering became legitimate naval action, on the one hand, or plain piracy, on the other. To make matters worse, the crews of some so-called privateers were often composed of about equal numbers of the rival parties in the current war, so that ships changed hands with remarkable frequency and often singular lack of turmoil. Mutiny thus also became almost respectable.

Quite apart from these ridiculous aspects, the British northern whaling industry was also beset by inefficient management. None-theless, a number of factors played into its hands. First, Dutch whal-ing began to decline about 1770 and continued on the downgrade rapidly after 1790. The Germans turned their attention more and more to sealing, while the Americans suffered almost complete tem-porary eclipse by the end of the war in 1783. The British were thus

## The South Pacific, as Seen by Samuel Enderby

This map is most startling to all of us who are used to viewing the Pacific as from the South Pole, and usually split in half so that the major land masses of the earth may be preserved in single pieces. We have come to regard the Pacific as a vast empty expanse of water with a few islands dotted about its southern portion. The fact is, it is an immense horseshoe-shaped gutter, bowing to the east, inside which lies a huge submerged continental promontory extending from the East Indies and Australia to Tonga and Chatham Islands and embracing several huge archipelagoes, including the whole of New Zealand. Beyond this, a further and even vaster tongue of comparative shallows and suboceanic ridges stretches three quarters of the way to the Americas and is dotted with more or less parallel lines of islands, reefs, and shoals. The dry land amounts in the aggregate to only an infinitesimal area compared to the water surface, but it constitutes a fairly even distribution covering the whole inside of the horseshoe.

Europeans entered this area from opposite sides: first, from the Indian Ocean going east via the Indonesian archipelago; second, round Cape Horn from the South Atlantic going west. The exploration of the Pacific went on from both sides and met in the middle. Apart from a few early voyages of a truly exploratory nature undertaken to circumnavigate the globe, most of the discoveries stemmed from the westward advance of the spermers. By following this whale, the Nantucketers and British crossed the main gutter from the Galápagos to the Gilbert and Ellice archipelagoes straight along the equator, where the sperm whales happen to congregate in large numbers. From this so-called "On-the-Line" fishing, they branched out to the left to the Vasquez Ground, thence to New Zealand, and to the right to the Japan Grounds. Finally they pressed forward along the northern edge of the continental shelf and entered the Sulu Sea inside the Philippines, there meeting the East Indiamen on their way to the China coast from the Indian Ocean.

Meantime, the British merchantmen carrying the reluctant early colonists had reached Australia and, finding a plethora of whales in those waters, they initiated bay whaling after the southern right whales, and took to sperming on the continental shelf to the northwest. In a matter of two decades the Pacific, from being a vast *aqua incognita*, became a whalers' pond.

# Map 7  The South Pacific, as Seen by Samuel Enderby

Modified Zenithial
Equidistant Projection
Scale 1:70,000,000

- - - - - - -  Limit of Continental Deposits
·················  Shallows Delimiting Oceanic Island Groupings
←— - - -  Seasonal Migrations of Southern Right Whales
←— - - -  Advance of the Spermers

left an almost clear field and the number of British whalers rose steadily from fifty in 1770 to two hundred and forty-seven in 1788, of which no fewer than thirty-one were Scotsmen. Apart from the Scots, however, almost the entire increase in the fleet was occasioned by certain novel activities in the Pacific, which was just too far away to make privateering feasible and where wonderful events were taking place.

The ultimate decline in the northern whaling was caused basically by the progressive extermination of the right whales in the North Atlantic and Greenland seas, so that the whole enterprise finally became uneconomical. In the South Pacific, however, early voyagers found anew whales of the same or very closely related species in enormous abundance. The British merchantmen who transported the involuntary colonists to Australia were quick to notice this potential harvest and they also soon learned that these southern whales had most convenient habits. They migrated around a fixed route, arriving in the bays, inlets, and river mouths of Tasmania, Australia, and New Zealand on precise schedules every year. This was something unknown in Europe since the time of the Basques and off the American east coast for almost two centuries. The reports on this to their owners by ships' captains prompted such perspicacious men as the Enderbys to divert as many whalers as possible to the Australian run and to supply their ordinary merchantmen visiting those seas with whaling equipment. It was in 1789 that Sam Enderby sent the first British whaler, the *Emilia*, into the Pacific via the Horn. She was a blunt-nosed, tubby, three-masted vessel built specially for sperming with a try-works amidships on deck, which set the pattern for all professional spermers for half a century. She returned to London in 1790 with a full cargo of sperm products. The following year several of the convict ships started whaling along the Australian coast, after unloading their human cargoes. One Captain Thomas Melville took four whales that year and saw such numbers his reports became a little hysterical. Ships poured into the area and twenty returned to London the following year with full holds. Despite the fact that it took the whalers four months to reach Australia, and although the East India Company still disallowed whaling east of the Cape of Good Hope, activity increased annually. The enterprising Sam Enderby, noting this, fitted out the *Rattler* and with what we must consider strangely modern foresight — and the assistance of the Navy, as we have seen — dispatched it simply to explore. His effort was fully justified, for he obtained the first really reliable information on the congregating areas and seasonal movements of the sperm whales throughout the eastern Pacific, which stood the Enderby Company in good stead for half a century in face of the massive American world-wide competition that was to come during that period.

This initial flurry was almost wholly directed at sperming, but, as we have said, both the mariners and the early colonists, from the first, had their eyes on the abundance of right whales. From this a new industry called "bay whaling" sprang up. The business really began in Tasmania, which was first settled in 1803 by a man named Bowen. With him were some convicts, a few free settlers, eight soldiers, and a remarkable man named Ebor Bunker who brought them all in his whaler, the *Albion*. One of the settlers was a man named Collins, whom Bowen appointed the first harbor master, and he, in partnership with Bunker, started bay whaling in the Derwent River inlet the very first year. They were very successful, and the practice slowly spread to southeastern Australia and thence north up to Queensland and west along the south coast and around into the Indian Ocean.

Bay whaling was conducted in the same old offshore manner that we have already met among the Basques and New Englanders. Clinker-built, open boats of cedar, about thirty feet long, double-ended with a small deck aft, with from five to eight oarsmen, were launched from shore when whales were sighted. The crew consisted of a harpooner, bow oar, midship oar, tub oarsman, who handled the line coiled in an open tub amidships, after oarsman, and a headsman, who wielded a twenty-seven-foot sweep held by a leather thong in lieu of a tiller. As always, the harpooner changed places with the headsman as soon as a whale was struck and fast to the harpoon. This strange custom gave rise to what was probably the first whaling law in British jurisprudence. This stated that as long as a harpoon stayed in a whale and the line was in the headsman's hand, the animal was a "fast fish." If anybody cut the line or in any way prevented a kill, he became subject to a fine of not less than ten pounds and not more than a hundred pounds.

Whales were at first so numerous off the Tasmanian coast that what was described as their "snoring" once kept the governor awake in his residence by the shore of the Derwent Inlet, but the business was so profitable that it soon became overcrowded, and as many as twenty boats sometimes put off after one whale. The whales arrived like clockwork toys on certain dates in June in Tasmania, and were subsequently slaughtered wholesale. As the remnants moved over to and along the Australian coasts, fleets of little boats waited for them in almost every inhabited bay and inlet. The Tasmanian and Australian aborigines made excellent whalemen and were consequently exploited by the colonists just as thoroughly as were the North American Amerindians by the Yankees. The bonanza could not last under these pressures, and after a slow decline in their numbers, the whales finally failed altogether to turn up in Tasmania in 1841. By this time there were 300 American and some French whalers working the south coast of Australia alone, while many more of the 675-strong Yankee fleet, which employed over 16,000 men, were in adjacent seas both sperming and cutting into bay whaling.

Meanwhile also, New Zealand had become an almost equally profitable hunting ground. The country was still the unclaimed domain of its native Maori inhabitants, and while it offered outstanding opportunities for exploitation, nobody made any move to annex it. Sperming was already under way off the north coast of New Zealand in 1794, and the Bay of Islands became a rendezvous for these high-seas men. Contacts were made with the Maori chiefs for fresh food and other trade. The results were appalling. The rough whalers cheated and mistreated the natives, who, being a magnificent warrior race, replied in kind. They seized one ship, named the *Boyd*, and killed and ate its entire complement, except one woman, a clubfooted boy, and two small children. Nor was this an isolated event, for the whalers persisted in interfering with the Maoris' bloodthirsty internal tribal wars while using them also in marauding among their own European and American rivals. A vast amount of blood was shed, and the whole state of affairs became so deplorable that the whalers finally banded together against the Maoris in 1810 and set up fully defended camps and settlements along the coasts.

The right whales migrated annually north, in May, to the New Zealand coasts to calve. Passing Kapiti Island, they entered Cook

Strait and congregated in Cloudy Bay. In June they moved to the Chatham Islands. In October they went off north or east. About 1828 the number of sperms in surrounding seas began to decline, and the slaughter of the right whales then really started in earnest. Ships came from Sydney and other Australian ports, landed a gang who set up a try-works ashore, and went on up the coast to collect a cargo of flax. Then they sailed for Australia and returned after the whaling season to pick up their shore party and whale products.

These shore stations were little different from the more permanent settlements in Tasmania and Australia. Small boats put off daily after the whales, towed them ashore from distances of as many as three miles if the weather was good, or anchored them offshore if it was bad. The oil extracted at these works commanded a much better price than that from the Greenland fishery because it was fresh when tryed-out and not extracted from rotten blubber that had been stashed in barrels in a ship's hold for months. From two to thirteen tons of oil were obtained from a single whale, and the average ran over six tons. The business was highly profitable in itself, but there was, in addition, a brisk trade with the Maoris. Every whaler brought a cargo full of guns, rum, tobacco, blankets, knives, pipes, fishhooks, and so forth, to exchange for flax, live pigs, potatoes, and curios.

The New Zealand bay whaling was almost exclusively in the hands of the Australians at first. The British and Americans — that is to say, the deep-sea men, the spermers, and the English ships that came to the Pacific round the Horn — did not take any active part until about 1835. Meanwhile, the relations between the Maoris and the whalers had become so violent that the British Government was bombarded with requests to intervene. Even the cannibal chief, Te Rauparaha, appealed for missionaries to be sent to help him, and the first arrived in 1836. The whole country was formally declared a territory of New South Wales, Australia, in 1839 and a lieutenant governor was appointed to examine all land claims. He arrived in New Zealand the following year and signed a treaty at Waitangi with forty-six of the leading chiefs, although that same year a company in Sydney actually bought the whole South Island and part of the North Island for two hundred pounds, plus an annuity of one hundred pounds to another group of chiefs. This private land-grab was later nullified by proclamation, and the whole country came formally under British aegis.

Meanwhile, the right whales had been declining in numbers even more rapidly than in Australian waters, and small wonder! It was estimated that American whalers alone took away £140,000 worth of bay-whale oil in one year, when the pound was worth a great deal more than it is today and in whale products represented a tremendous fortune. By 1850 bay whaling was virtually defunct and the sperming had moved to more northern areas. The main sperming grounds were: the northern, between Queensland and New Caledonia; the middle, between Sydney and New Zealand; the western, from Tasmania to the Leeuwin Islands; and the eastern, extending from New Zealand to the Chathams; but these were still very minor areas compared to the great Vasquez Ground north of New Zealand, that around the Ellice Islands, and the string of vast offshore grounds stretching across the Pacific athwart the equator. The so-called "golden age" of American whaling was dawning and the international fleet moved away from the Tasman Sea area. But it left some odd footprints.

In July of 1842 a curious man named Ben Boyd, who had been a wealthy stockbroker in London, arrived in Sydney on his private yacht named the *Wanderer*, preceded by three steamships full of provisions. He built a seventy-six-foot lighthouse and a township at Twofold Bay, and started bay whaling and sperming. He first lost his steamers, then quarreled with everybody, and finally lost most of his capital in London due to a "crash." He sailed for California, where he was even less successful, and then attempted to set up a republic in Papua. He finally disappeared on Guadalcanal in 1851. However, his assistant, one Oswald Brierly, stayed on in Australia. He was a recognized Royal Academician at the age of twenty-five and continued to paint in Australia. He also went on a voyage of scientific exploration in H.M.S. *Rattlesnake*, on which the famous Huxley had shipped as the official naturalist. He made a considerable study of the southern whales, and when he finally returned to England — to become official royal marine painter to Her Majesty Queen Victoria, incidentally — he ran afoul of that irascible old gentleman, Professor Richard Owen, who was noted for making sweeping statements about almost any matter zoological on no grounds whatsoever, other than the supposed authority of his name and position. Among other asininities, he had seen fit to state that right whales existed only in the northern hemisphere, and nobody had dared question him, despite the multimillion-dollar industry founded on these beasts in the South Pacific. Such is the provenance of orthodoxy, however, that when he was not only challenged but shown to have talked complete nonsense by Brierly, he resorted to outright trickery by stating that the southern right whales were "a different species."

The effects of Professor Owen's mendacity have lingered until the present day, for there is still debate as to whether the southern black right whale is truly a different species and whether it is completely isolated from its remaining northern cousins. These mammals do not customarily live in the intervening warmer waters of the tropics, but they do migrate annually towards the Tropic of Cancer and of Capricorn from the colder waters of the north and south, and they have quite often been taken wandering about in mid-ocean near the equator. There is no reason why they should not occasionally stray from the Arctic to the Antarctic and vice versa; further, there do not seem to be any really valid reasons for separating the two except on geographical grounds. This, of course, is begging the question. At most there may be four groups to which specific names have been given: *Balaena biscayensis* for those in the North Atlantic; *Balaena australis*, rather muddlingly, for those from the South Atlantic; *Balaena antipodarum* for the South Pacific; and *Balaena japonica* for the North Pacific populations. In the Southern Hemisphere they inhabit a wide belt of ocean ringing the Antarctic from the Ice-front north to the coasts of South America, Australia, and South Africa. Today they are rare in all areas.

While the South Seas lack a representative of the bowhead, they are the habitat of most other oceanic species, and they appear to be the chosen areas for certain groups and for a variety of lesser-known types. Among these is a little, twenty-foot relative of the black right known as the Pigmy Right Whale (*Neobalaena marginata*). This has been recorded only from southern areas, only a few specimens have been found stranded, and nothing is known of its habits. Externally it looks just like a little black right, but it has a small triangular dorsal fin. Internally it displays some very odd features.

First, it has only four fingers in its flippers; but much stranger are its ribs. It has more than any other whale, and they are flattened and immensely broad from front to back, forming an almost solid barrel of bone around the internal organs. What this is for we do not know, but it has been surmised that it is to hold the body out in deep-diving operations. Despite the fact that no other baleen whale makes deep dives, this theory is considerably strengthened by the fact that the ribs are but loosely attached to the backbone, presumably so that they can bulge outward to counteract pressure.

Truly Australian whaling became extinct with the end of the bay whaling about 1850, but several ports in that country, Tasmania, and New Zealand continued to make gestures towards the spermers for twenty-five years. Thus, Sydney remitted all port charges to whalers in 1871, and Otago in New Zealand offered five hundred pounds to the first ship which would refit there, but found no takers. It was over half a century before an entirely new industry sprang up, using motorboats to pursue quite another kind of whale, which we shall have cause to mention later.

The end of the Australian enterprise did not mean the end of either British South Sea whaling or the British industry as a whole, though it presaged a critical period in whaling throughout the world. There were many contributing factors, but principal among these was the discovery of petroleum. Meantime, the British whaling fleet in the Arctic had fared no better, and by 1850 was reduced to thirty-one ships. Ten years later it suddenly revived, for reasons we will soon learn. The high tide of British whaling was about the year 1819 at a time when the American fleet was at its lowest ebb. As the latter increased again, the British declined and they had already practically given up the effort when the Civil War broke out.

It is the great outburst of Yankee activity following this interlude which we must now turn to examine.

## 12

# Late Noon in the West

### (*American III*)

THE *John W. Nathan* rose and fell with creaking yards and what appeared to be enormous complacency upon the endless, glassy, pale-blue swell that heaved in from the Pacific. Apart from her gently rocking yardarms and a few odd lines that dangled listlessly from her rail, she was spick and span and her canvas neatly furled. There was even a glaring white awning stretched amidships between the try-works and her poop, and two people were lolling in hammocks slung over the transom. Though her stubby lines and dull-black sides proclaimed her to be a whaler, her general appearance and behavior would better have suited a sultan's yacht. She wasn't even anchored.

A ridiculously small dinghy, in build most oddly like the big ship herself without her spars, languished at the end of a light line aft, and performed its own lesser dance upon the oily swell. It was early morning and although it was the first of December, the heat was oppressive, the air completely unmoving, and the sunlight so intensely shining despite a general haziness that it hurt the eyeballs to look at the water. Also, there was silence except for a distant, inter-mittent rumbling that sounded like thunder behind a range of moun-tains, but which was, nonetheless, felt through the feet more than heard through the ears. Small sea birds wandered about on the ab-solutely smooth sea, leaving endless arrowheads upon its shining sur-face, or creating little stars as they suddenly went below upon urgent business of their own. A man wearing a clean white shirt slithered down the line into the dinghy.

Captain Joshua Nathan emerged from a financial reverie which he had been indulging unabashedly and uninterruptedly since break-fast in one of the hammocks. He stretched mightily, yawned, and listlessly picked up a spyglass. The other hammock swayed and the face of an astonishingly young and beautiful woman peered over its rope edge.

"Do you see anything yet?" Mrs. Joshua Nathan inquired drow-sily.

The captain said nothing for a long time while his glass swung in a wide arc to the north along the seemingly interminable shore towards a far distant headland. His beard jutted out underneath the telescope even farther than did the peak of his cap above it. His wife smiled frankly at his earnestness. Then she made a very tactless re-mark.

"I don't think the silly things will come back at all," she began. "They can't be that stupid, and then there are all those other vultures waiting for them up north." And she would have gone on in that vein had Joshua Nathan not turned to starboard instead of to port to admonish her. As he did so, however, his roving telescope swept the nearby shore and the vast fields of gently heaving kelp that intervened. He immediately became rigid and let out a low gurgle.

"What is it?" gasped Maria Nathan, swinging herself agilely out of the hammock, for she had got to know the significance of that strange sound. Her husband was speechless, so she came up quietly beside him. Then she saw what he was staring at and it was so close she did not need a spyglass to see what it was. The kelp was heaving mightily over an area of a square mile as if some underwater volcano was about to burst forth.

"So they did come," she said quietly. "But where from, and how did they get by the boats?"

"That's what I'd like to know," roared Captain Nathan, coming suddenly to life. Then he jumped for the companionway, shouting as he went for all hands aboard to put in an even more than immediate appearance.

Matters from then on moved with lightning speed, but not a little confusion. All officers, except the second mate and a teen-age cadet, and two thirds of the crew were absent in the five whaleboats, with most of the harpoons and other equipment, seven miles up the coast. They had been there for three days, spending the nights ashore where their fires could be seen from the *John W. Nathan* and by a lookout left on the headland. They were waiting for the coming of the Devil Fish as they plowed slowly through the kelp beds to their winter breeding grounds far to the south. Thus, the ship's company consisted for the most part of the members of the commissariat, with some young apprentices, the cooper, the carpenter, and a very ancient Chinese who performed miracles with a sail needle in return for an astonishingly small quota of rice and plain water. What is more, there were only the little dinghy and one somewhat damaged whaleboat aboard.

The safe and probably most intelligent thing to have done in the circumstances would have been to signal the boats and then wait patiently for their return, but young Yankee whaling captains were not much interested in safety, and though intelligent enough, they regarded the exercise of this quality a deterrent to action in an emergency. So it was that after a great deal of shouting and mad scrambling 'tween decks, the battered whaleboat was lowered away and an assortment of cooks, apprentices, and the carpenter flung themselves into it, while Captain Nathan, two seamen, and the ancient Chinese filled the little dinghy, lowering it almost to the water line. That the Oriental went along was due solely to the fact that he happened to be pursuing his trade in the dinghy on account of the heat when the crisis occurred. The two boats then set off at a rapid stroke towards the glistening, heaving kelp beds.

The dinghy arrived first because of the more experienced oarsmanship of the two sailors, and the captain stood rather uncertainly in her bow holding a harpoon at the ready. They pushed in among the masses of seaweed, followed by the whaleboat. Some monumental risks were taken by whalemen, but none could ever have been more dubious than this, as immediately became apparent.

First, the dinghy became fast in the weed; then the whaleboat tried to maneuver around her both to lend a hand and to make haste into the clearer shallow water beyond towards the shore, but she ran afoul of something and nearly keeled over. Thinking this to be a sand bar, the cook helpfully unshipped his scull and jabbed it downward with the idea of punting, but it went right down unexpectedly so that he fell clean overboard. Everybody was very excited and the other men roared with laughter. This produced the most extraordinary and unexpected response.

The whole sea and the kelp all around them suddenly rose up in small mountains, one of which showered spray upon them and then, as the shiny strands of weed slipped from it, resolved itself into a horribly corpselike, mottled, gray mass. This swung around before anybody really knew what was happening and charged the whaleboat, hitting it squarely amidships and splintering the gunwale. Then, surprisingly, it backed off and charged the dinghy.

Captain Nathan was ready for it, and yelling encouragement to the other boat's crew not to take to the water, he lunged forward with the harpoon and every ounce of strength at his command. Red blood spurted skyward in a great jet, and the hideous gray mass plunged beneath the boat. Then the cook's head appeared between the two boats. His mouth opened and he gave vent to a high-pitched scream which was cut off short as he was abruptly jerked below the surface. Meanwhile, the whaleboat had filled with water and rested completely awash, held up by the kelp, with the men sitting stupidly, submerged up to their waists. And thus the tableau held for almost a minute while nothing happened except the singing of the line as it rushed out through the cleat abaft the dinghy, with which the old Chinese was wrestling manfully, cursing in his own language. Then things changed.

With a roaring noise the bull whale, for such it was, came up directly under the waterlogged whaleboat and well-nigh cracked its skull on the unexpected weight thereof. It shattered the keel and threw most of the remaining men into the water, where they imme-

diately became entangled in the kelp. It then turned below the water and, raising its tail, struck with ten-ton blows of solid steel-strong
sinew at the dinghy. And the mighty bludgeoning rained down at
ten-second intervals, so furiously agile was the devilish creature.

By what could only have been a miracle, the first strokes missed
the frail craft, and this gave its two experienced oarsmen just enough
time to pull away, but so crazed and intent upon murder was the
beast that it continued to lash the place where the boat had been.
This gave the old Chinese an opportunity which, despite his frailty
and long lack of practice, he seized with unexpected adroitness.
Hefting one of the lances, he drove it to the hilt five times into the
underside of the brute near the base of its tail every time that portion
of its anatomy flashed aloft. This so enraged the animal that it
stopped its hammering and rushed headlong shoreward, dragging
the dinghy and an enormous mass of kelp along with it. In a moment
it burst out into the clear, shallow water just seaward of the surf
that boomed upon the sandy beach.

But the encounter was not yet over and the real test was still to
come. The maddened whale plunged straight into the breakers and
then, wriggling around with its belly actually on the bottom, it cunningly waited for an incoming wave to make it water-borne. Then
it charged directly at the little boat, its tiny useless eyes clearly visible above the surface and jets of blood spurting behind into the
creamy foam. Captain Nathan just had time to yell out, " Save yourselves, men! " when the beast was upon him. In a last supreme effort,
more in self-defense than by design, he thrust his second harpoon
directly into the creature's blowhole, which, as any whaleman
knows, is normally the most useless point to try to penetrate. But
by some further miracle, or perhaps the sheer force of the strike,
the Devil Fish let out a strange squeal and lunged straight downwards and, although they only found out much later, it actually
broke its jaw on some rocks at the bottom, and knocked itself
out.

The captain sank slowly into the belly of the dinghy and listlessly disentangled his right leg from several coils of the line that
was attached to his second harpoon. This line was quite slack; had
it not been, he would long since have been yanked overboard, or
his leg would have been torn from his body. There was silence but

for the booming of the surf. And it was a full five minutes later before anybody stirred or spoke. Then the old Chinese pointed.

"Flish! He come up! " he sang out.

And sure enough, a great gray bulk was slowly rising to the surface by the kelp bed. Red rivulets snaked out into the clean, clear water all around it. It did not move.

It was many minutes before the last man had struggled back to the waterlogged whaleboat, and they were then two less a company than when they had set out. The cook had not reappeared and now one of the apprentices had also vanished. It was two hours later that the first of the ship's boats arrived on the scene, all aboard manning oars and a sail set to catch the gentle breeze that was springing up. The dinghy was still anchored to the dead Devil Fish by the two harpoon lines but had been maneuvered into the kelp alongside the smashed whaleboat.

So it was that Captain Joshua Nathan took his first gray whale and lost a fine cook, a promising hand, and a good whaleboat, for there was hardly a timber or plank in the last that was worth repairing. And so it was, also, that he swore to fill his barrels with the oil of these cunning creatures whatever might be his other losses. He filled twenty from that first animal, and he filled the rest before the spring, for he started out that very day after the remainder of the school, and he kept right after them all through the winter right down to the Gulf of California and back. But he never lost another man or a boat, although he hunted the whales like one possessed. Nor did he ever venture into the kelp beds again. Instead, he cut a channel through them and then came upon the beasts in the clear water to landward.

Others were not so successful as he, and not a few of them lost their lives, but he filled his casks three years in succession, during which his wife never once offered a single prognostication upon the migration of any whale or the behavior of the Devil Fish in particular. This was a great relief to Captain Nathan.

AFTER the War of 1812, the Yankee whalers found themselves in a new world. The economic structure of the Union had changed. The industrial age was dawning, population was already growing apace, a new kind of wealth had begun to accumulate, and the Congress was looking to overseas trade as well as to home agriculture to round out the economy. Living, as we do today, almost a century into the age of petroleum, we often fail to realize the enormous importance of animal and vegetable oils prior to the discovery of this mineral substance. Enormous quantities of oil were needed for lighting, for heating, and even for cooking, while lubricants were in ever-increasing demand. Also, animal oils were essential to wool and other textile manufacture and to many other growing industries. While cotton, linseed, and some other vegetable oils were available in fair abundance, animal fats and oils were preferable for many purposes and whale oil constituted by far the most valuable and important of these. There was thus a great incentive to get the whaling industry going again for, unlike the years following the Revolution, there was now a large and growing demand for its products in America itself.

The New Englanders set to work immediately after the end of hostilities. By 1818 there were fewer than forty whalers left, but by the following year sixty-three had been commissioned, and by 1821 there were eighty-four. Although the Nantucketers made a valiant effort again to lead the country in the field, the troubles with their sand bar thwarted their every move and New Bedford took first position, both in the size of her fleet and in the volume of whale products she imported. Offshore whaling was dead, the black rights had become almost extinct, and the Greenland rights had already retreated so far into the Arctic Ice that it was no longer worthwhile dispatching more than a few ships in their pursuit, and in competition, to boot, with the still fairly active Hollanders and the Britishers, who had had a free rein in those seas throughout the war. Thus it was to the much more valuable sperming that the Yankees turned, and for this, larger ships were needed that could remain at sea for years and circumnavigate the world. To be economical they had to be just too big to overcome Nantucket's wretched sand bar.

Not only was the build-up of the whaling fleet in America very rapid; the extension of its operations throughout the world proceeded at a quite extraordinary pace. The first American whalers had rounded the Horn and entered the Pacific in 1791, and those ships which managed to avoid the war continued to follow that

route annually. Their operations in the Pacific slowly extended up
the west coast of South America, where sperm whales are fairly
plentiful close to shore in April and May. The Chileans were already
engaged in the business and the Americans appear to have learned
a great deal from them. By the end of the war, American ships had
pushed north of the coast of what is now Ecuador, where sperms
are still abundant until the end of September. In 1818, the first
Americans ventured out into the open Pacific, due west along the
equator, fishing for the first time through areas that were to become
known later as the famous "Galápagos," "Offshore," and "On-the-
Line" grounds. Within two years from that time, moreover, they
had crossed the Pacific entirely and were not only working the
Christmas, Phoenix, and Gilbert Island grounds, but had even turned
north and reached the Japan Grounds in latitude 30° N. Thus, the
major routes of expansion were already laid by the time the shipbuilders of New England got the new fleet of whalers off the stocks,
and as soon as these were fitted out, they sailed directly to the
Pacific. And the fleet continued to grow, the number of vessels
rising from 203 in 1829 to 421 in 1835 when what is popularly
known as the "golden age" of American whaling really began. This
was an extraordinary affair that might well have changed the course
of history but, for reasons that may appear historically most unusual,
it did not do so.

Although it created a number of fortunes at home and carried
Americans all over the globe, it left practically no lasting impression upon either this country or the world. Despite every economic
advantage, the industry remained throughout its history a neat little
home-grown affair, and despite the most incredible exploits of those
who sailed the ships to almost every island and into every port in
the world, the American whaleman remained a home boy to the end.
Americans still had more than enough to do exploring, opening up,
and settling their own home front to be bothered with founding a
world-wide empire or colonizing distant lands. They went out to get
the oil to light the lamps of Boston and, when they got home with
a load, as often as not they went back to the farm, trekked West,
or went digging for some much-needed minerals. Thus, when a
series of disruptive events hit the industry in rapid succession, and
the prime necessity for whale oil was eliminated, the whalemen just

stayed on the farm and the whole business petered out without leaving any outstanding imprint on the world. But while it lasted, this age had a glorious history.

It is always harder to gain a clear insight into a period of success than into one of failure. When necessity calls, invention results, and when invention is even a little ahead of the times, success can almost be assured. In this case everything was set up just right for the enterprise. The country was a fast-growing economic child demanding raw materials and new power sources in ever-greater quantities and, thus, it provided an almost inexhaustible market for oil. The people had a long experience in shipbuilding, had pioneered the routes, and had plenty of trainable man power. The only other whalers — the Hollanders and British — were undermanned, somewhat worn out by wars, and were too hidebound in their ideas. The former had thrown everything into the Arctic and the right whales; the British were still inexperienced, had a comparatively small fleet, and were beset by all sorts of official restrictions. Last, and most important of all, the oceans of the world were then positively swarming with sperm whales, whose numbers had hardly been so much as touched except in the North Atlantic. Every factor was propitious.

Far too much has already been written about this period of whaling history. Whole libraries are devoted to the subject; the logbooks of a large number of the whalers themselves, in which day-to-day accounts of their activities may be studied, are still extant; and almost everybody, it seems, who can claim any connection with the whaling families of old and a great many who certainly cannot do so appear to have written a book on the subject. Then there are the firsthand reminiscences of every kind of whaleman from captains to part-time deck hands like the famous Melville. This mass of literature is of every quality and varied worth. Quite a lot of it is arrant nonsense and some of it pure fabrication. One might suppose that there is nothing left to say and nothing to be added. Nevertheless, it is extremely hard, if not impossible, to find any single, good, over-all account of this period that both puts it in its proper perspective and at the same time brings to the fore its really salient features. The whole picture is so cluttered with shouts of "Thar she blows," blown-away topgallants, stove-in boats, and the varying prices of whale oil that it becomes well-nigh impossible to ascertain just what the hard-bitten skippers and owners were up to, where the ships went, why, for what, and with what success. These essential facts can be summed up very simply, but, first, we must obtain some clear understanding of the actual volume of the business and of its real time span.

To take the latter first, the build-up began, as we have said, in 1818, and it then continued progressively to a high point in the year 1846 when the fleet consisted of no fewer than 736 vessels — 680 ships and barques, 34 brigs, and 22 schooners, aggregating 233,262 tons burthen. From then on, the numbers declined by ten-year intervals as follows: to 635, 263, 169, 124, 77, and then to 46 in 1906. The first real drop occurred in 1857 when a serious financial slump hit the country as a whole. Four years later the Civil War broke out and the number of whalers took a plunge from 514 vessels of a total of 158,745 tons to 263 vessels of only 68,553 tons. By the end of the Civil War the "golden age" was over, though American whaling persisted until 1916. Thus, the whole period concerned lasted just fifty years, and the "golden age" for thirty.

Coming then to the financial aspects of this period, we find ourselves confronted with a mass of most regrettably conflicting statistics. Nothing can be more misleading than statistics, even in the hands of experts, and there are almost no things that can be more boring; nevertheless, the simple law of averages still pertains, and the outcome of averaging the sundry available statistics makes interesting reading. During the period 1835 to 1860 the annual imports of whale products averaged 117,950 barrels of sperm oil, 25,913 of common whale oil, and 2,323,512 pounds of baleen, valued in all at about eight millions of dollars of that period, which, of course, had a much greater purchasing power than the dollar of today. Sperm oil was worth 80¢ to $1.62 a gallon, ordinary oil 34¢ to 79¢, and baleen 34¢ to 58¢ a pound. In the peak year of 1846 there were more than seventy thousand men employed in the fleet alone and the vessels were valued at over twenty-two million dollars, while the total value of whale products imported reached the colossal figure of seventy million dollars.

Some individual vessels made incredible profits. The *Lagoda* in twelve years earned $652,000 and in one year paid a dividend of 363½ per cent. She cost less than $5000 to build! Some of the whalers saw the whole period through; the *Maria, Rousseau, Triton,* and *Ocean* were broken up only after ninety, eighty-seven, seventy-nine, and seventy-five years of work respectively. The *Maria* was built in Massachusetts in 1782 and broken up in San Francisco in 1872. The distribution of ownership of the fleet is also of great interest. In 1847 no fewer than thirty-four ports were engaged in whaling, the nine leaders being in the following order: New Bedford (254 ships), Nantucket (75), New London (70), Sag Harbor (62), Fairhaven (48), Stonington (27), Warren, R.I. (23), Provincetown (18), and Mystic (17). Where the ships went after whales proves to be even more significant.

In the year 1847, sixty small barques and some schooners went after sperms in the North Atlantic, only one ship went to the northern fishing in Davis Strait, thirty-two barques went after sperms in the Indian Ocean, one schooner went to the Pacific after sperms, and six hundred ships and barques went to the same ocean, a fifth of them exclusively for sperms. The same year, the first American whaler entered the Sea of Okhotsk inside Kamchatka on the Siberian coast and found an enormity of bowheads assembled there to breed. This initiated a whole new industry, but at the same time presaged the real beginning of the end of American whaling.

The method of whaling from American ships during this period was unvaried. It stemmed directly from the original Basque plan and was in no way dissimilar to that of the Hollanders on the high seas. The whalers were heavy, tublike wooden ships with blunt, almost flat, bows and abrupt square transoms. They carried steeply cocked bowsprits of considerable length and stepped three masts, the fore and main being square-rigged, the aft or mizzen usually fore-and-aft-rigged. Officers' quarters were aft and although not luxurious were more spacious and just as comfortable as the average modern cabin cruiser, often with a double, spring-mattress bed slung on gimbals for the captain and his wife, who many times was aboard. The crew's quarters were in the forecastle and were cramped, dark, airless, and verminous with three tiers of narrow board bunks forming a V and just enough space between for the crew of two to three dozen to stash their slop chests and to grab filthy meals in relays seated upon them. The deck was cluttered with boats, gear, and tools, and a large part of it between the fore and main masts was taken up with a large brick try-works containing two or more huge metal pots in which the oil was boiled. The rest of the vessel below decks was hold space, the main deck usually being about six feet below the upper and all below free. Stores and provisions were kept between decks; the lower hold took the oil in casks which were fashioned aboard by the cooper; these were made from bundles of staves and rings shipped from the home port.

When whales were sighted, three to eight small, open, double-ended shallops, hardly different from those of the Basques, were lowered and manned by the usual complement. As always, the harpooner changed places with the steersman if he struck and made fast to a whale. Then the oft-told procedure of burning lines rushing between the cleats, entangled human limbs, desperate backing and pulling on the oars, lancing, shouting, cursing, bloody foam, flailing tails, and miraculous escapes took place. But when all was over, the dead whale was either towed to the mother ship or flagged and picked up by her, and then the really hard work began. The crew went overboard upon the corpse and started cutting-in. A bewildering assortment of knifelike tools on long pole handles was used to cut the blubber from nose to tail in a variety of prescribed manners. The long strips, about twenty-four inches wide, were then hauled aboard by block and tackle and winches. There, they were chopped into square blocks and fed to the try-works. The fires were started with wood, but were kept going with the "crackling" that came out of the pots themselves after the oil had been melted out. The work continued round the clock until all the blubber and, in the case of the right whales, the baleen were aboard; then the corpse was cut free and abandoned.

Despite a fairly regular quota of deaths by accident and a lot more by disease and ship jumping on exotic, girl-infested islands, the fishing continued inexorably throughout the years. A few mutinies occurred and quite a number of ships were wrecked or foundered; a slightly larger percentage were lost to privateers or took to one form of piracy or another, though usually of a milder variety in this increasingly settled and enlightened era. Some just took up general trading. But, still and all, the slaughter of sperm whales went on throughout the oceans of the world, the profits piled up, and the street lamps of Boston, New York, Philadelphia, and other great, new

cities continued to shine. Then "Progress" stepped in and adminis-
tered a series of sledge-hammer blows to the whole preposterous
business.

The forewarning came in the slump of 1857, the real blow in the
discovery of petroleum in 1859, and the *coup de grâce* in the form of
the outbreak of the Civil War in 1861. The effects of the discovery
of petroleum emerged only slowly as adverse factors in the whale-oil
industry because this development was cloaked by the hysteria of
the Civil War. It is, however, this phase of the period and its after-
math that provide us with the really interesting and significant aspects of American whaling history.

Greatest damage was done to the Yankee whaling fleet initially by
Southern privateers, but there was a lot more aiding and abetting
in this wholesale destruction by nonbelligerents than is generally
realized or than the history books state. There are numerous allu-
sions in the contemporary records of other countries that clearly
indicate what can, at best, be described as sharp practices by many
governments, both colonial and others. The Hollanders impounded —
which is merely a polite term for seized — a number of whalers in
the Orient, and the British developed a regular trade in what they
termed "abandoned" vessels which somehow invariably turned up as
supply ships for the Confederates. The over-all result was that the
whaling fleet was reduced by almost two thirds.

When the war ended, there was an all-out business boom and the
price of whale oil and baleen shot up to ridiculous and, as was soon
proved, quite unstable values. By this time, the east and west coasts
of America were linked overland and the latter had started on its
mushroom growth both in wealth and importance. Although there
were still sperm whales in the Atlantics and in the Indian Ocean,
there were many more left in the Pacific, and almost the whole remaining whale fleet was concentrated in that ocean. The passage from
the Pacific to New England and back had always been tedious; now
it became somewhat absurd, and the whalers began unloading whatever quota of oil might be needed for local consumption on the West
Coast. Then they took to unloading their entire cargoes there, leaving also what was needed for the East Coast to be freighted thence
in the barrel in primitive "tankers." Finally, the transcontinental rail-
way reached a point of efficiency that permitted such bulk products

## The North Pacific, as Seen by the Yankees

Although this map is intrinsically the same as that upon which we showed this area from the point of view of the Japanese, its content is quite other and the movements it displays are wholly contrary. To the whalers running out of San Francisco, the Pacific was no longer the end of the universe; it was their world and, in the case of Hawaii, even their home base. The sailors paid little attention to the Kuro Siwo, and the steamers could go anywhere at will, provided fuel could be obtained. The whalers' interests were threefold at this period.

First and foremost, they were interested in the North Pacific bowhead whales, which calved in the Sea of Okhotsk and retreated in summer through the Bering Strait to the string of seas lying between the Arctic Ice-raft and the northern coasts of Asia and America. Second, they awaited the annual migration of the gray whales down the American coast; and third, they still did some sperming, for which they had to go via Japan or Hawaii to the warm waters of the Central Pacific.

There are ice problems in the North Pacific, but they are confined to the ladderlike formation of seas lying against the southern, or under, side of Asia because the Kuro Siwo holds even the drift-ice back from the open ocean. The winter freeze seals off the arctic seas and makes the Bering Sea impractical, and after a major part of the whole whaling fleet was caught and destroyed one year in this ice, the steamers took to wintering at the mouth of the Mackenzie River in the Beaufort Sea, or went south to engage in the gray-whaling or to refit.

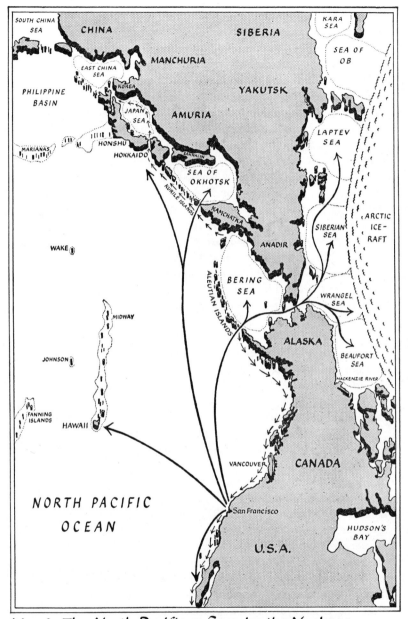

## Map 8  The North Pacific, as Seen by the Yankees

Bohn Projection

Scale 1 : 54,000,000

← − − −  Annual Migrations of Gray Whale

←———  Principal Routes of
San Francisco Whalers

to be transported across the country economically by land, and San Francisco stepped into the lead as the principal importing point for whale products. But there were also other factors that contributed to this change of venue.

As the sperming in the open Pacific became better organized and supply bases were set up for the victualing and refitting of the high-seas men at points like Honolulu in mid-ocean, the whalers began to find more time on their hands for off-season activities. One was offered them in the discovery of the vast numbers of valuable bow-heads in the Sea of Okhotsk, and when they penetrated the Arctic via the Bering Sea, they found an even greater bonanza of these whales there. However, they immediately went after them with such determination and such lack of foresight that they had totally extinguished this source of wealth in a quarter of a century. Just how ferocious this onslaught was may be gauged by the accounts of whale after whale killed and abandoned untouched, except for the extraction of its baleen. This was one of the stupidest and most wasteful actions in history and one that is almost inconceivable to us today. The basic trouble was that it cost about eight thousand dollars to build and equip a whaler, but bowhead whale-oil fetched only 30 cents a gallon, while its baleen then commanded a price of four dollars a pound. One bowhead whale might give a ton of baleen and thus pay for the whole voyage. Why should the whalers bother to go through the laborious and time-consuming business of cutting-in and trying-out the blubber?

Although the northern Pacific and Arctic whaling grounds were very far distant from San Francisco — nearly three thousand miles to the Bering Strait, a thousand on to the Mackenzie or the Lena, and still another two hundred to the Ice-front, to Banks Island, or to Cape Chelyuskin, to all of which the bowheads eventually retreated — the passages were still infinitesimal compared to the voyage back to New England via the Horn. Therefore, more and more whalers were registered on the West Coast and more and more companies built factories to process their imports in that area. The baleen-whale hunting in the North Pacific and Arctic was not, however, the only digression indulged by the American fleet in its declining phase after the Civil War. There was another diversion presented by a unique annual phenomenon that took place up and down the California coast.

No two coasts in the world are identical, but there are many that can be closely approximated in various widely separated parts of this planet; I have in mind those of Maine and western Scotland, of Chile and Norway, and of countless palm-girt tropical beaches. There are others, however, that are absolutely unique, so that if one were dropped upon them blindfolded from a spaceship, one would recognize them by smell or sound alone, provided one had been upon them at least once before. Such is the coast of California. There is a quality about its light that, although quite indefinable, is not found elsewhere; the sound of its endless and enormous oily rollers tipping on to its narrow beaches is quite distinct from that made by any other swell on any other coast. And it looks different. Nowhere else can the sea be such a pale blue under a brilliant sun, and nowhere else are such vast beds of kelp seaweed found moving lugubriously up and down just below the surface offshore. These kelp beds extend intermittently all down the west coast of the North American continent and provide a most distinctive habitat for a very particular fauna which once included great numbers of primitive beasts known to science as *Rachianectes*, to a limited number of the public as the Gray Whale, and to the whalers of old as the Devil Fish. These animals once migrated up and down this coast in huge congregations, feeding among the kelp beds and scratching their itching skins on the rocks of its beaches. The scientific name, in fact, means literally the "gray rocky-shore swimmer."

The gray whale is the most primitive of existing baleen whales. It reaches a length of forty-five feet, and the head is very small compared to the body. The baleen plates are small, cream colored, and individually very thick and heavy. In color the whale is a strange mottled or dappled gray of various shades. It has no fin on the back, but a slight hump rises about two thirds of the way aft between nose and tail. Under the throat there are two or four deep, fore-to-aft pleats in the skin. The females are larger than the males, and the young, which are born in late January, are about seventeen feet long. Incidentally, they are weaned in seven months when twenty-five feet long. They have regular rows of hair all over their heads.

These animals used to live in great numbers in the North Pacific, where they formed two groups, or tribes, one migrating annually down the Asiatic east coast from the Arctic to Korea, the other down the American west coast, reaching south to latitude 20° N. in midwinter, and then returning north again. Gray whales apparently were once much more widespread throughout the world, as was discovered in 1937 when the Hollanders drained a new portion of the Zuider Zee in their country, and a skull and part of a skeleton of one was unearthed. Later, another was dug up in the same area. They have very strange habits for whales. The males appear to have strong possessive feelings about their females and young and they will — and we use the present tense advisedly because, although gray whales were thought to have become extinct when they vanished from the American coast about 1895, they were rediscovered in fair abundance in Korea by Roy Chapman Andrews in this century — attack anyone or anything molesting them. Lone bulls will also attack boats on sight, especially small ones, and they are very agile, powerful, and persistent creatures. They can swim in shallower places than any other whale and during the breeding season will actually rest in only two feet of water on shoal beaches during low tides. Their normal cruising speed is about four to five knots and they do not appear to be able to do more than nine or ten. They love to splash about in the breakers inshore because they are terribly prone to all manner of parasites and are often literally covered with barnacles and huge lice (actually species of crustaceans). To free themselves of these, they rub along sandy bottoms and scratch themselves on rocks and this often produces large open sores, for the skin is very thin. All kinds of other parasites then enter the wounds which, when they do eventually heal, leave large white spots.

There is one creature that scares them into a frenzy and this is the killer whale, upon the approach of which they either dash hysterically for the shore, or become so terrified that they fall into a state of advanced catalepsy and just float like dead things, often bottom side up. The killers delight in tearing off the gray whales' lower jaws and pulling out their tongues, but then, killers will do this to anything they can't swallow whole.

The Siwash and other Amerindians of the West had hunted these mammals among the kelp beds in dories for countless aeons, and the Spanish made some halfhearted attempts to do likewise in the early days of the settlement of California but these animals were then left alone until two Provincetown whalers who had victualed in the Hawaiian Islands in 1846 and had empty holds were led to them by a Chinese pilot. This man's name is given simply as Chiang, which is vastly less committal than Smith or even "that man" might be as a definitive name and leaves us somewhat exasperated. We would sorely like to know who he was among that vast clan, where he came from, and how on earth he came to know all about gray whale hunting in the Californian kelp beds; but this he did. There are endless fables about Chinese junks trading with our West Coast Amerindians and even with Aztec Mexico before the fifteenth century, but there is no proper record of the later peaceful Chinese invasion. The result of this Chiang's pilotage is another sad passage in the history of whaling, for a not inconsiderable part of the Yankee fleet forthwith took to making an annual side trip to these coasts to slaughter the gray whales.

Scammon has estimated that about eleven thousand were killed between 1846 and 1875, and during the following twenty years all the rest were taken. Not a single one was seen in 1895. Each yielded about twenty barrels of good oil, and some large ones caught on the southward migration when they were covered with thick blubber gave up to seventy barrels. During the whole winter, which included the breeding and mating season, they appeared to eat not at all; their stomachs were invariably empty and their blubber was shrunken to a measly, thin layer of tough oilless hide. Now it has been discovered that they feed during the summer in the Arctic on small crustaceans of a group known as amphipods — those hopping things that look like squashed shrimps which come leaping out from under bundles of damp seaweed lying on sandy beaches. The Japanese call the gray whale by the euphonious name of *koku-kujira*.

The end of the gray whales coincided with the disappearance of the North Pacific black rights, the retreat of the bowheads into the dangerous ice floes of the Arctic, the decline of sperm whales throughout the Pacific, and the general adoption of petroleum as a source of both power and light. And then, as if these blows were not enough to cripple the age-old industry, two more innovations loomed upon the technical horizon — steam and the harpoon gun. These will be described in greater detail later on, as they proved to be the foundations of an entirely new whaling industry — the greatest of all, the one which has lasted until today and the one which so far surpasses all previous efforts put together that it would render them all worthless of mention were it not for their purely historical interest. Nonetheless, these innovations sounded the death knell of the old industry and that of the sailing ships. In fact, they brought about an almost complete eclipse of American seamanship, because this country clung stubbornly to sail for thirty years while the rest of the world converted to steam and placed their naval activities, their merchant marines, and even their whaling enterprises on this entirely new basis. While the British and Norwegians were perfecting the steam chaser and even experimenting with the factory ship, the Americans were indulging in ridiculous experiments with four-thousand-ton wooden sailing ships and monstrosities with twelve masts. The first American steam whaler did not sail till 1880, and when steam was finally adopted in this country, it was too late either to save the industry or even to find a sufficiency of whales to fulfill the remaining meager needs of industry for specialized animal oils.

In the meantime the port of New Bedford alone had added to its whaling fleet, having increased its number from 254 in 1847 to 329 by 1857. Those of all other ports declined rapidly. Almost all of them were operating in the North Pacific and during this period a great disaster occurred: the major part of the combined Yankee fleet was caught in the North Pacific ice in 1870 and lost.

As high-seas whaling shrank, the fleet coalesced and adopted a regular annual schedule. It wintered in San Francisco and then sailed north in spring to await the breakup of the ice in the Bering Sea. It then pushed north through the straits, pursuing the whales into the leads among the Ice-front and into the bays and inlets to the east along the Siberian coast via the Wrangel, Siberian, and Laptev Seas, on the one hand, and along the Canadian coast into the Beaufort Sea, on the other. Thus, it extended its operations as far as Cape Chelyuskin to the west and to the coasts of Banks Island in the east. In the fall it retreated slowly south, fishing all the time, and then returned to San Francisco, or went south to Honolulu or Panama, to refit and unload those cargoes which were destined for the eastern seaboard.

With the introduction of steam, the whalers took to wintering in the north while freighters took back their cargoes. Steamships cost more than three times the initial outlay for a sailer, needed almost twice as many crew, and were extremely expensive to operate because coal was so scarce and costly to buy and transport. Fuel for the four-thousand-mile trip to San Francisco could be saved by keeping the whalers in icebound northern anchorages for the winter. By 1893 a substantial number of the steam whalers wintered in the mouth of the Mackenzie in the Arctic Ocean. At that time there were only thirty-three whalers registered in San Francisco and twenty-two of them were steamers.

The development of steam in whaling was primarily a Scots innovation and it will be explained in proper detail when we survey the activities of that people in the next chapter. Although it failed to save the American whaling industry, it did help to maintain a not inconsiderable business until the end of the nineteenth century. During the decade from 1895 to 1905 there were still fifty-one registered American whalers out of San Francisco, aggregating only 10,184 tons burthen, but producing steadily a return of just one million dollars net per annum. In this final period the whalers reverted to coastal, offshore operations little more advanced than those of the early colonists. Payment of crews was still on the lay system with the captain receiving one eleventh and crewmen one one-hundred and fiftieth. If the ship returned empty, the crew got one dollar apiece.

By 1906 there were just four American ports left in the industry: New Bedford with twenty-four ships, San Francisco with fourteen, Provincetown with three, and a lone brig out of Norwich. The slight revival in the East was due to a most extraordinary development that has never been chronicled and is, outside of a few specialized official studies, simply not known at all.

A large proportion of the best harpooners, steersmen, and all-round whalemen had for long been Portuguese-speaking Africans from the Bissagos Islands off what is now called Portuguese Guinea in West Africa. Whaler crews were always the most incredibly polyglot outfits with every West European racial and national type mixed with native-born Americans; Orientals of many kinds, including Japanese, Chinese, Filipinos, sundry Malayans, a few Hindus, and Singhalese; Kanakas from the West Pacific Islands; Australian Blackfellows; Amerindians; Eskimos; and even some South American

Amerindians. One British vessel had a Russian captain, Dutch purser, Arab first mate, Nigerian boatswain, and ten other nationalities among its crew.

In almost all crews the Negro African figured very prominently, and those from Portuguese West Africa proved particularly outstanding as whalemen. They usually far surpassed all others of whatever racial or national origin in this art, and many of them settled along the New England coast, where they became known, and still are known, as "Bravas," which, for once, is more a term of endearment than of opprobrium. They are hard-working, honest seamen, and when all others abandoned the old sailing ships, they not only clung to them, but kept patching them up with loving care, and making payments out of their earnings on the rotting hulks on a sort of primitive installment plan. Eventually they came to own almost all that remained of the fleet, either by purchase or by default of others. In some cases even, they obtained the ships as outright gifts and they sailed them all over the earth with their own crews and made a modest profit by whaling in the old and tried manner while the rest of the world slugged it out with submarines, dreadnoughts, and even the first airplanes. The last of the grand old whalers foundered on Cape Hatteras in 1924 with a full hold. Today, only the proud *Charles W. Morgan* remains partly entombed in concrete at the Marine Historical Society's beautifully reconstructed whaling port at Mystic, Connecticut.

But we have run ahead of our story in order to complete the history of the last American whaling effort. Actually, this came to an end as a really effective enterprise about 1870 when other peoples with new techniques started operations upon an entirely new group of whales in hitherto untouched sea-countries. Thereafter, the effort was merely a relic of a former glory, although it presents some extraordinarily interesting side lights to any who regard themselves as "students." Quite apart from this, these remnants are strangely intriguing.

There are also certain aspects of the "golden age" itself which are tacitly omitted from most accounts, but which are of enormous importance to a proper understanding of the industry. One is the behavior of the sperm whales; the other, that of the human beings involved in their pursuit.

The sperm whale is perhaps the strangest of all mammals found upon this planet. Not only is it vastly aloof from all other animals and very different from its nearest living relative — the tiny pigmy sperm — it seems to be constructed upon a quite unique plan. It is a highly specialized animal dependent upon what one might at first suppose to be a very specialized food — namely, squids. Most people don't even know what a squid is, yet these animals probably make up a greater aggregate bulk of pure animal matter on this earth than any other two kinds of living creatures put together. They exist in countless millions of apparently endless masses in every ocean and sea in the world, and almost three quarters of this planet is covered by oceans and seas which are on the average nearly two and a half miles deep. Throughout this vast volume of liquid there are probably more squids than anything else.

These animals, however, migrate constantly all over the map, and in order to keep up with them and to save time and effort in obtaining a good meal, the sperm whales follow them around thousands of miles of oceanic passages per annum. Their exact movements are not yet fully comprehended, but it is recognized that they are concentrated in certain areas at certain times. (These areas will readily be seen on the end-paper maps.) There are thirty-six great areas of such concentration, all of which were originally discovered by the whalers, but the coming and going of the whales between the early and the late part of summer makes no sense in the over-all. It can only be said that they are in one area at one of these times, and in another, usually adjacent area, during the other. Where they go in the winter is not known at all.

The behavior of the whalemen, especially those from America, is even less explicable and no better understood. As we remarked above, it appears to have been dominated throughout the so-called "golden age" by an overpowering desire to get back home. Nonetheless, vast numbers of whalemen succumbed to the obviously worthwhile charms of maidens, grass-skirted or not, in all parts of the world. They left an ample progeny but neither their language nor any other remnants of their culture. Many of these deserters, in fact, were Americans only in name, and they often came from the very places where they finally abandoned their ships. This is perhaps explicable, but what induced the native-born Americans to go a-whaling? Was it an economic necessity; was it an excess of adventurousness; or was it simply inborn? The answer seems to be none of these.

Although America needed oil desperately at that period and was willing to pay handsomely for it, she did not offer anything like high enough individual returns to induce young men to leave an enormous, limitless, almost virgin field of profitable agriculture, mining, trade, and industry to risk their lives chasing whales in the tropics; yet the young men went to sea in droves. What is more, Americans had ample opportunity for adventure right in their own back yards and had just been through a devastating and vicious war, while they still had a whole continent to open up and explore. Gallivanting about on vermin-infested ships in climates they manifestly loathed, and to which they could not accustom themselves, was quite unnecessary. That they were inborn sailors need hardly be considered, despite the foibles of modern New Englanders, for the majority of the North-eastern colonists were landsmen and of Anglo-Saxon origin. They hated and distrusted the sea and usually had to be press-ganged into going upon it at the best of times.

The answer to this question is no clearer than that offered for the behavior of the sperm whale. Perhaps Melville came closer to explaining both in his famous tale *Moby Dick*, wherein men just went to sea by mistake and the whales kept bobbing up in odd places for no apparent rhyme or reason.

## *13*
# Afternoon by the Ice
### (*British III*)

A MESSAGE from the *Truelove*, Cap'n, sir," announced the seaman, pulling his forelock.

"Thank you, Bates," the captain said without looking up from the calculations that had been occupying him all morning. There was silence in the cabin while the hard, cold sunlight poured through the skylight.

Then the air was split by a sudden explosion, as if a giant had snapped some vast timber across his knee, and the whole ship gave a convulsive shudder. The captain jerked his head up and looked the seaman straight in the eye.

"What the devil are you waiting for?" he snapped.

"She's going, sir," the man almost screamed. "She can't take it, I tell you, she can't . . ." But the captain cut him short.

"Get out!" he ordered.

"But I tell you she's going, sir," the seaman persisted.

Captain Silas Hardwicke looked at the man askance, and uncontrollable rage began to well up somewhere inside him. He had never before encountered such behavior on his or any other ship. That an ordinary seaman should address his captain at all, except under orders, was unthinkable enough, but that he should persist in doing so when he had been commanded to leave, and that he should heap insolence upon insufferance by presuming to instruct an officer in his duties, practically calling him a fool to his face, was just more than the captain could comprehend. Had the man's behavior been even a little less outrageous, he might have been thrown into irons, but it was so unprecedented that the captain was left speechless. And while he was seething, the door opened and his first mate stepped in.

Mate Angus MacNeil had a red beard, light-blue eyes like gimlets, and tiny feet on which he moved about quickly and without sound. Captain Hardwicke had a great respect for him and placed the utmost confidence in his judgment and counsel. One look at his face now showed that all was definitely not well.

"I think she's going, sir," MacNeil announced simply. "The ballast's awash and she's opening up somewhere. The pressure's coming that hard the noo."

The captain's rage abated abruptly and he looked from MacNeil to the seaman Bates and then back again. He asked casually, "How long have you been aboard, Bates?"

"Nigh on ten year, sir," the man replied, bobbing and pulling time and time again on his forelock.

"And he's the vurruh best aboard," Angus MacNeil put in hurriedly, sensing the situation.

"In that case, he may go," said Captain Hardwicke, "but he should learn to keep his mouth shut." And he turned his attention to the message which he still held in his hand. Then, as his eyes fell on what had been written there by the officer of the watch, he let out a noise like a bark.

"Wait!" he snapped. "I've got a job for you, Bates, that'll give you a chance to do all the talking you want. Listen to this, Mr. MacNeil. The *Truelove* is caving in and Captain Barron requests all hands we can spare to offload her. We've got to get the men over there before we need her crew over here . . . that is, if I heard you correctly," he added.

"You did that," replied the mate.

"Then it's up to you, Bates, to get your scurvy mates over to the

*Truelove* on the double," the captain barked at the cringing seaman. "And I want willing volunteers, not a bunch of mismated loafers. Besides, for once you'll have to think for yourselves, if you can, because no officer leaves this ship. Now get out!"

Able Seaman Bates darted for the door, still vigorously pulling on his forelock, and Captain Hardwicke turned to his mate.

"Now this is what we do," he began and his orders continued for a full fifteen minutes, during which Angus MacNeil pulled up a chair, sat down, filled and lighted his pipe, but said nothing. When the discourse was finished, he sat staring moodily at the floor and at his tiny feet.

"Arrach is the man you want," he said. "He's only a lad, but he's a vurruh queer one. The Shetlands he comes from, and methinks he was spawned by a seal. He fears neether the water nor this hell-spawned ice, and I'll wager he'll know better what to do than we . . . if he feels like knowing," he added.

"I thought he was particularly foolish," Captain Hardwicke suggested. "I've never heard him talk but he's raving about lights in the sky or little men in the bilges. The boy's daft, in my opinion."

"Not in mine, Silas," said Angus MacNeil, as one old friend to another. "He's queer all right, but he knows things we don't. Besides, he says he'll be marrying a girl in Stornaway, and if he says so, I have a fancy he will. That means he'll be getting home, and if he can, the rest of us can go along with him. Have him cut the damned ice where he will and I'll lay you ten guineas he'll go right to the vurruh plank that's stove, and before she fills up, at that."

Captain Hardwicke looked at his mate in amazement. He'd never heard him offer money on a bet before and he'd never known him to sound so assured about anything that was obviously silly. That he would risk his ship on the chance that some crazy young Islander would know better than thirty experienced mariners which plank in a hundred-foot hull was giving way to the absolutely unpredictable pressures of several hundred or thousand square miles of shifting ice was not only preposterous but somehow unbelievable. Nonetheless, for some cause beyond his powers of reasoning, he nodded his head in assent. And at that moment the ship gave another tremendous heave, a noise like thunder rolled through her from stem to stern, and the table actually shifted on its gimbals. The sound of many running feet could be heard on the icy deck above.

"You'd better get started," Captain Hardwicke said.

And half an hour later two parties went over the icicle-festooned side, bundled up in every scrap of clothing they could find, and armed with a variety of lines and tools. One, led by a very busy and vociferous seaman named Bates, immediately straggled out across the endless, glaring ice in the direction of a tiny black point near the western horizon like a fly speck on a vast hospital wall — the doomed ship *Truelove* entombed in her prison of frozen sea. The other, which comprised all the officers, the carpenter, the cooper, and the smithy, just stood about, whacking their arms across their shoulders, puffing jets of frosted vapor from behind the fur trimming of their face hoods, or stamping their feet on the ice so that it rang like metal sheeting. Only one man in this second party was doing anything. He was a thin youth, with strange, almost colorless eyes, jet-black brows, and a tiny pointed beard. He did not even wear a hood but had a towel wrapped around his head, and he did not puff steam like the rest. He moved slowly along the straining sides of the ship, pressing a hand or a cheek against her frozen planks, and he seemed to be listening. Why his flesh did not freeze to the slick paint nobody could understand, but he did not even seem to notice the cold.

It was a strange scene. The great ship lay still under the glistening sun, with a slight list to starboard, like a dead thing, and her tall spars and wide yards spread black against the searing white sky. She looked as if she were just resting gently while some kindly sea thing caressed her; yet she was, for all useful purposes, already a hulk and might just as well have been rotting on the bottom. Between such a position and a more useful future stood nothing but a strange mystical youth who professed he talked with fairies and who ordered his eating by lights he said he saw in the sky. Yet the ship seemed to have confidence in this creature, as did the other men standing stupidly around. Not once did she crack, shudder, moan, or shift during the whole long hour he moved slowly around her sides.

Then the boy stopped suddenly athwart the foremast on her port side. He placed both hands and his right cheek on her side and she instantly gave a tremendous shudder.

"Fruch nahil," or something sounding like that, he called out, stroking the great ship as if she were a sick sheep. "She is hurting here. 'Bout twa ells below," he called, and he pointed down into the ice.

Without a word Angus MacNeil picked up a harpoon, and pacing off twenty feet from where the lad Arrach was clinging to the ship's side, he described a semicircle around him on the ice.

"Now break the muck out!" he shouted. Then he attacked the ice with a pick, starting at the farthest point.

And as the dozen men labored, noises like the discharges of blunderbusses would, every now and then, shatter the silence, and showers of smashed ice would burst into the air and go tinkling off across the flow. So great was the pressure that the whole area threatened to heave up and split right under their feet. But eventually someone broke through into a horizontal crack and the whole place came apart. Great sheets of clear ice seemed to crawl out of the previously smooth surface as if possessed and moved across one another. The ship gave a tremendous shudder and let out a tortured scream. Her yards rocked back and forth aloft and more ice shifted. The men jumped back and waited, but the movements went on with that slow inexorableness known only to ice. There was thunder in the air and beneath their feet. Then, slowly the upheaval subsided and all was quiet again.

"Now get her side cleared!" the mate barked. "Only He knows how long we may have."

And once again all hands turned-to with picks, grapples, and lines like ants attacking a continent of sugar. But a few minutes later they heard the sound of water running. A plank, right on the water line and just exactly two ells below the surface of the ice, was completely stove-in, disclosing a shattered timber to one side and an inwardly bulging sealing plank to the other. The icy arctic waters were flowing silently into this gaping hole as into a millrace, and they were splashing on into the bilges within the ship like a waterfall. The entire company sprang into action.

And so busy were they all, lowering a mat to the hole and bolting and pinning timbers over it before the ice should close in again, that nobody saw the incredible procession that had been approaching them from the west. The first notice they had of it was a raucous metallic blast. The vital work momentarily forgotten, all hands leaped for either the stem or stern of the ship to see what manner of monster might have crept up upon them thus unheralded over the open vastness of the ice. But what met their eyes was far stranger and much more uncanny than any sea monster that a Northlander could conjure up in his wildest tales, for there, not half a mile away, was a full-rigged ship belching black smoke from somewhere amidships and calmly sailing right through the solid ice. And, what was more, right behind her followed the *Truelove* with a thin towline tying her to the smoking one. The apparition gave three more raucous hoots and the ice rang beneath the men's feet in answer.

"All aboard!" yelled Captain Hardwicke. "For your lives, men. Aboard and save yourselves!"

Just in time the cooper leaped for an ice-covered line and hauled himself to the scuppers. He was the last man up, and just as they hauled him over the side, the ice below gave way with a noise like a cannon, and clear black water opened up right where he had been standing.

Within minutes the steamship *Ardnamucken* was alongside and had thrown them a line, and half an hour later, tied between her and the *Truelove*, they were moving out towards open water along a narrow lane through the ice. The *Ardnamucken* wheezed and thumped on ahead, white foam boiling from her flanks. She forged ahead contrary to all the laws of nature, but by noon she was in the clear.

"It's a fine thing sometimes that the ability to read is reserved for the upper classes," Captain Hardwicke remarked casually to his mate. "Your ideas of education for everybody may seem fine in Scotland, Mr. MacNeil, but I warrant we'd not have got her tight if that craven old porpoise hunter, Bates, could have read your message."

Angus MacNeil puffed twice deliberately on his pipe, then he removed it from his mouth, spat over the rail, and observed, "And I'll wager another ten guineas ye'd never 'a found the bloody hole if the lad Arrach had 'n read the Scriptures. You'll be owing me the ten guineas for that."

And Angus MacNeil found an extra ten guineas, in gold, in his wallet when he signed off in Hull two months later.

THE INNATE DUALITY of the second British whaling effort becomes clear only after one has followed either one or the other of its aspects from its beginning to its specialized zenith, and thence through its declining phases to its ultimate end. We have done just this and seen that, once the possibilities of a "southern fishery" were realized, a special fleet was built to exploit it. The owners of this fleet, however, were in many cases the same merchant traders who built the whalers which engaged in the "northern fishery," so that both their records and official statistics tend to cloud the issue rather than to reveal the complete dissimilarity of the two enterprises. From the turn of the eighteenth century the British industry was split into two quite separate projects employing quite different techniques.

The southern fishery came to a rather abrupt end in the middle of the nineteenth century. By this time the third phase of American whaling was going full blast and followed its quite separate and individualistic history to its gentle end in the present century. To complete the picture, we must now turn back to a point some fifty years before the beginning of the nineteenth century and investigate the other part of the second phase of British whaling — that in the north — and, in turn, follow it to its conclusion. This is a very important period in the history of whaling as a whole, for without a proper understanding of its progress, the origins of the modern industry will be quite incomprehensible. This phase began about 1760.

In that year there were just forty British vessels engaged in whaling, despite the enhanced bounty. All were registered in England, and all were engaged in the Arctic, all but a few in the Greenland seas (see map page 163). It was in that year, moreover, that the first tentative gesture towards participation in the business was made by a people who were, in one way, new in the field, but were, in another way, virtually the originators of the whole business — at least in western Europe. These were the Scots.

The Scots' whaling fleet was never large and their activities never became widely known, but their influence was very great and it was these people who eventually shifted the whole industry into the high gear that made modern whaling possible. What is more, they made a very considerable success of the enterprise, and derived from it much higher comparative profits more consistently than did either the English or even — when we come to compare the end results of

the three industries statistically — the Americans. Although there had
been little actual whaling tradition in Scotland, a certain group in
that country were an ancient maritime race of fishermen with countless centuries of experience in this field behind them. These are a distinct race and they are not Scots, though this is seldom realized even
by the nationals of that country. This has a very important bearing on
our subject, and we must therefore digress a little in order to try
to unravel this most tangled skein of history.

Just as the English are basically a mongrel people, so, to a lesser
extent, are the inhabitants of Scotland. In England there are two
main strains that have kept surprisingly distinct in culture, habits,
physical structure, and even, to some extent, in language in the purer
sense; one is the continental, land-loving Anglo-Saxon; the other is
the restless, sea-roving Norman, or Norseman. The latter people
started subduing the former in 750 A.D., completed the job in 1066
A.D., and then goaded them into founding an overseas empire by all
manner of maritime activities, which they have always loathed. In
Scotland also, there are two quite distinct peoples who have kept
somewhat apart for more than two thousand years. One, the Scots,
were tribalized, wore kilts, played bagpipes, were primarily sheep-
herders, and were originally continental landsmen not too distantly
related to the Saxons. They came to Scotland from Ireland! The
other group, fewer in number, for long submerged, and often not
recognized at all, are entirely different. Until quite recently, speaking from a purely historical point of view, they had neither a collec-
tive name nor even individual tribal or family names. They are the
dark-haired, sallow-skinned, narrow-faced people of the lochs and
isles of the west coast, the same stock, basically, as the Black Irish,
the Cornishmen, the Bretons, the original stock of Portugal, and
also those ancient neolithic peoples of Scandinavia who left us records of their whaling exploits engraved upon the faces of rocks in
Norway eight thousand years ago. Among these strange and wonderful people were numbered the dreaded Picts who, clothed in
nothing but a wash of blue dye known as woad, so scared the Romans that they built their famous walls from sea to sea across the
northern borders to keep them out of England.

Since the so-called Norsemen of history were really preponder-
antly of this same race — only the jarls and other rulers being de-

scendants of the warrior nation, the Aesir, led by their priest-king Wotan out of central Asia at the beginning of the Christian Era — there has always been a complete understanding between the indigenous populations of the Orkneys, Shetlands, Hebrides, the west coast of Scotland, and a large part of Ireland, on the one hand, and those sea rovers who came "a-viking" among them in the seventh to eleventh centuries, on the other. In fact, all these peoples became part of the Norse kingdom at that time and remained so until the early fifteenth century. They are a maritime race of fishermen and boatbuilders, and they are, incidentally, the originators and makers of whisky. They are not tribalized, but have always lived in gross, inbred, family groups, the size of which was governed by the size of the island, loch-head, or other piece of habitable land they happened to live upon. They originally lived in round houses with walls made of boulders, whales' ribs for rafters, and domed over with blocks of peat. My family had some of these for storing seaweed for manure, and the foundations of these very houses were probably laid down before the Romans reached England, and possibly several millennia before that.

These "Black" Scots, or perhaps we might call them Picts, have always been the boatbuilders of Scotland and seem, in fact, to be the main source of that breed of engineers for which the country as a whole is so famous throughout the world today. Be it noted that the names Carnegie, Bonnalie, Rennie, and such are not Scottish but Pictish names. These mariners had been voyaging all over the world in their little, deep-draught smacks for hundreds of years, so that when the Hollanders, English, French, Spanish, and even the Portuguese first reached the most outlandish coasts in the New World, Africa, and even islands in the Indian Ocean, they found so-called "Scotsmen" already there, busily engaged in trade and commerce and usually surrounded by a small tribe of half-breed offspring. There are some deathless expressions of surprise recorded by dumfounded Spanish navigators when they encountered these early colonists thus pre-empting some of their more choice "discoveries." The reason for this emigration from Scotland is the clue to all Scots enterprise and success; namely, the virility of this prolific race in a country where arable land and other resources are extremely limited. It is, in fact, a sort of viking.

The entry of the Scots into the British whaling business coincided with the real beginning of the build-up of the English fleet. In 1765 there were 33 English and 8 Scots whalers; ten years later there were 95 English and 9 Scots; in 1785, 136 English and 13 Scots; and by 1788, 216 English and 31 Scots. This year marked the high point of British Arctic whaling, and also the beginning of the southern fishery, as we have seen. The American Revolution reduced the combined fleet to 51 ships, and though Britain was at peace for a time thereafter, press-ganging continued and this, combined with a drastic reduction in the bounty to twenty-five shillings a ton in 1792, again more than halved the fleet. Thereafter, it averaged about a hundred, though it dropped to only 50 in 1800 and rose to 150 in 1816, which marked the opening of the decade in which British whaling as a whole reached its highest tide.

The British first visited the Davis Strait in 1773 when the Dutch were still whaling there with 182 vessels. Ten years later a group of Dutchmen — the Germans — gave up whaling and turned to sealing exclusively, and the Hollanders' fleet began to decline rapidly, though it was not till about 1820 that they too gave up whales in favor of seals. In the meantime the British slowly forged ahead, or perhaps we might better say, hung on, despite twenty years of almost continuous wars. During this time, Hull emerged as the leading English whaling port and in 1816 she sent 64 ships to the two fisheries. Meanwhile, the Scots fleet grew healthily but slowly, and its profits remained surprisingly stable. The most significant aspect of this build-up phase of British whaling was, however, the whalemen's first real encounter with a phenomenon that was new both to them and to seamanship as a whole. This was the Arctic Ice.

Now, the Arctic Ice is composed of three quite separate things. First, there is seasonal ice, which is just a lot of frozen sea; second, there are icebergs, which originate on land, act like and are, in fact, great hunks of "rock" that can float; and third, there is the permanent Arctic Ice-raft. This is, comparatively speaking, only a few feet thick, but at the present time extends over the whole Arctic Ocean like an immense, inverted, shallow bowl. It is not, however, rigid, homogenous, or even permanent, for it revolves very slowly like a huge wheel, while its component parts flow in and out of each other in the most complicated and sometimes amazing manner.

Ships caught in its edge will drift hundreds of miles into its middle and sometimes perform all sorts of gyrations, crossing their own paths before either breaking up and sinking or being spewed forth again from its edge, sometimes at the opposite side of the world. And when we say that it is not *permanent*, we mean the expression to be taken in both of two quite different senses.

First, the actual ice (or, say, any one cubic yard) of this raft is constantly changing in a variety of ways, as it may melt away at any time, while new volumes of water are continually freezing and making more ice, and snow falls upon it and some of this becomes congealed into the mass. There are some areas in the Ice-raft that are, however, much older than the rest of it, and some of these appear to be very ancient. They are known as palaeocrystic islands and they have become of great importance of late to our polar defense system, because they are much more permanent and stable than the rest of the raft and, being visually distinguishable, can be mapped and make ideal airfields on which large supply bases and permanent weather stations can be erected. Second, it now appears very probable that the whole Arctic Ice-raft itself, as an entity, may not be a permanent feature of our planet. In fact, up till five hundred years ago there may not have been any such thing for some thousand years. This possibility is of the utmost importance to a proper understanding of the history of whaling as a whole, for it may make it possible for us to explain some of that history's more peculiar aspects. The reasons are as follows:

There are many students of climatology who think that the whole Arctic Ice-raft did so completely vanish about 700 A.D., at the end of the cold period which brought on the so-called Dark Ages in Europe, and that it then suddenly came back again about the year 1450, when the first of a series of most terrible winters is known to have descended upon Europe, and the temperature dropped to a point from which it is only now recovering. One climatologist — Professor C. E. P. Brooks — further contends that such change-overs can take place in one season, because once an ice-raft has shrunk to a certain size, it can no longer either maintain itself through the summer or grow at the edges. His theory is very cogent, but to be explained it requires many more background facts than can be assembled and presented here. Whether it is valid or not is, however, comparatively unimportant; what is vital to our story is the mere possibility that the Arctic Ice-raft could have vanished between 700 and 1450 A.D. and then suddenly formed again, because if it did so, it would explain the sudden expansion of the Norse, how they could sail all over seas that were till recently ice-bound, and how they could settle colonies in Greenland. It would also explain why those colonies later withered away just about 1450, and the Norse themselves retreated into virtual oblivion. Further, it would give us a completely different picture of the Arctic whaling of the sixteenth, seventeenth, and eighteenth centuries, for these must have represented a period of much greater rigorousness than the present, though one of slowly ameliorating temperatures.

The western Europeans and even the Norsemen knew nothing about ice when they first went to Spitsbergen, and their ships were hardly suited to its penetration. Unless the Basques really reached the Greenland seas in the early sixteenth century, it was the Hollanders who first came to grips with both sea ice in general and the Arctic Ice-raft in particular. And they appear to have tackled it with their usual methodical perseverance, just as if it were some specially aggravating type of coast. When there were leads opening into it, they sailed right in after the whales, and if these leads then closed up on them, they went to work with pickaxes and crowbars and tried to dig basins in the ice in which to keep their ships afloat, just as they would have done had they been caught on the mud flats of their own Zuider Zee. They also developed all manner of tedious methods for warping their clumsy ships for miles through the floes, and they consequently learned quite a lot about ice movements and what may be called its "squeeze play."

It was the British, however, who first tried the novel idea of fortifying the ship against the ice, rather than trying to keep the ice away from the ship. The first ship so built, with an enormous thickness of timber forward and specially heavy thwarts, sailed in 1790. It was not a success and was crushed early in its first season. This failure was perhaps due more to overconfidence in the protection that would be afforded by the new devices than to either faulty construction or the impracticality of the idea. It was seventy-five years before any real success was achieved along these lines and then it was the Scots who solved the problem by applying an altogether new factor to the technique, as we shall see later.

During this period, whaling continued in the Greenland seas with varying fortunes. Several times the British fleet sustained tremendous losses — as in 1821, and again in 1830 when nineteen were lost and twenty-one others returned completely empty — and these failures were nearly always due to the ice. Reference to the map on page 139 will disclose the principal danger point for the whalers. This was in the narrows between the Davis Strait and Baffin Bay. The ice in Baffin Bay is seasonal and is not a part of the Arctic Ice-raft. It spreads down from the north in autumn and, becoming jammed into these narrows, performs there most horrendous tricks. It may suddenly congeal or just as suddenly break up and then rush about in a manner that can truly be described as mad. When a storm sweeps into the strait, the ice blocks appear to become seized with the frenzy of things possessed and actually leap right over each other like ten billion multi-ton battering rams, among which it is hard for any ship to survive. Yet the old sailing whalers did survive such conditions year after year, for the route they followed was invariably from Resolution Island at the south of Baffin Island to Melville Bay in northwestern Greenland, thence over to Lancaster Sound, and on into the Gulf of Boothia (see map), then back south, down the east coast of Baffin Island to Home Bay, and finally round into Cumberland Sound. Thus, the fleet had to pass through the narrows twice each season, and sometimes they missed their weather and got caught there. Out in the East Greenland Sea they had to contend with the true Ice-raft and a plethora of icebergs to boot, and both seem to have been much worse in those days than they are at present.

A new type of vessel was developed for this northern fishery. This combined certain features deemed advantageous in the perpetual fight with the ice with other more general changes that were taking place in ship design. While the southern whalers clung to the tublike, blunt-prowed, high-sided, barque-rigged construction of the typical Yankee spermers, the northerners, and particularly the builders of Hull and the Scots, moved steadily towards clipper lines, lowering the freeboard, slimming the whole design, adding length, schooner transoms and bows, lengthening the spars, and adding ever more fore-and-aft canvas. Some of these ships, though wonderful sea boats, were extraordinarily ugly, with spars pulled far forward of the upright, and most ungracefully straight lines. One can sometimes hardly believe that they could have been as depicted in contemporary drawings and paintings, and perhaps they were not, just as one can likewise hardly believe that some of those ladies painted by the old masters could have been the mistresses of any man, let alone French kings. Nonetheless, the changes wrought in the ships certainly increased both their efficiency and the speed with which they went to and returned from the whaling grounds. Instead of taking half the season to get there and back, they finally made the passage home so rapidly that they were delivering fresh blubber to the try-works in Scotland. Still, the industry was just holding its own when a number of things took place that at first gave it a great boost, but finally brought about its collapse.

The first of these developments is seldom mentioned, and we don't know exactly when it began or when it started to affect the industry. This was the use of whale meat and bones for the manufacture of fertilizer. The first mention of this most important process appears in an advertisement in a London newspaper as early as 1812, wherein the resultant product is called "manure," but no official records of this manufactory appear to have been compiled until nearly forty years later, though the practice became of ever-increasing importance. The second event was the application of artificial power to ships, in the form of the steam engine.

Steam power had been known to the Greek-Egyptians of Alexandria in the early Christian Era and had been used by them to run pumps. The Arab scientists of the Middle Ages made it known to European savants in the form of certain toys, but it was not until the Englishmen Savery, Papin, Newcomen, and especially Watt experimented with it in the early 1700s that it became known as a usable source of power. It was first applied in a mobile form by Richard Trevithick in 1800, in a carriage, and then by Stephenson in his "Rocket," which, being made to run on two tracks, constituted the first railroad. Two years later one William Symington built a steam-propelled tug named the *Charlotte Dundas* for use in the Forth to Clyde canal in Scotland, but it was not till 1811 that a passenger steamer with side paddle wheels was launched on the Clyde. In the meantime, Robert Fulton had built his famous steamboat on the Hudson River, which operated commercially between New York and Albany. It was from these practical demonstrations that certain Scots engineers got the idea of augmenting the sails of ocean-going ships with steam power. Moreover, it was, to a considerable extent, the problem of the northern ice that prompted these experiments and led to the exercise of the most vigorous efforts to perfect them.

The first two steamers to prove their worth in the Arctic were named the *Pioneer* and the *Intrepid*, and they steamed north together in 1850 in search of the British explorer Franklin, who had disappeared in 1845 somewhere north of Canada trying to find the northwest passage to Asia. The first steam whaler sailed from Hull in 1857 and several more were ready the following season. The next year the British whaling firms tried to reorganize the whole industry around steamships, and a vessel named the *Empress of India*, built of iron at Peterhead, and with bows reinforced to a thickness of twelve feet to withstand the ice pressure, joined the fleet, but the first ice it encountered penetrated it and the whole plan was a signal failure. However, the engineers were undaunted and continued to experiment.

It was an English master of an English ship who turned the scales in the favor of steam. His name was Barron and he had got his sailer, the *Truelove*, firmly stuck in the ice of Baffin Bay. Although the ship was in sight of open water, her crew had toiled all day, warping her only a mile, when one of the new steamers, the S.S. *Narwhal*, hove in sight, banged her way straight through the ice to the *Truelove*, took her in tow, and pulled her out in an hour. Captain Barron wrote: "After toiling all day we succeeded in getting only a mile. The S.S. *Narwhal* came to our relief, and towed us into clear water without the least difficulty." There was prejudice against steam in many quarters, but the British whalers were quick to appreciate its advantages. It had taken them an average of sixty days to get through the Middle Ice in the narrows twice a year; the earliest steamers went straight through it in sixty hours!

In 1830 there were ninety-one registered Scottish whalers, all sail, of course; in 1857 there were sixty, out of seven ports, and still all sailers; but by 1873 the entire fleet out of Dundee were steamers, and Dundee stayed longest in the business because she needed a certain quota of whale oil every year for her own thriving jute industry. The conversion to steam was, in fact, very rapid, and its adoption made possible the solution of many of the worst problems presented by the ice. Not only did it increase the speed and certainty of movement and reduce the risks, but it made possible the first successful reinforcement of the ships. This started a train of events that has ended in our modern icebreakers, the power of which is sometimes almost incomprehensible even to those who run them. Yet, the first steamers were merely sailers with a very small auxiliary power unit, so ridiculously small, to our way of thinking, that it seems almost inconceivable that it could have moved the ship at all, let alone push it through ice, or permit it to tow other vessels. These ships, ranging in tonnage from 275 to 500 tons, were propelled by engines developing only 36 to 70 horsepower, equivalent in actual push to the real pulling power of one or two good dray horses!

The introduction of steam power was not the only factor involved in the passing of the old whalers and of the second phase of British whaling. On the one hand, the supply of available whales was once again giving out — this time the arctic rights — while, on the other, industrial technology was already producing substitutes for whale products, and a completely new technique for whaling suddenly sprang up in the hands of another people. The English more or less gave up whaling altogether in 1875, but the Scots managed to continue and to make handsome profits, due to their readiness to change their procedures and to their general versatility and enterprise. The Modern Period of whaling, based on the great rorquals, began in 1880, when the Scots had a fleet of twenty-five steamers. In 1890 they were still making a profit with seventeen and, although the numbers went steadily down, they continued to employ seven in 1904.

The reasons the Scots could do this were various, but it was mostly because as the right whales vanished, they took to hunting the white whales, or belugas, which gave fine oil and most valuable leather, blackfish, and other lesser species, while they also developed sealing to such a pitch of efficiency that they almost destroyed the market. Then again, the "Black" Scots were, as we have said, one of the most ancient races of "sea farmers" in the world, and they knew all manner of other profitable commodities that could be collected in, on, or by the northern seas. One of these was eiderdown, the feathers of the eider duck which were in enormous demand throughout Europe and America for stuffing pillows, mattresses, and covers for the beds of the wealthy. Finally, the Scots had an entirely separate whaling industry all their own, employing small fast schooners to hunt the vast schools of bottle-nosed whales on the open ocean.

The Bottle-nosed Whale (*Hyperoödon rostratus*) is both a most singular beast and a member of the most peculiar and least-known tribe of whales. These are the ziphioids, and they are toothed whales. There are about sixteen known species of ziphioids, clearly divided into five genera. Four of these genera cover Baird's and Arnux's Beaked Whales (*Berardius bairdii* and *Berardius arnuxii*), Cuvier's Beaked Whale (*Ziphius cavirostris*), and some half dozen species of Strap-toothed Whales (*Mesoplodon*), among which the best known is Sowerby's Whale (*Mesoplodon bidens*), and a small, rare creature known as *Tasmacetus shepherdi*. Ziphioids are of world-wide occurrence but, with the exception of the bottlenose, are seldom seen, and are either little known or only known from a few bones. They are washed ashore from time to time like other whales but, being of no economic importance, they have usually been ignored, so that their skulls, skeletons, and other preserved remains are rare even in museums. They are known collectively as beaked whales.

Although they are definitely toothed whales, as distinct from baleen whales, the teeth per se are usually reduced to only two in the lower jaw with a row of minute, rudimentary ones embedded in the gums of the lower or, in rarer cases, in both upper and lower jaws. However, the very rare member of the group, known from only three specimens washed ashore in New Zealand and named *Tasmacetus shepherdi*, has nineteen functional teeth on each side of both upper and lower jaws. Sometimes the two teeth of certain *Mesoplodon* reach a considerable length and protrude well above the beaklike upper jaw, just as do the lower tushes of a wild boar.

There are at least nine known species of *Mesoplodon*, all but Sowerby's Whale being exceedingly rare and very primitive anatomically, as far as we can ascertain from the very limited number of their skeletons that have been examined. The single pair of teeth in the lower jaw occupies a different position in each species, ranging from the extreme fore end (in *Mesoplodon mirus*) to about midway back on either side (in *Mesoplodon densirostris*). All these whales are about twenty feet long, rather slender, and have pronounced beaks. Their color seems to vary greatly; all but three are known only from two or three specimens; and three come only from the Southern Hemisphere.

Cuvier's Whale, named after the famous French zoologist, has a rostrum rather like that of a goose, flowing smoothly into the front of the head, unlike most other ziphioids, which have pronounced beaks and bulbous foreheads. It is apparently a fairly common species and has been found all over the world. It grows to a length of about thirty feet.

Baird's Whale and its relative, Arnux's Whale, from the Southern Hemisphere, are distinguished by having two, instead of one, pairs of teeth at the front of their lower jaws, though those of the females, as in most ziphioids, seldom show through the gums. Baird's species reaches over forty feet in length; Arnux's only thirty. Both are black above and white below, and they have very pronounced beaks. There are distinct forms of Bottle-nosed Whales in the Northern Hemisphere (*Hyperoödon rostratus*) and in the Southern Hemisphere (*Hyperoödon planifrons*). They are heavy-bodied animals, the males reaching thirty-five feet in length, and the females twenty-five feet. The young are about ten feet long when born. There is a pronounced forehead which becomes more exaggerated in the males with advancing age. This is supported by a forward-curving crest of solid bone. The skulls of all ziphioids are bilaterally unsymmetrical, which is to say that if you look down upon them, one side is quite different from the other, as in the sperm whale. There is a small fin far back on the body, the flippers are very small, and there is a single crescentic blowhole. The tail flukes, looked at from above, have a unique form among whales, having a convex hind edge instead of being notched or concave as in all other species. Under the throat there are two longitudinal grooves, or pleats, constructed like those of the baleen whales. These animals also show other characteristics that in some way appear to point towards the baleen whales; for instance, the roof of the mouth is covered with large horny papillae in rows which, being basically the same structure as the ridges on the roof of our mouths, are fundamentally the same as the baleen plates of the *Mysticeti*. This does not mean that the latter were derived from the bottlenose, but it does show something of the way in which baleen was evolved. Bottle-nosed whales change color with advancing age. The young are almost black, then go brown, and later yellowish white. They may develop spots on the underside and flanks, and aged females may be marbled all over. Old males sometimes develop a white forehead, and the dorsal fin may go white.

The bottlenose have strange habits also. They travel about in small family parties, but hundreds of these may join up when they migrate north in spring and south in the fall. At these times vast masses of them travel along at considerable speed and with extraordinary singleness of purpose. They are completely indifferent to man or his works, and will never leave a wounded member of the school. They are the most dangerous of all whales to hunt, as they can jump clear of the water, will flail with their tails, butt with their heads, and even bite, and they can sound quicker than any other species. What is more, they can stay below for two full hours. Most surprisingly, they can turn their heads almost as much as a right angle to either side or downwards and they seem to have good vision above water. The stomach is divided into a series of compartments, which probably has something to do with digesting the cuttlefish upon which they seem to feed almost exclusively. Ten thousand cuttlefish beaks were once taken from the stomach of a single bottlenose.

Like sperms they have a hydrostatic organ in their heads, presumably to aid them in deep-diving after their food. This contains as much as 225 pounds of fine spermaceti. In addition, a full-grown male yields two tons of ordinary blubber oil, and also has a mass of fat around the lower jaw which is called *anarnak* by the Eskimos and is a violently strong purgative.

The bottlenose fishery was a traditional affair in the Faeroe, Orkney, and Shetland Islands, and some records were kept in those places from about 1800 onwards. During the first seventy-five years of that century over seventy-eight thousand of them were killed. The practice was taken up by the Hebrideans and then by individual fishermen all down the west coast of Scotland. In 1880 the Norwegians fitted out a ship specially for the business and caught thirty-one the first year. By 1890 they had seventy ships so engaged and were killing two thousand annually, so this fishery finally merged with their other whaling activities, and the Scots monopoly came to an end. The hunting was carried on from small schooners and smacks with a crew of about ten, and most of the harpooning was done directly from these, since the bottlenose will come right alongside and even rub itself against boats. The principal hunting ground lay between the Gulf Stream and the Arctic Stream where those currents meet — about 64° N. to 72° N. and 2° W. to 12° W. — in the East Greenland Sea, and where these whales used to congregate in great numbers in July.

The bottlenose fishery was the last independent activity in the Late Period of whaling, and even it was ultimately absorbed into the Modern Period due to the vastly improved techniques of the latter. The old whaling would have succumbed to steam power alone, but even if this had not been invented, it would have come to an end anyway with the invention of the harpoon gun, for this made it possible to take the rorquals, and these were always the most numerous, the largest, and the most valuable animals in the sea. It is, therefore, to this period that we must now turn.

# Part Six

## The Modern Period

## *14*
# Evening in the North
### (*Norwegian I*)

THE *Vikna* announced her arrival, long before she herself became visible, by a dark-brown wedge of smoke that jetted upwards and apparently forwards over the horizon. Even this seemed somehow aggressive, and the Boy experienced his first serious misgivings as he watched this blemish grow above the steel-gray surface of the heaving ocean. Then a stubby bucket-topped spar and a madly raked stack appeared beneath the plume of dirty smoke, and a glistening white disturbance could be discerned beneath them. The Boy's nemesis was arriving slightly ahead of schedule.

It was half an hour before the little vessel rounded the headland and nosed into the bay, her engine-room bell clanging madly and billows of black smoke rolling ahead of her brutal prow. As she came to an abrupt and shuddering stop in the sound and let go her anchor with a tortured clatter, the Boy regarded her with little less than terror.

And there was much about the *Vikna* that was terrifying. She was painted a nasty gray all over and her stack was grimed black halfway to the engine-room housing from which it directly protruded. Her bows were far too high, knife-sharp but widely flared, and they were cut off abruptly above by an ugly, triangular steel platform upon which reposed a grim-looking, stubby gun. Her rail swept down almost to the water line amidships and then just seemed to peter out aft, while an enormous mass of metallic confusion rose from within above her bulwarks, as if there were just too much to be decently contained within her belly. She had an aggravated and aggravating appearance from all angles, and she did not seem to have been born of the sea. Rather, she had the air of some piece of mining machinery temporarily set afloat, and loathing every moment of the experience as only an inanimate machine can loathe a task for which it was not specifically designed. The Boy set off with leaden feet down the rocky path from the headland towards his humble home. It lay only a mile below, and gentle blue smoke arose from its gray slate roof.

An hour later the Boy was viewing the same scene, but from a very different angle. His home was still a mile away, but now he looked up at it, for he was hanging over the cold steel bulwarks of the *Vikna*. His father, having signed a dirty official form stating that the Boy might ship for the summer season as a junior deckhand apprentice, although he was not yet twelve years old, had departed shorewards in his tubby dinghy, and the Boy was left to wait for further instructions on deck, his small carpetbag at his feet. Three others had been signed on with him, but they were men — one an engineer, the other two such old seamen that they could almost have been described as ancient mariners. As they all spoke Norsk, they had immediately gone below with the mate, and the Boy was left alone in the late northern dusk. Suddenly the deck began to shudder.

Normally, any ship up-anchors before turning over her engines, but everything was done differently on the *Vikna*. Not till she was going full speed astern did a weathered old engineer amble from below and attack the anchor winch. Jerking back a lever that caused a jet of white-hot steam to spurt across the deck, he set the squat machine to work and the chain started to come thumping in through the hawsepipe. Almost immediately the *Vikna* began to move backwards towards the mouth of the sound. The whole procedure was quite unseamanlike and altogether irregular, but it worked, and within minutes the gray brute had spun completely around on her stem and, with anchor still dragging, was barging straight out to sea, full steam ahead. And she did not stop going full steam ahead for five days and nights, impervious and apparently quite indifferent to the elements. Captain Olsen was of a demeanor just as implacable as his ship. He either spoke not at all, or gave staccato barks in Norsk. He apparently stood watch twenty-four hours a day, and he ordered a change of course every so often, but for no reason that could be discerned by anybody. In fact, if these maneuvers had been plotted, they would have been found to trace a course like a drunken ant with a limp, wandering about a table top covered with honey.

On the fifth day at dawn, however, the Boy, who had been sent aloft into the little bucketlike crow's-nest at midnight, spotted just what he had been told to watch out for. Far on the larboard quarter three white plumes were rising from the sea like the fountains seen in the gardens of French châteaux. The Boy yelled down to the bridge and pointed, and he was careful to frame his announcement in Highland Gaelic because nobody had so far addressed him in English since coming aboard five days before, and nobody had answered him at all when he had asked a question or volunteered a remark in that language. The response from below was immediate.

The *Vikna* changed course so abruptly the Boy was almost thrown out of the nest. She literally turned half left, keeling over to an angle of about forty degrees. Then she shook herself like an infuriated wart hog, and two tremendous white billows rolled from under her bows. Men shouted and iron-clad boots rang on metal decks. Captain Olsen charged out of the wheelhouse, vaulted the canvas-fenced bridge, and set out along the raised catwalk over the foredeck to the gun platform. The chief engineer emerged from a black, rectangular hole in the metal wall below the bridge and jumped into the cage behind the main-deck winches. Four seamen catapulted out of the forecastle and deployed about the decked-over forepiece, opening hatches and cranking levers. Then the *Vikna* got down to business.

If she had banged her way over the ocean before, she could now only be described as plowing under its surface. Unlike other boats, which rise above the waters with increasing speed, she literally burrowed into the water, and when she met a wave, she went straight through it, either splicing it apart, if it was small enough, or making a hole through it, if it was too large. The only comparatively dry place aboard her was the nest, but even this was constantly drenched with spray. The Boy clung on desperately and sucked salt water from his upper lip. The little ship seemed to be possessed; she had the obvious intent of a predaceous animal in sight of a meal, and yet she remained an implacable machine.

In no time at all, it seemed to the Boy, they were upon the gentle white fountains. These were now about a dozen in number and bunched together within an area of about an acre. The *Vikna* barged right in among them and then suddenly swung to starboard in answer to, and almost simultaneously with, a wave of Captain Olsen's hand. Then, just as suddenly, a bell clanged in her loathsome metallic vitals, her decks juddered up and down, a turmoil of creamy foam boiled forwards along her ugly flanks, and her engines thumped to a dead stop for the first time. An appalling silence reigned. This was instantly shattered by a colossal explosion.

The Boy, far aloft, was projected clean out of the nest and found himself clinging to the steel signal cable. He had completely missed the progress of events below and now, while he dangled in mid-air kicking frantically for a footing on the crosstree, the engine-room bell gave another clang, and the *Vikna* keeled right over again, only to set off full speed astern. At the same moment the main-deck winch came to life with a roar, and a cloud of steam rose up to envelop him. Out of this came raucous shouts, brief commands, and other incomprehensible epithets in Norsk. Then the winch came to a jarring stop and the *Vikna* made a sort of profound curtsy into the sea. This brought the Boy together with the masthead.

There followed a half hour of comparative calm while the Boy regained the safety of the nest, the *Vikna* plowed steadily astern, and the winch roared intermittently. Then the engine-room bell clanged once again, the deck shuddered once more, and everything fell silent for nearly five minutes. The pause was interrupted by violent oaths from Captain Olsen. Next, the gun exploded again, and a snake of rope curved out over the sea ahead. The captain roared, the bell clanged incessantly, the winch screamed, the deck shook, the mast waved madly back and forth, and mountains of salty spume rushed forwards from the wildly thrashing screws. But this time it was soon over.

The *Vikna's* engines died away and she drifted slowly backwards while the spume flattened out around her and great floods of beautiful ruby-red blood swirled among it, forming little whorls and curlicues. Something bumped against her hull, and Captain Olsen let out a shout. Everybody but the engineer left his post, and all other hands emerged from holes in the metal monster. They all gathered on the starboard bow and peered over. Something vast and shiny wallowed there just below the waves which washed unconcernedly over its curved bulk.

After a time the main-deck winch rattled once more as it reeled in the slack on the line and drew the dead monster hard against the *Vikna's* plates. Then two seamen lowered a loop of steel cable from a block suspended from a davit aft, and after a bit of angling they set a subsidiary winch into action and the vast, batlike tail flukes of the whale appeared above the waves. Seizing flensing knives with long handles like those used of old, the seamen jabbed away until both flukes were sheered off close to the stem of the animal's tail. Then a strong length of chain was linked round this stub, and the whole set free. Meantime the mate had gone overboard on to the forward part of the body of the beast and thrust a long pipe with a razor-sharp cutting end — like a huge hypodermic — into its vitals. To the upper end of this an ordinary hose pipe was now screwed and then, with a violent hiss, compressed air was turned on. The whale immediately began to inflate like a vast balloon, and as it did so, it slowly rolled over so that its glistening, white, fluted belly came uppermost. Ten minutes later, the mate planted a steel pole with a red and black flag on top of the thing, just as if he were claiming some newly discovered island for some stupid empire. Then he jumped back inboard, the bell clanged once more, and the *Vikna* charged off at a tangent at full speed.

The Boy had watched all this from aloft. Nobody had as much as glanced up at him, let alone called to him. And now, as the gray brute upon which he rode rushed away from the great, pathetic, wallowing corpse, what did he see straight ahead? Four more gentle fountains rising from the waves. For the second time that morning he yelled below in strident Gaelic, and then it all began again.

And thus it continued intermittently for four months. There were days when the *Vikna* simply banged straight ahead; there were others when she would back and fill, lurch madly from side to side, clang, shudder, belch black smoke, and end up drifting in a whirling sea of bloody foam. But the end was always the same, another red and black flag drifting off abaft. There was something utterly relentless about her performance, even when she suddenly spun about at midnight and charged off on another course, zigzagging for days among quite unseen currents and other sea obstacles, gathering up the flagged corpses with unerring skill and unfailing accuracy like some supernatural steel terrier. Even when towing a line of these monstrous balloons into the sound, there was nothing proud or even majestic about her. She remained always just a horrible, overefficient hunk of insensible metal, a sort of latter-day djinn temporarily released from Captain Olsen's private store of bottles. The last the Boy saw of her was an angry plume of dirty brown smoke curling from beyond the horizon. Then he rose from the mossy sod and tramped back home with leaden feet.


ALTHOUGH man is essentially a land animal, his ancestors — which is to say, "apemen," and probably even their progenitors, the "men-apes" — have dwelt upon, or at least visited, coasts since time immemorial. The earliest of our line were doubtless indistinguishable from various other "apes," and they behaved accordingly. They literally grubbed for their food, and they would seem to have relished seafood then just as they do today, in common with many other creatures, such as the Japanese macaque monkey. Tropical forests do not abut on to the seashores, so the true apes, such as the gorilla, chimpanzee, and orangutan, have no opportunity to go fishing or clamming. Nevertheless, these creatures relish the natural salts found in fish and other marine products just as much as do any other animals. Man's earliest ancestors were terrestrial creatures more like baboons, as opposed to arboreal animals like the apes, and they wandered about the earth and must from time to time have reached foreshores. There they doubtless dipped into pools and sampled whatever moving thing they could grasp in their hands.

This brief flight into the field of anthropological speculation is, at this juncture, most germane to our record of man's pursuit of the whale, and for two reasons. First, even today a not inconsiderable number of dead whales are washed up on seashores all over the world, and the farther one goes back in time, the more such creatures should have been so beached, because they were much more numerous in all seas before man started to slaughter them systematically. Men-apes probably, therefore, came across many dead whales, and what could have been more glorious a find to a family party of such lowly creatures who were at least partially carrion-feeders and certainly scavengers. Such a mountain of ripe flesh would keep their potbellies filled for a whole season, because, even in the tropics, it takes a quite unrealized length of time for a whale carcass to decompose. In fact, the heat generated by decomposition through normal bacterial action so raises the temperature inside the body that it starts to cook the flesh within a matter of hours. I once lived with a dead sperm on a tropical beach for three weeks while cutting out its skeleton, and although the stench was terrific and rancid oil poured continually out of the carcass in rivulets under the blistering sun, and although the beast had been dead at least a month before I found it, the great masses of flesh beneath its blubber were perfectly fresh when cut out and they remained so until I left, even though scattered about a muddy foreshore. Of much greater importance to our story, however, is something quite else which must have occurred to some apemen who wandered about beaches in search of a meal.

These primitive parodies of ourselves had, at a very early period of their evolution, discovered that a recalcitrant nut, an animal's skull, or any other hard object containing edible material could be opened more easily by pounding it either on a stone or, conversely, with a stone. Certain wasps use small stones to tamp down the mud with which they construct their nests; some birds break snail or clam shells by dropping them from a height on to rocks; and chimpanzees will batter away persistently and with enormous intent upon all things that appear to be hollow with anything serviceable that comes to hand. It is obviously thus that our ancestors came by "tools."

Now, tools have an evolutionary procession of their own which is, to a certain extent, altogether separate from that of the humans or other living things who use them. Man's ancestors, at some very early time, hit upon the idea of shaping stones — first, by breaking, and, later, by systematically chipping them — to fit various purposes. The primitive banging stone attached to the end of stick became a mace or hammer; with one pointed end it became a pick; with one wedge-shaped end, an axe. Meantime, knives, scrapers, chisels, and sharp points for boring or drilling were invented. Similar tools were developed in wood and bone for work on softer substances. The process was a laborious one of trial and error, and it extended over hundreds of thousands of years. Then came one of those major advances that occur in the evolution of any series of things after which one may say that something new has been added though it remains hard to say just exactly how, when, where, or why it came about.

At some stage, apemen conceived the idea of using tools by what we now call remote control. Instead of waiting until you caught your horse or rabbit to bash in its head, you lurked behind a convenient bush and *threw* your stone at the quarry as it passed by. It is strange to reflect that this apparently most simple and basic stratagem appears to have been quite foreign to life on this planet until man appeared. Monkeys may occasionally lob some object at an adversary; digging dogs and baboons can shower you with stones; and certain fish can shoot blobs of water at flies; but no animal actually throws things deliberately.

The first projectile was probably a thrown stone, but some apemen, with that latent strain common to all men, early noticed that a sharpened stone at the end of a stick did a much more deadly job, and thus the spear was born. But this did not hold fast in the quarry. Next came some even cleverer character who, presumably noting that a high proportion of both men and beasts struck by a spear still got away, conceived the idea of attaching the spear to a line. It probably took the first half of the recent ice age to figure this out, but the end product was the harpoon, which is nothing more than a series of arrowheads, joined one in front of the other. The idea very probably originated with the triangular arrowhead, the two backward-pointing tines of which so greatly increase the holding power of the whole device.

There is some evidence that the harpoon may have been employed on land, but its most obvious use was manifestly in water, where even a dead prize may sink beyond reach before it can be retrieved. We have traced the history of man's pursuit of the whale back to the inhabitants of Norway about the year 8000 B.C., when offshore whaling was definitely in progress there. Also, as we have already noted, peculiarly large harpoons were employed by certain maritime peoples of the Iberian peninsula just twice as long ago, in 16,000 B.C. But these were still not by any means the oldest harpoons.

This *tool* has one of the most ancient and venerable histories, and yet it changed little throughout twenty millennia. Even the coming of the age of metals did not alter its basic pattern, though some early Iron Age harpoons had three rows of tines arranged at 120-degree intervals around the shaft, and for special purposes these were recurved so that the tips of the tines ran parallel to that shaft. The harpoon was originally a throwing device, but in rather early times men conceived the idea of *shooting* the thing mechanically. Presumably, fish-harpoons had been shot with bows for countless thousands of years just as they are today by many riverine tribesmen in the Amazon and other areas. The first time, however, that something stronger than a human arm was needed to shoot a harpoon was probably when the Norse tried to attack the larger whales, either from land — as we noted them doing in the fjords during the Dark Ages — or from ships large enough to carry the machines necessary. Thus, it was the Norse who invented the "harpoon gun." The idea of a *gun*, however, is, usually, inseparably associated in our minds with an explosive charge, while the device used by the Norse was simply a vast bow, catapult, or ballista.

Our earliest ancestors, equipped with harpoons, while perambulating the beaches must have conceived the notion of hunting fish offshore, and, along with them, porpoises, dolphins, and finally the larger whales. This idea persisted throughout the ages, and one of maritime man's primary objectives has always been to devise ever more efficient methods of doing this. Some of the results of his endeavors were rather extreme and economically very silly — notably, sailing wooden ships into the arctic ice and then pursuing hundred-ton monsters in cockleshell boats with tiny, hand-thrown harpoons no more efficient than those used by Stone Age man twenty thousand years before. Thus, the next really great step forward in whaling came when a true harpoon *gun* was invented. This came about in 1864, but this too had a history of its own.

About the year 1730 some Englishmen started experimenting with a harpoon gun, but it was a hefted device like a heavy blunderbuss that shot a converted hand harpoon from a long barrel by means of an excessive charge of black powder. The whole thing was so dangerous and so heavy that it had to be fastened by the base of its barrel to a rowlock mounted on the whaleboat's gunwale. It was not a success for several reasons. First, an extreme prejudice to the device arose among the whalers of the period because they were still pursuing right whales, and these are very shy and nervous creatures, with acute hearing. The monumental explosion of the guns put these animals to immediate flight, and thus greatly reduced their availability for slaughter at any one time or place. Worse, however, was the lack of technical knowledge in the construction of the guns. Metallurgically, they were very weak, and they often blew up. Worst of all, the line had to be attached to the harpoon head at the *front* of the shaft (which, of course, had to go into the barrel) and since the charge was weak, the drag of the line, however carefully and freely coiled, tended to pull the harpoon to one side as it traveled between the gun and the whale, and thus often caused it to miss the target completely. The experiments were therefore soon abandoned, and the whole idea of harpoon guns got a very bad reputation. It was a century before another attack was made on the problem. The belief then was that both the charge and the harpoon should be so strong the line could no longer exert any appreciable drag.

In 1809 a man named Svend Foyn was born on the island of Nøtterøy near Tønsberg in Norway. He lived there, apart from endless voyages, until his death in 1894. His whole life was devoted to the whaling industry, and notably to the invention of the first workable harpoon gun. This he finally achieved in 1864, but it was not adopted by the industry till 1880. Thus, once again, we come back full circle to the people of what we call Norway, after just about a thousand years, to mark the final stage of man's pursuit of the whale. Before plunging into this, however, we must digress into still another little pocket of interest in order to keep our record clear.

The English — that is to say, those people who originally developed, spoke, and still speak the language called generically by that appellation — have a positive genius for either disregarding other languages or fractionating them or translating them in a way that has practically nothing to do with the original native verbiage. Just as they persist in calling the *Hollanders* "Dutchmen," and the *Deutsch* "Germans," they have always referred to the inhabitants of Norway as "Norwegians" with glorious disregard for the usage and wishes of its people. That country is called *Norge* by the Nordmenn who live there. The "d" in the latter happens to be wholly silent, so the word comes out as "Normenn," or "Norman," if properly pronounced, which explains the age-old puzzle of why the French-speaking Normans who conquered England in 1066 A.D. turn out to be none other than Norse, or Norsemen. We ought to have called both parties the Nordmanni, which is the old plural form of the name for these people, all along; have referred to their language as Norsk; and to their country as Norge. There would then have been less confusion, and we might never have encountered that ridiculous and quite unpermissible practice of calling them "Vikings," which was never the name of anybody but is the Norman, or Norse, word for "discovery," or, more accurately, "expeditioning."

Incidentally, this may be a good place to explain why Scandinavians sometimes appear to cross out some of the "o's" in their writing. The "ø" is not an "o" at all, but quite another letter denoting the sound "eu" as in the French *peut* or nearly as in the English "beautiful." The really troublesome thing about this is that when written in longhand, it is "ȯ," with a little comma above it, but when printed, it is crossed, thus: "ø." The final confusion comes with the capital in longhand, which *is* crossed out, "Ø," but in a very fancy way.

The word *Norse* has now come into common English usage as the name for the people of Norge up till about 1200 A.D., and that monstrosity *Norwegian* for those people since that date. This may serve to explain why we refer to the first Nordmann period of whaling as that of the Norse, and the two latter-day periods as Norwegian I and II, rather than simply calling them all Norman I, II, and III, which we would sorely like to do. We would also like to write Tønsberg, for the benefit of the English-speaking world, as Teunsberg!

The biography of Svend Foyn has been chronicled most adequately in several languages, and very thoroughly by his own people, but it warrants brief reiteration since it concerns one of the half dozen really important names in whaling history — to wit, Tiglath-Pileser, King of Assyria; François Sopite, the Basque; Captain Christopher Hussey of Nantucket; Samuel Enderby of London; Svend Foyn of Norge; and Captain Carl Anton Larsen of that same country. At the age of fourteen Svend Foyn was at sea on a sealing ship. Ten years later he was already experimenting with guns, and becoming very successful and prominent in the whaling industry, with consequent financial returns, so that he was soon thereafter investing heavily in this work. The industry did not back him properly for some time and he spent, in all, 360,000 kronen on his experiments before he had the proper answer. This was an altogether revolutionary device.

The first practical model weighed about a ton and was mounted in a steel swivel shaped like a huge rowlock, so that the gun could be elevated or depressed and the whole moved around a complete circle while steel springs took up the recoil. This was erected on the bows of the vessel. The barrel was four feet in length and was muzzle-loaded with no less than 350 pounds of black powder in a cheesecloth bag which was pounded down with a ramrod. This cannon had a three-inch bore and was provided with a wooden handle at the back for aiming. The harpoon consisted of a shaft fitting the barrel and an explosive head of rather complicated design. To this was attached 400 fathoms of rope.

The "head" was really a kind of shell with a tail to which the rope was attached. Imagine a shell composed of two parts: a pointed solid bomb in front, and a cylinder behind. Then cut four length-wise gutters in the latter and fit exactly into each, large barbs pointed at the back, with a forward-directed tine on the inside, and hinged to the body of the shell at the front end. You will thus get a smooth shell with a tail, but one from which four arms may be spread outwards, to north, south, east, and west when looked at end on. The idea was to shoot this "shell" into the whale and then have the arms open inside the beast so that they formed a star and thus a firm anchor for the rope. Svend Foyn therefore included an explosive charge in the solid front portion of the shell. In order to detonate this, he further introduced a glass vial of sulfuric acid, and then de-signed the "arms," or barbs, of the hind portion so they would turn upon entering the whale's body and thereby crush this vial and re-

lease the acid which set off the charge. In turn, this charge, even if
not lethal in itself, caused the arms to fly open, thereby firmly an-
choring the rope to the quarry. The modern harpoon is little different, though improvements have been made in design, new explosives
are used, and even an electric charge has been tried as a substitute
for the chemical one.

This invention was far-reaching in its implications because it not
only greatly enhanced the chance of hitting whales up to some fifty
yards away, but also greatly increased the likelihood of remaining
fast to them once struck. It also made possible the pursuit and capture of the fin whales, or rorquals, which had always before been
beyond man's reach because they sink promptly when dead, and
often even before they die. The device thus did away for all time
with the ridiculous little shallop, or whaleboat, for a one-ton gun
had to be mounted on a large ship. Here, however, was where Svend
Foyn and the industry ran into a snag that held up the universal
adoption of the gun for fifteen years.

There were plenty of vessels big enough to carry the gun, but in
the mid-eighteen hundreds there were none fast enough and at the
same time maneuverable enough to bring the gun within fifty yards
of the fast rorquals with sufficient surety to make their pursuit
worthwhile. On the other hand, there weren't enough right, sperm,
bottle-nosed, or other whales left to render the use of large, slow
ships practicable. The adoption of the gun had therefore to await
the development of a special type of ship, the "whale chaser." This
was also a Norwegian invention and it was perfected rather rapidly.

It turned out to be a small, sturdy vessel, thirty feet long by
twelve to thirteen feet in beam, but with a draught of only eight to
nine feet. It was, at first, schooner-rigged, though the taller mast was
almost amidships and mounted a small crow's-nest, while the shorter
was far aft and carried only a small steadying canvas which was
either gaff-rigged or a trysail. The smokestack rose from the middle
of the after third of the vessel, and there was a small wheelhouse
fo'ard of this. A platform extended over the rather tall bows and
upon this the gun was mounted. These little vessels looked rather
like the early steam trawlers and drifters, but had flared bows, a lot
of sheer, a very low freeboard, and rounded bottoms to facilitate
rapid turns. They rolled, pitched, and performed other quite inex-

plicable gyrations in a manner that cannot possibly be described. The only thing they almost never did was sink, though they often technically foundered (which means simply going below the surface) and several of them turned turtle. In both cases, however, they almost always bobbed up again, and right side up to boot! I spent a season on one of the later models in my youth, and fortunately I must have been born with a most firmly attached stomach or whatever other wobbly organs cause seasickness in so many people because, even in what appeared to be perfectly calm weather, that little vessel danced about perpetually. In a storm she once stood absolutely upright on her transom and then, having mounted the wave that caused this odd performance, she proceeded to head straight down its other side like a sperm whale sounding, altogether without regard for the admittedly somewhat confused area where air met water.

The sails on these vessels were soon abandoned, except for the little after steadier, and the ships gradually increased in size to a length of about a hundred feet, with proportionately greater beam, but still shallow draft, and their speed was stepped up to twelve knots. The modern chaser today can make fifteen knots and thus keep up with a blue whale unless the creature is in a very great hurry. The crew has increased to a dozen.

The invention of the whale chaser led to the extinction of the old whaling industry, the creation of an entirely new enterprise, and the disappearance from this field of virtually all people except the Norwegians. The business began in 1875 when the first chasers were laid down, and it got under way in earnest in 1880 when four of them were launched. They were of only thirty-two tons capacity and were manned by a captain, three engineers, a steward, and three seamen, but they did nine knots. The results of their first season were so encouraging that they brought an immediate investment response. Nevertheless, the enterprise took another decade to build up to its full potential.

This first phase of the Modern Period of whaling, which we call Norwegian I, may be divided into four distinct subphases of exactly ten years each, conveniently dated 1880 to 1890, 1890 to 1900, 1900 to 1910, and 1910 to 1920. The first was a period of slow build-up and some expansion, starting from the coast of Norway and reaching

Iceland along the ancient Norse oceanic highway. The second marked a sudden thrust to the Antarctic, the establishment of the first permanent shore stations beyond the Atlantic, and a very large expansion of the whaling fleet and of capital investment in the industry. The third saw the establishment of Norwegian whaling stations all over the world, but it also marked the beginning of a recession in certain areas, due both to a reduction in the number of whales, and to certain national restrictions. The fourth marked the consolidation of the Norwegian whaling monopoly but also saw a rapid and almost complete revolution in technology that brought an end to this phase and the beginning of another, which we call "Norwegian II." This is the truly modern industry, founded on the floating factory ship and only made possible by the invention of the Kvaener cooker, which we shall introduce in more detail in the next chapter. The whole period which we call Norwegian I was based upon the use of the shore station, either permanent or seasonal, and this operation represents a recrudescence of the engineering principles first put to use in this industry by the Hollanders at Blubbertown in Spitsbergen.

The details of the history of the rise and expansion of Norwegian shore-based whaling are as outstandingly dull as are the details of any other history, except to a few profound students and those with some emotional interest in the business. Nonetheless, they are startling enough to warrant some brief over-all elucidation. The facts have been published innumerable times and in several different ways, each as muddling as all the others. If anyone really wants to know exactly how many barrels of each kind of oil resulted from the activities of those chasers operating in any one area during any one season, he may find this recorded in any of four languages and in masses of statistics in at least a dozen different serial publications. If, on the other hand, simple souls like ourselves want to know just what went on in the field of whaling as a whole between 1880 and 1920, they will be very hard put to it to find any single lucid exposition of fewer than three hundred closely printed pages in any language. This period is more precisely documented than even the "golden age" of American whaling, but it is just as complex and much less commonly understood.

In 1882 a shore station was established at Sorvaer in Norway with a view to processing blue whales taken offshore by steam chasers. The first surprise came when sei whales were found to be much commoner than blues or finners, although only nine had ever been recorded as having been washed up on the shores of all Europe until that time. Forty were taken in 1883. At about the same time other stations were established at Tromsö and farther north in Finmark. From these, rorquals of all kinds were hunted, the chasers returning to port each night. The practice spread from Norway to Iceland by 1888. The job entailed the construction of a slipway headed by heavy winches that could haul the largest whales out into the air and of buildings to house try-works. The whales were cut up so that blubber oil might be kept separate from meat oil; glycerin and other products could be collected from washings; baleen extracted and cleaned; and some residue from bones and the try-pots ground and converted into bone meal and fertilizer. The so-called "manure" industry had made considerable strides since the period when it was first mentioned in a newspaper advertisement in England. These first stations together averaged fifty-eight whales per annum between 1880 and 1885, and one hundred ten per annum during the following decade.

In 1891 the second subphase of the period was initiated, this time by a Scots outfit named the Tay Whale Fishing Company of Dundee. They sent four steamers — not chasers — to the Antarctic, where they spent the whole of 1892, wintering at the Falkland Islands and returning north in February of 1893. They took only seals, but they saw a superfluity of whales, notably rorquals. Then, in 1892 the Germans dispatched one sealer from Hamburg, and in the following year they sent two more to the same area. They also brought back reports of great numbers of rorquals, which so stimulated the Norwegians that they sent an experimental steam whaler in late 1893 to the same seas. This vessel took whales, but only of species other than rorquals. She returned to her home port in 1895. However, nothing of a practical nature was accomplished in the south thereafter for eight years, although the whole industry went into a turmoil over the idea of all-out Antarctic whaling by the new methods then being perfected and already employed in the northern fishery.

During this decade also, the Norwegian fleet steadily moved outward across the North Atlantic. Establishments were planted on the

Faeroes in 1892, on the Outer Hebrides in 1895, and in the New World on the shores of Newfoundland in 1897. In 1896, 2081 whales were taken, and there were twenty-five chasers working out of Finmark and eighteen out of Icelandic stations. The following year there were twenty-five at the former and twenty-three at the latter.

The turn of the century initiated great changes in the industry and ushered in the golden age of Norwegian shore-based whaling, which reached its zenith in 1910. It began with serious and extraordinarily stupid troubles at home. Man is still virtually an uneducated, though presumably a thinking, creature, and so uninformed is he on some occasions that it becomes hard to believe he thinks at all. Misinformation is rife everywhere, but among specialized groups it sometimes tends to become a mania, and very often this centers upon the very matters in which those groups specialize. Fishermen are not by any means the worst offenders in this respect, but they can be very averse to change, and the Norwegians as a whole are a notably stubborn people. Sometime during the rise of latter-day whaling, Norwegian fisherfolk gained the impression that the offshore pursuit of rorquals drove migrating fish away from their coasts. This entirely false notion slowly became an obsession, supported by many quite erroneous beliefs and deliberately fostered by irrelevant traditions. A moment of reflection would have demonstrated to anyone, and particularly to the fishermen themselves, that since the whales ate either the fish or the food of the fish, or both, their elimination could only *increase* the number of fish. Nonetheless, the clamor became so great that it erupted in serious riots at Mehavn, and these in turn prompted the Norwegian Government in 1904 to ban the taking or landing of whales off or on the coast.

Instead of retarding the whaling, however, this action spurred its expansion because the companies promptly built stations on foreign shores, notably the Shetland Islands, Iceland, the Hebrides, and later on the west coast of Ireland, and even on Spitsbergen. More stations were built on Newfoundland, and seasonal ones on Greenland. This movement also resulted in some finite effort being made towards a southern fishery, and in the following year, 1905, one Captain Carl Anton Larsen organized the Compañia Argentina de Pesca in Buenos Aires to exploit the sea-countries south of Cape Horn by means of chasers working out of the islands of South Georgia. In the same

# The South Atlantic, as Seen by Captain Larsen

When Captain Carl Anton Larsen went to the Argentine at the turn of the century to investigate the potential of the whale stocks in the South Atlantic, he viewed the Antarctic as any of his more ancient Norse ancestors would have done. However, he also surveyed the area as a modern ecologist as well as a seaman and he appears to have done so with extraordinary perspicacity.

South of Tierra del Fuego lies a comparatively narrow ocean strait named after Drake; beyond this the indented, island-girt coast of Graham Land juts northward from the antarctic continental mass. One would naturally suppose that these narrows constituted the division between the Pacific and the South Atlantic Oceans, but this is not the case. Due either to the fact that the world tides originate on the Pacific side of these narrows and then flood through to the east in endless succession, or to the fact that the Americas have been slipping or drifting to the west, as the geomorphologist Wegener has suggested, there is a wild geographical distortion off the tip of South America. The Pacific bulges through into the South Atlantic and the bulge is ringed with shallows, reefs, isolated rocks, and islands. Within these is a comparatively shallow area named the Scotia Sea, and this has a unique physical make-up. Other notable geographical features of the area are the vast continental shelf off the east coast of Patagonia and the enormous sea of pack ice beyond the Scotia Sea which chokes the Weddell Sea and extends to the Antarctic.

Captain Larsen perceived that the best whaling grounds were around the southern edge of the Scotia Sea, thence east towards Bouvet Island, and on into the southern Indian Ocean. The best places to set up bases for whaling operations were, first, in the Falklands, to process those from the Argentine Basin, second, on South Georgia for those from the Scotia Sea, and, third, on the South Sandwich Islands for the Atlantic Antarctic Basin fishing. Captain Larsen's primary concern was rorquals, and of these the blues and finners migrated annually north and south from the pack ice to the open southern oceans. The humpbacks were strung out along the edges of the continental shelves. The distribution of a number of hitherto unimportant little island groups thus became of paramount importance, and their positions vis-à-vis the confirmation of the continental shelves almost equally vital. With modern steam whalers the matters of ice, currents, and even of winds took secondary places.

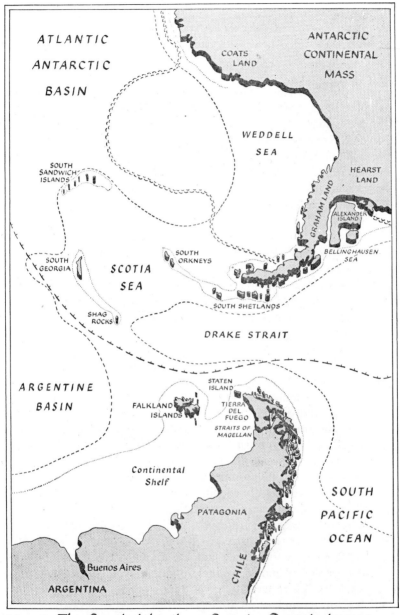

ATLANTIC
ANTARCTIC
BASIN

COATS
LAND

ANTARCTIC
CONTINENTAL
MASS

WEDDELL
SEA

HEARST
LAND

SOUTH
SANDWICH
ISLANDS

GRAHAMLAND

ALEXANDER
ISLAND

SOUTH
GEORGIA

SCOTIA
SEA

SOUTH
ORKNEYS

BELLINGHAUSEN
SEA

SHAG
ROCKS

SOUTH SHETLANDS

DRAKE STRAIT

ARGENTINE
BASIN

STATEN
ISLAND

FALKLAND
ISLANDS

TIERRA
DEL
FUEGO

STRAITS OF
MAGELLAN

SOUTH
PACIFIC
OCEAN

Continental
Shelf

PATAGONIA

CHILE

Buenos Aires

ARGENTINA

## Map 9  The South Atlantic, as Seen by Captain Larsen

Polar Azimuthal
Equidistant Projection
Scale 1:25,000,000

⊥ ⊥ ⊥ Approximate North Limit of Drift Ice
〜〜〜〜〜   "      "      "   "   "  Pack Ice
............... 100 Fathom Line   ------ 1000 Fathom Line

year, the first Norwegian station was founded in the Pacific, at Vancouver, although Norwegians had already been supplying, manning, and sailing a fleet of chasers out of Japanese shore stations for some years.

In 1906 the Japanese Government banned the operation of all foreign whalers from their ports, and also denied command of any Japanese ship to any but their own citizens. Whaling in Japanese-owned, Norwegian-built chasers with rating Japanese and subordinate but controlling Norwegian double crews continued for twenty years. Meantime, stations were established at other points all around the Pacific — on the Galápagos Islands, along the coast of Chile, on the Sandwich Islands, and finally in Alaska and Australia. Along the routes to the Pacific, both east and west from Europe, other outposts were built — on the coasts of Brazil, in Portuguese West Africa, in South Africa, in Mozambique, and on such distant oceanic isles as Kerguelen.

By 1905 there were no fewer than eighteen stations on Newfoundland alone; the first all-year station in Spitsbergen was used in 1904; and by the following year the activity was so great around the Falkland Islands that the British Government sought to levy from it their usual impositions. They demanded payment of twenty-five pounds sterling for permits to whale in their waters, and they endeavored to charge a royalty of ten pounds on each right whale, ten shillings on each sperm, and five shillings on all other whales taken there. The idea, of course, did not bear any fruit except international friction, and the law was repealed in 1908 when a new ordinance was promulgated demanding a flat license fee and prohibiting the killing of female whales with calves. No such licenses were ever issued, and the prohibition on killing nursing mothers was ignored. The latter idea did, however, signify the first move in an entirely new approach to whaling, namely that of conservation.

By 1910 Norwegian whaling was really in high gear and was going full blast all over the world. The production in the North Atlantic, exclusive of Newfoundland and Greenland, in that year totaled 59,000 casks of oil and 60,000 sacks of fertilizer, the product of some 2000 whales. There were six companies working in the Faeroes, another six in Iceland, seven around the British Isles, and two in Spitsbergen. At the same time, six other companies were operating out of

South Georgia with fourteen chasers which produced 103,000 casks of oil. Three companies in the South Shetlands with eight chasers killed 1560 whales to produce 32,500 casks, while still another Chileno-Norwegian firm obtained 8000 casks from an additional 400 whales in that area. Stations at Valdivia and San Pedro in Chile, others at Durban and Saldana in the Union of South Africa, more in Mozambique, and still others in Brazil and Australia swelled the vast total.

This new "southern fishery" developed at an astonishing rate between 1906 and 1911, while the northern declined — the same story as that of the right-whale fishery. While the total of oil from the south rose from 4200 barrels to no fewer than 306,000 during this period, that from the north dropped from a peak of 69,000 in 1908 to 38,000 in 1911 and continued downward thereafter. Since only six barrels represent a long ton, more than 57,330 tons of whale oil were harvested in the last year of this decade. In this peak year also, something entirely new was added — a development in the long evolution of "tools," in the sense that we discussed them earlier — the exact origin of which is, for once, known. This was the first floating factory ship.

Actually, two such ships sailed that year, but to widely separated areas. The first went to the southern fishery and was based on Kerguelen Island in the southern Indian Ocean; the second left its home port months later, since it only had to make the short passage to the Spitsbergen grounds; and both were immediate successes. What is more, they solved a number of problems that had frustrated the modern whalers for twenty years. Their full activities rightly belong in the second period of Norwegian enterprise, and they will be discussed in detail in the next chapter. Suffice it to point out here that they obviated the necessity for shore stations; they saved vast amounts of time and fuel going to and from whaling grounds on the part of the chasers; and finally they offered provision for rendering the whole whale, instead of the blubber alone, on the high seas.

From this date onwards, the Norwegian industry entered the fourth decade of its first phase, and this, as we have noted above, was one of rapid change-over from shore-based operations to the full-fledged oceanic operation of today. The first two factory ships sailed in 1910. By 1912 the Norwegians had 157 chasers, 11 transports, and no fewer than 37 floating factories at sea. Nothing could better indicate the revolutionary impact of this new device.

At the same time, shore stations began to close down at an increasing rate. By the end of the decade (1912) the northern fishery was completely given up and this was not by any means entirely due to the ban on all whaling out of Scotland issued by the British Government. Meanwhile, the southern activities continued to rise, reaching a secondary peak during the First World War when the demand for oil, fertilizer, and other whale products — notably glycerin for explosives — reached a new high. Whales killed in the combined northern and southern industries by Norwegian firms alone — and there were some others operating by then — amounted to the following totals for the seasons from 1913–1914 to 1918–1919: 10,659, 8514, 9611, 11,792, 6474, and 4305. The dip from 1914 to 1916 was occasioned by shipping losses consequent upon the outbreak of hostilities, blockades, and so forth; that subsequent to the 1917–1918 season to the sudden decrease in demand at the cessation of hostilities in the latter year.

After World War I, the industry floundered in an organizational and financial morass for five years. This was due partly to normal postwar confusion, partly to the collapse of the northern fishery, partly to lack of equipment, and, to some extent, to a distinct diminution in the number of whales in the more accessible parts of the southern oceans, which had been exploited so drastically during the war years. Despite the formation of an over-all authority to control the industry by the Norwegians in 1915 — known as Den Norske Hvalfangerforening — the British had managed by the end of the war to insinuate themselves into the whole business through astute financial manipulations. In point of fact, by then they held a controlling interest through capital investment and they forthwith proceeded to block all efforts to conserve the whales — something the Norwegians had at long last come to realize through practical experience was absolutely necessary to preserve the industry. There were numerous international conferences on this, and grandiose proposals were drawn up. Everybody agreed on the principles; everybody signed and ratified the agreements, except the British. Meanwhile, the stock of whales continued to be depleted, and this proceeded at such a rate that new sources of raw material (new whaling grounds) became an urgent necessity.

In the continued absence of any constructive conservation plan, they were sought and found, within the south polar ice, by none other than the now famous Captain Carl Anton Larsen. These were the last resorts of the whale, and this discovery marked the opening of the final period of whaling. The story will be chronicled in the next chapter. The fate of the whale provides food for solemn thoughts. It took over five hundred years to eliminate the right whales as a profitable source of raw material. The sperms lasted two hundred years, but the open-ocean rorquals were decimated in just forty years. Meantime, narwhals, belugas, bottlenose, and sundry other species were disposed of in even less time. Fortunate it was that one last retreat remained to the blue whales, the finners, and a limited number of other species, including some wandering sperms, among the vast and difficult fastnesses of the antarctic ice; and even more fortunate was it that man grew up mentally just in time to realize that some methods could and should be devised to save these great beasts. Had it not been for the Second World War, however, and the consequent ascendancy of America as the controlling power in international affairs, this last stock of whales would doubtless also have been eliminated, for it was only America's new-found ability to twist the British lion's tail by means of the acute dollar shortage that finally forced Britain to ratify the conservation code and thus make it a truly international mechanism for the protection of the whales, albeit an inefficient, shaky, and still somewhat powerless one.

The sperm whales and, to a lesser extent, the right whales have made and are still making a remarkable and unexpected comeback. Very fortunately, these animals, despite their enormous bulk and comparatively long, though by no means excessive, gestation period, appear to have a solid standing in the over-all economy of nature on this planet and at this particular time. The dinosaurs died completely away, so did countless great mammals, including the large proboscidian called the mammoth, and there seems to be only one explanation as to why they did so. Those creatures, it appears, simply came to the end of their allotted time, and they died as species just as we and other animals die as individuals. In some manner which we don't quite understand but which in the case of the mammoth has been very succinctly propounded by Tolmacheff, those types simply could no longer breed fast enough to maintain their numbers, and when the number of individuals of any species drops below a certain critical point, that species heads rapidly to extinction. In the case of the so-called dinosaurs, a brief cold period, combined with the depredations of small mammals upon their large eggs, may have hastened the process; in that of the mammoth, slaughter in pits by primitive man may have helped; but in both cases the creatures were apparently already doomed by some natural law of birth and growth, decline and death that applies to all of life. Extinction has nothing to do with sheer size, though bulk over certain limits is not efficient on this planet. Countless other types, great, medium, and small, have likewise vanished, but whales, despite their highly specialized form and, in some cases, their truly vast bulk, are apparently not yet scheduled for extinction. Happily, they have not yet run their full course, and they still seem to have a remarkable, inherent, individual virility and a pronounced specific vitality. The sperms have made such a comeback in the last half century that a modern, though limited, industry has now again been created upon their capture and products.

It is to be hoped that the rorquals will display a similar virility, for products derived from them are still sorely needed, and they have, from a purely aesthetic point of view, considerable intrinsic value of their own. There is nothing that reduces man to his proper dimensions more rapidly and completely than contemplation of a fully-grown blue whale at play in the open ocean, and nothing humbles man quite so readily as the sight of one of these animals on land. Man needs no one thing more than humility. At the same time, the larger whales present the greatest challenge to our physical prowess and mental agility, and their pursuit and capture provide probably the greatest release for our puerile, but nonetheless real, striving for conquest. The best man to guide the first rocket ship to the moon or to Mars would probably be a young whale-chaser captain. Despite the proportionately puny equipment of the early whalers which was pitted against the scared and bumbling right whales and the slightly more efficient but more massive devices the whalers of the Late Period employed against the mighty, toothed sperm whale, it is the battle between the modern sailor and the rorquals that has really brought this struggle into its proper perspective.

The fin whales, notably the mighty blue whale, the greatest creature, apart from certain extinct sharks, that ever lived on this planet, are not terrified lumps like the rights, nor brash hunters like the sperms. They are slick ocean travelers of almost inconceivable power and agility, and although they feed on piffling minutiae or small fish, they have the fighting spirit of the sperm, sometimes even of the killer, and power unknown to either. An eighty-foot female blue whale held fast by a modern harpoon head attached to three thousand fathoms of line once towed a ninety-foot, twin-screw steam chaser, with its engines going full speed astern, for seven hours at a steady eight knots, covering over fifty miles without letup. The thrust of a rorqual's tail, using the typical cetacean semirotary sculling motion, has been estimated by British naval engineers to exert a drive over twenty times more efficient than that of any screw of similar dimensions we have so far devised. What is more, the streamlining of a rorqual far surpasses that of any submarine yet built by man. These were the animals that the Norwegians set out to capture with the aid of Svend Foyn's gun and steam chaser.

There are only six kinds of rorquals — the Blue, or Sibbald's Rorqual; the Finner, or Common Rorqual; the Sei, or Rudolphi's Rorqual; the Piked, or Lesser Rorqual; Bryde's Whale; and the Humpback. Purists prefer to separate the last and reserve the name "rorqual" for the first five. Of these, the piked and the sei have already been described, and while these have always formed a small quota of the take, the modern industry was generally based on the finner, then on the humpback, and finally, in its latest phase, on the blue. The first and last of these have much in common; the humpback is remarkably different.

This mammal was originally of world-wide distribution, but it seems always to have preferred the cooler, temperate seas, though it was once plentiful off such warm coasts as California and northern New Zealand. It also occurs in the Antarctic polar ice masses. It is known to zoological specialists by the rather delightful name of *Megaptera boöps* or *nodosa*. The generic name is a Latinization of the Greek words *megas*, meaning great, and *ptera*, a wing or fin, while *boöps* is derived from the Greek *boöpis*, meaning "ox-eyed." The alternative *nodosa* refers to the strange nodules that occur about the fore edge of the vast flippers and all over the head, in regular areas but in a different pattern in each individual. The actual form of the beast, although basically cetacean, defies description and can only be partially displayed by a picture (see Appendix E). The animal appears to be permanently humpbacked, or at least curved over like a classical drawing of a dolphin; the body is short and very deep; the head is huge; but the jaws are very wide. The dorsal fin is small, recurved, and set very far aft, and the tail flukes are rather large and are serrated along their hind edges. Most distinctive of all are the flippers, which are tremendously long, narrow, and shaped like a jet-plane wing, thick on the forward edge and knife-sharp behind. These have wartlike bumps all over the leading edge and are nearly one third the length of the whole animal. A fifteen-foot flipper is not uncommon on a fifty-foot whale.

These nodules, although irregular, are distributed in definite areas corresponding to the arrangement of the sparse hairs on other rorquals. One series reaches from the blowhole to the tip of the snout; others spread along the upper jaws. Another group usually occurs on the chin and others dot the lower jaw. Each nodule is usually surmounted by a few stiff bristles. Some seventeen deep grooves pleat the underside of the beast from chin to navel, spaced about eight inches apart. The baleen is only about two feet in length, but there are up to four hundred plates per side. It is almost black.

Apart from the gray whale, this species is more of a coast frequenter than any other large cetacean. It enters bays and even ascends rivers, and it seldom gets into difficulties in shallow or muddy waters. Why it enters such confines is not clear, for its food seems to consist almost exclusively of the usual krill, though some fish and many oddities, like small turtles, sea birds, and holothurians, have been found in the stomachs of this species. They migrate in the winter in both hemispheres into warmer waters to mate and give birth, those in the Northern Hemisphere mating in April, while the Southern population indulges this activity in September. Their migrations are as regular as a moon clock and their passing along coasts can be predicted by working out the rhythm of the seasons in the appropriate hemisphere and then applying the simple rule that the humpbacks go to the poles to feed in the warm half of the year and return towards the equator to mate and breed in the cold season.

The mating of humpbacks can best be described in slang: it is "quite something," and has intrigued whalers since early times because it is so noisy. Apparently, these fifty-foot creatures become highly skittish at this time, frolicking about and administering ten-ton blows to each other with their flippers while lolling side by side on the surface, by way of expressing their mutual affection. These "caresses" are stated to be audible for miles. Even in the absence of sexual stimulation and provocation the humpback is more boisterous than any other whale. It has all manner of navigational procedures; it dives in all kinds of ways, stays below for quite unpredictable lengths of time, often leaps clear out of the water, and seldom does anything systematically. It is not a silly beast, even by our standards, but it certainly behaves like a very sportive one. Doubtless it is in reality just as concerned with earning a living and just as generally bothered and bored as any other animal, including ourselves.

In color the humpback is basically, or originally, black above and white below, though in varying proportions depending upon age. The flippers are white below, and the tail flukes are usually so, but the actual color of all but the immature is an appalling mess. Due, perhaps to the humpbacks' habit of invading shallows and of rolling and frolicking about in such waters, their skins are invariably scarred and abraded, and this in turn results in their becoming infested with all manner of loathsome hangers-on. Huge sessile barnacles and masses of stalked barnacles festoon their sides and cluster in all cracks, crevices, folds, and other interstices. Vast "lice" — actually, strange, almost bodiless, but many-legged creatures known as pycnogonids — meander all over them by hooking their sharp claws into the skin, and myriads of lesser, more-numerous-legged crustaceans scurry hither and yon about their person. Certain molluscs bore into their blubber, just as they do into driftwood, rock, or even concrete; plume-headed worms either sink their gelatinous bodies into the poor beast's flesh or construct voluted calcareous tunnels on its surface; and only Nature knows what other freebooters bum rides on

the patient beast's exterior or in its inner recesses. Internal parasites
are legion. An adult humpback is, in fact, a parasitologist's paradise
and a happy hunting ground for any conchologist, helminthologist,
or crustaceologist who might run out of free-living specimens for
study.

The poor humpback was attacked with gusto by the modern
whalers; first, because it was a coast-loving species; second, because
it was everywhere numerous; third, because it yielded a large amount
of good oil for its size; and fourth, because it had already been
hunted to a limited extent. Being a rorqual, or, rather, a fin whale,
it sinks when dead, but various offshore whalers had early learned
that it would eventually rise again because of the gases formed by
the decomposition of its internal matter. The first phase of modern
Norwegian whaling was directed at the true rorquals — the finners
and the blues and, parenthetically, the seis and Bryde's Whale —
but the whalers met and slaughtered humpbacks everywhere. So
great was the destruction of this species, moreover, that it was reduced to uneconomical numbers within twenty years. By 1920 it had
become a quite minor part of the annual catch, and today it is purely
incidental. The number caught, despite a more liberal quota for this
species, amounts to less than 2 per cent of the annual catch, yet there
was a time when it was so numerous that a special industry was devoted to its pursuit at a place called Wanganumumu in the channel
just inside Cape Brett, in New Zealand, using large motorboats and
huge steel nets. In 1910 humpbacks formed over 95 per cent of the
catch in South Georgia waters; by the end of the First World War
the proportion had dropped to less than 10 per cent. The species has
not become extinct, and it shows signs of a healthy comeback, but
it is just too easy to kill to be able to multiply, despite modern conservation laws.

Although the modern Norwegian industry was deliberately devised to capture the true rorquals, it took almost half a century to
learn how to do the job adequately and economically. In the meantime it so reduced the number of humpbacks throughout the world,
and of finners, seis, and blues in the North Atlantic, that at one time
it showed distinct signs of going the way of all previous whaling
enterprises. The fortunate combination of Captain Larsen's discovery
of new whaling grounds in the antarctic ice, the invention of the

floating factory and of the Kvaener cooker, and ascendancy of the U.S.A. as an international power with the means to enforce proper conservation principles saved both the industry and the whales. The present-day result of these happy circumstances forms the substance of the following chapter.

## 15

# Twilight in the South

### (*Norwegian II*)

B Y SOME incredible and altogether unusual concatenation of
meteorological circumstances, a dead calm had continued for
three days and nights. The whalemen were frankly nervous; the
factory men came on deck, sniffed at the sky, and went below again
without looking at the sailors. The Shetland Islanders are not talka-
tive folk at the best of times, and having been seamen for ten thousand years, they do not normally behave any differently when afloat
than when on shore, but even these mariners went about their business rather quietly. Their responsibility was the running of the ship,
as opposed to its machinery, which was the concern of the Scots,
the whales, which was that of the Norwegians, or the management
of the whole enterprise, which was carried on in spacious quarters
below the bridge by an international group of technicians, office
personnel, and other specialists.

A corvette delivered a pod of blue whales from Catchers II, III,
and IV, which had been working in splendid isolation under the
guiding genius of Captain Ole Olsen, followed by Captains "Beg"

Olsen and C. F. Olsen, like terriers on the scent of a bloodhound. Since no whales had been delivered for two days, the whole ship's company was immediately in a turmoil, mindful as ever of its quota, of the rapid passing of the season, and thus of their individual bonuses, and worried by the leakage of radio intelligence regarding the better luck of other expeditions. The bosun had the *hval kra* ready and waiting for the first whale that could be maneuvered into position at the base of the slipway. Within seconds, it seemed, the great body was gliding up to the afterdeck, and the head flenser was upon it before it came to a stop. The whalemen attacked the body like ones possessed, while winches raced and a fantastic web of twanging wire cables grew above the corpse, apparently with total disregard for safety, so eager were the crews to get the whale into the works.

They had just rolled the body over so that the head flenser could mark the cuts on the other side when a short blast from the siren brought all hands to a temporary halt. Then a loud-speaker blared, "To save time, weather report; to save time, weather report . . . [unprintable] weather expected, wind rising to ninety, exceptionally narrow front and localized, but sure to hit us. That is all." The substance of this was then repeated in Norsk. For a moment after the awful voice went dead, as only an intercom can do, nobody moved. The Shetlanders glanced at the sky and, already in the silence, a gentle moaning could be heard somewhere aloft. Then a thick Scots burr remarked, "Aye, she's a-comin'," and immediately the winches began to clatter again and the long-handled flensing knives flew once more.

An hour later, whale number two was on the afterdeck, and all was furious activity. Steam belched from the cooker traps, blubber-boys raced back and forth feeding these gaping maws with strips of oozing fat, and flensers whirled and danced. On the forward deck the lemmers cursed while they hacked away at vast steaks that rose from the deck on vibrating cables. Winches rattled and roared here too and bone saws screamed as every man strained his every muscle to clear the decks of as much whale as possible before the weather broke.

Almost all the operations in the processing of a whale on a modern factory ship are fraught with danger, even in the best of weather and when the annual quota is already assured, but under pressure and after a lean period of enforced idleness and with a storm approaching, too many whales to come, and the sky darkening by the minute, any crew can become careless. The first accident coincided with the first cry of "bada" on the second whale.

Either the winchman jumped the gun in his eagerness and ripped the great mass free before the chief flenser had completed his last cut, or the flenser did not give early enough warning, or the boy was just not listening. More than a ton of flesh, with the eight hundred-odd baleen plates attached, literally catapulted out of the whale's gaping mouth at the same moment that a heavy steel pulley and grappling hook swung across its path. This was flipped aside like a flying steel ball, caught the boy behind the ear, and smacked him to the scuppers. He was quite dead before he hit the bulwark. The chief flenser just looked at the winchman. Neither spoke. The work did not stop even when the medicos hurried on deck.

This accident slowed the tempo on the afterdeck somewhat, but the clatter forward was so great that the crews there did not know what had happened until disaster struck them also. A cable snapped, depositing a vast hunk of bone and flesh on one of the power saws, which shattered while racing at full speed. Bits of steel flew in all directions, engines raced, and men screamed, but when the sound and the fury died away and the men examined themselves and each other, nobody, surprisingly, was hurt. Nevertheless, this too slowed down the work so much that whale number two had to lie on the afterdeck, pink and bloody and completely denuded of blubber, waiting to pass through "Hell's Gate" to the forward deck. Everybody aft, from the bosun and his Shelties to the tiniest blubberboy, moped and cursed the lemmers and the engineers. Then the loudspeaker blared once again, announcing that the ship was coming about. By this time a fresh breeze was blowing and light flurries of snow were sweeping by.

The storm hit so suddenly that even the radiomen were taken by surprise, despite the fact they had been glued to their squawk-boxes all day. What is more, as is the way in the Antarctic, a towering sea came almost on the heels of the first wind. Within minutes, the usual pandemonium began and, to make matters worse, the Corvette heaved in sight again through the thickening gloom, quite unannounced, with four more whales in tow.

The bosun was still bawling at the skipper of this vessel anent the arrangement of the new whales when the real trouble began. Head to the wind, the factory ship had begun to pitch lazily, her engines turning just enough to give her way, but then something happened that none, even among the Shelties, had expected. A gigantic rogue wave came by across the sea and tossed the mighty vessel into a wild roll just as if she had run aground on a mudbank. This caught a group of flensers by the rail on the starboard side, smoking their pipes and waiting for the lemmers to get their work done on whale number one. Whale number two, ready to go through the gate to the forward deck, was not anchored to the deck and, being bathed in oil, blood, and grax, suddenly slipped, its seventy-odd tons coming up against the gear to starboard with a sickening thump. By what could only be regarded as a miracle, nobody was actually killed, but some gruesomely mangled bodies, among them the head flenser, were brought to light when the engineers finally grappled the vast corpse and winched it back to the center of the deck. Then the Corvette let out a wild bellow for help.

The sudden and unexpected roll of the big ship had caught the thin-skinned Corvette as she was backing alongside, without a whale between her and the factory ship to act as a fender. The backwash from the factory ship's mighty roll brought the Corvette against her, broadside, so that the little vessel let out a report like gunfire, and the big ship resounded like a drum. Something gave in the Corvette, and by the time she recovered from her second roll, water was flooding her engine room, from above. Then the final disaster occurred. Until then, all that had taken place could be regarded as either a normal hazard on a whaling expedition, or so odd as to be excusable, but for this last catastrophe somebody was definitely to blame. It was, after all, the ultimate sin of whaling. Three whales had broken adrift.

To the newsman who clung to the now heaving rail of the factory ship, high above the afterdeck, what took place thereafter was beyond comprehension. In fact, he was momentarily convinced that the mother ship was sinking and that the entire crew, including even the Shelties, were panicking, and he got ready to leap for the nearest life belt, though this would, of course, have been quite useless in the towering, ice-cold seas that were by then roaring past the great hull in never-ending succession and ever-mounting fury. His flight was fortunately prevented by the manager, who came strolling up, a pipe clenched between his teeth.

"Damned bloody fools," he blurted as he peered over the rail at the seething mass of some two hundred men milling about on the deck below, apparently without reason. "Who in hell's name let that happen when we've only got one lousy, stove-in corvette?" And he went off, mumbling to himself and cursing.

The newsman, frightfully conscious of his ignominious position aboard, which was not only that of an interloper but also that of one on the greatest sufferance, said nothing but tried very hard to look as if the very idea of abandoning ship could never have so much as entered his mind. He remained, clinging to the rail and shivering, and not entirely from the biting cold. And what he witnessed so amazed him that he was quite unable to write about it for several years afterwards.

Somehow, out of the human maelstrom on the deck below a pattern slowly began to emerge. This was dominated by a steady stream of engineers converging upon the starboard rail at the point beyond which the Corvette's masthead waved madly back and forth. Meantime, the confusion on the fo'ard deck had resulted at long last in space being cleared for number two whale to be towed through the gate. As soon as the afterdeck was thus relieved of this encumbrance, everybody, including even the blubberboys, vanished, and it was left clear for the engineers.

These methodical Scots now appeared in swarms, toting all manner of bits and pieces, like ants removing their larval packets from a demolished nest. Then larger parts came sailing out on the end of a web of cables and followed the stream of men and other material over the side onto the bobbing Corvette. And all the time the wind rose, so that the huge, floating behemoth heaved about, its oily decks canting first this way and then that, and wet snow congealed to ice on the windward edges of everything.

All things that were not firmly battened down came loose and careened about the deck until cornered and securely anchored down by the ever-present Sheltie sailors, who somehow managed to keep out of the way of the engineers, but who always seemed to be ready with the necessary gear when things went wrong or some particularly outrageous piece of machinery had to be hoisted. So transfixed was the newsman that he might have frozen to the rail and there passed into a statuesque coma, to be chipped out by a laconic seaman after the storm. But fortunately the manager came by that way again an hour later, still mumbling profanities. And when he stumbled into the newsman, he opened his mouth with sorry disregard for the howling subzero wind, and his pipe fell to the deck.

"You blasted imbecile!" he roared. "Get the hell below before you freeze to death. Can't you see we're busy, or do you perhaps think you're getting a story?" And with that he shoved the newsman through the nearest door and slammed it behind him. Then he shouted, with the same volume he had employed to make himself heard over the roaring wind outside, "Now, look here! If you think the company's permission for you to be aboard allows you to go snooping around and getting in the way every time some bloody fool slips a whale, you're very much mistaken and I'll have you confined to your quarters."

The newsman stared at him in stunned silence, not that he could speak, anyway, because the lower half of his face was frozen into a solid cake of ice. Life on a floating factory was strange at the best of times, but sometimes it became completely impossible. Getting in the way, indeed! And then a sudden thought struck him. What on earth had any of this to do with the manager? And when he realized that it had absolutely nothing to do with him, the newsman tried to laugh, but when he found he couldn't, another thought raced through his mind and he dived for the nearest companionway, heading for the hospital to get very definitely in somebody's way as quickly as possible, because he was convinced that his face was frostbitten and that his jaw was going to fall off.

But the newsman's jaw and the manager's corvette were both saved by the skills of the technicians, and both returned whole and sound to their home ports. What is more, the expedition's quota was exceeded.

THE TWO PHASES of modern whaling, which we call Norwegian I and II, blend one into the other during the brief period of a single decade, between 1910 and 1920. We can divide the two phases just as well at the beginning of this decade — when the factory ship first made its appearance — as at the end, which marked the prohibition of Norsk whaling on British coasts and the final abandonment of shore stations in the north by the Norwegians themselves. Moreover, there was a primitive floating factory at work in 1903 and there are still a fair number of shore stations running today in various parts of the world — no fewer than five were established in Australia in 1951 alone — so that the blending is almost complete. This overlap should not, however, in any way be construed as meaning that the two periods are not absolutely distinct. Further, the change-over was not just a matter of putting a shore station on board a ship and transplanting it to new whaling grounds. A great deal more had to be done before Norwegian Period II could get under way.

The idea of the floating factory was presumably first initiated by François Sopite, the Basque, for the only evidence we have regarding the earlier Phoenician whaling activities strongly indicates that those peoples towed the whole animal ashore for processing on land. Since François Sopite's time, whaling technique has wavered back and forth between the shore station and some form of floating factory, each new industry starting on shore, then taking to the high seas, and usually ending up on shore again. Shore-based whaling requires less capital, but it remains economical only so long as a sufficiency of whales is available within a limited distance, and this one which can be traversed by the ships used during the time that it takes for decomposition to start breaking down the oil in the whale. As soon as the stock of available whales within this distance drops below a certain point, one of three things has to be undertaken. Either the station has to be moved, faster ships with a greater cruising range have to be employed, or the whales have to be wholly or partly processed at sea.

If there is still an abundance of whales available somewhere else, and efficient-enough ships can be employed, while the value of the products obtained is currently high, we get that most inefficient, bastardized procedure, so much favored by the British, Scots, and Yankees, whereby the whales are semiprocessed on the high seas and the products then freighted back to a shore station for refinement. This is even stupider than freighting crude mineral oils to the area of their consumption for refinement, especially with the introduction of powered ships. Using sail, the long and useless hauls did not matter so much, despite the deterioration of the oil, but when fuel has to be burned to effect the transport, the procedure becomes purely asinine. The modern floating factory is bad enough, filling its bunkers with twenty thousand tons of mineral oil in order to go and collect twenty thousand tons of animal oil; but at least the product gained is worth more than the product used. It was not always so.

In the past, whenever the supply of whales gave out inshore, better ships were devised and the animals were sought farther afield. This process could have gone on indefinitely but for one fact. The whales refused to cooperate: they started becoming extinct, or they retired to areas beyond the reach of man. As it became impossible to bring them back with any ship, man finally had to either abandon the whole business or go after the whales and process them entirely *in situ* in order to cover the vast cost of merely getting there. The factory ship had to come; it is the final and the only answer to current whaling. But the modern factory ship had to be something quite different from a Basque caravel with a brick oven amidships.

If the hackneyed phrase "the law of diminishing returns" were rephrased as "the law of aggravating returns," it would better fit the predicament of the whaling industry during the second decade of this century, for the more essential it became to process the whales on the high seas, and the farther those seas receded from the areas of consumption of the whale products, the more involved the whole process became and the greater the capital outlay it required. The complexities of the problem were already becoming overwhelming when World War I broke out. This added three more factors to the conundrum.

First, it gave an enormous stimulus to all manner of researches in many fields, which resulted in demands for products of hitherto unimagined refinement. Second, the cost of everything went up, and much equipment became, at least temporarily, hard to obtain, while, in the fiendish way of the so-called law of supply and demand, the value of many raw materials and notably that of whale oil slumped to unimagined depths on the cessation of hostilities. Third, the unbridled slaughter of whales during the war years so reduced the then available stocks — we speak of the years 1919 to 1923 — that almost any whaling, either offshore or on the high seas, looked unprofitable.

At that time not even a ship returning full of the best blubber oil could pay its way. A ship had to bring back not only enormous quantities of refined oils of many kinds, but also a number of rare substances obtainable only through very costly chemical and mechanical processes, and a considerable tonnage of lower-priced by-products, before it could even start to cover the cost of its voyage. When the whaling companies started totaling up the amounts of each that were needed to achieve this economically feasible objective, they were so stunned that they almost gave up the whole business. The little converted cargo vessel with two pressure cookers in her belly, some tanks, a surfeit of davits, and a large crew would no longer suffice as a floating whale factory. The ship had to be almost as large as the biggest liners afloat in order to carry the equipment needed alone, and then it had to be moved by a vast army of mariners, technicians, and even office personnel, all of whom had to be looked after. Next, there was the matter of catching the whales. This manifestly had to be done by chasers, and these in turn had to be manned, stocked, and serviced. Finally, the most crucial point of all loomed up. What about the whales? Where on earth were they still to be found in sufficient quantity and concentration to keep such a vast machine supplied fast enough to make its operation pay?

About 1920 there seemed to be no answer to this last question and the whole industry was slipping into a slough of despond when one man who was not fazed by the enormity of these problems came to its rescue. He had been born to whaling and he had pursued the business since his youth. Moreover, he had not traveled the world as a mariner only, but also as a scholar. His agile mind was not unique, but it was of rare caliber, more like that of a promoter, and somewhere between those types best exemplified by Cecil Rhodes, on the one hand, and P. T. Barnum, on the other. In other words, he was what we call a "businessman" in the truest sense. His name was Carl Anton Larsen, and his is probably the most important name in the whole ten thousand years of the history of whaling. He was born at Tjølling, near Larvik, in 1860 and he went to sea as a youth in the Arctic bottlenose-whale fleet. His life from then on became not only an integral part of modern whaling but practically its main theme.

As we have already noted, it was this man who organized the

Compañia Argentina de Pesca in 1903 to exploit the whaling grounds around the South Georgia Islands (see map page 327). His primary objective at that time was to get the Norsk chasers to work in places where whales were more numerous than in the North Atlantic. This he accomplished, and his initiative resulted in an extension of these enterprises to the Falkland, South Shetland, South Orkney, and South Sandwich Islands. These activities, however, constituted nothing more than another step in the world-encircling progress of the Norwegian whaling monopoly in its primary phase of shore-based operations. Similar moves were being made throughout the world, as we have already seen, but about this time they all began to concentrate on the Antarctic Ocean. The whales — specifically the rorquals — were already diminishing in numbers progressively from the north to the south. Then came the First World War.

By the end of the war the age-old problem had again arisen. There were already insufficient whales, not only in the north, but even in the south, to keep the shore stations economically employed. What was worse, there were so many stations, while the ships they employed were, by that time, so efficient and could range so far, that their activities had become almost contiguous all around the southern oceans. Only two alternatives remained. Either a truly efficient factory ship had to be developed and paid for, or a new supply of whales had to be found. As we have seen, the very idea of the former had overwhelmed the industry. Thus, at that time, only the second alternative seemed to remain.

In 1922, Captain Larsen took up the challenge and at the same time tackled singlehanded the first alternative. He raised the capital to finance the assembly in Tasmania of a small fleet, consisting of a twelve-thousand-ton freighter, which he bought from the British Government, and five little whale chasers commanded by the best gunners he could find. The latter came from as far away as Alaska and Norway. He had converted the freighter into the first real floating whale factory, using the very best equipment then known, and he sailed the whole fleet to the Ross Sea within the antarctic ice. This was the first modern whaling expedition and the true beginning of the last phase of both Norwegian whaling and whaling history as a whole. It was of enormous significance but was itself a complete failure both from an economic point of view and, to a

# The Antarctic, as Seen from a Spaceship

The last and current phase of whaling has carried the fleets into the Antarctic itself. This is partly an extension of Captain Larsen's movement to the Scotia Sea, and partly the outcome of his further pioneering with floating factories in the ice fields themselves, beginning with his experimental expedition to the Ross Sea from Tasmania in 1923. A lot of exploration had been done in the Antarctic before the coming of the whalers, but comparatively little was known about it prior to this event, and even its coast line was for the most part a blank on our maps. This latter is still not quite filled in, and there is no single published map showing all the most recent discoveries, yet the general conformity of the continental mass is now determined and has been compounded on this map by Mr. Charles Ballentine, cartographer to the American Geographical Society.

The most startling thing to emerge from this first general map of the continent is not so much the lopsidedness of the outline of its land mass, but its almost complete circularity when ice and land are taken together. The only kink in this is the Ross Sea with its open water and the great Ross Barrier, or Shelf Ice, that extends from this to within five degrees of the South Pole. If there is a single cause for this great indentation, it is not known, but the break in the ice may be the result of the conformity of the coast.

The coasts of the Enderby Quadrant are the least known; those of the Weddell Quadrant the best charted. Rorquals abound all around the periphery of the ice and migrate outwards in all directions annually. Sometimes they appear in unexpectedly great numbers and then just as suddenly they seem to become scarce. That they retreat into open or other suitable waters within the pack ice is certain, but just where these places are and whether they are permanent or not is not yet known in detail. Rorquals go to the Ross Sea, but sometimes they are extremely scarce therein.

Several large — in fact, vast — tracts of sea bordering the Antarctic have been set aside by international agreement as reservations where whaling is not permitted. The modern whale fleets operate all round the continent, however, for a few months each southern summer.

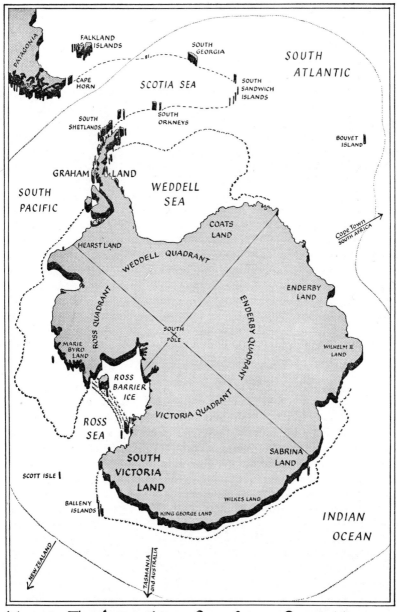

# Map 10 The Antarctic, as Seen from a Spaceship

Polar Azimuthal Equidistant
Projection
Scale 1:36,000,000

~~~~~~~~~~ Approximate Limit of Pack Ice
................... " " Drift Ice
- - - - - - Boundary between Pacific and
Atlantic Oceans

great extent, from the biological. This latter aspect of the endeavor should be noted well at this juncture because, from that date on, it becomes of ever-increasing importance. The principal cause of the failure was, strangely enough, the absence of sufficient whales.

Nobody, except "explorers," had ever before penetrated the Ross Sea, which is a vast gulf cutting into the Antarctic continent to within five degrees of latitude from the South Pole, and stretching between longitudes 160° E. and 140° W. All those who had been there reported vast quantities of whales disporting themselves in its remote, ice-locked expanses of open water, and Captain Larsen conjectured that this sea must be one of the only remaining resorts of the whales where they had never been molested and to which those that had been might have retreated. However, even he did not seem to realize that not only are whales unpredictable creatures at the best of times, but also that their normal habits involve movements still altogether unknown even to whalers, after centuries of practical experience, and behavior that has not yet been unraveled by the biologists, who only began to assemble the true facts about these unapproachable animals at the end of the last century.

Whales, both as a whole and as individual species, come and go seasonally or from year to year in the most extraordinary manner. It is not so much a question of where they go, as a matter of fact, but where they come from. For instance, a whole party of great lumbering beasts, more than a hundred strong, rushed upon a foreshore in the Dornoch Firth of Scotland in the fall of 1927 and became firmly wedged among the rocks between tide levels. Local inhabitants inspecting them decided they had never seen anything like them before, and they requested outside help in identifying the beasts. By great good fortune their appeal reached one of Britain's real experts, Martin Hinton of the British Museum, who went up to look at them. To his surprise they proved to be false killers, which had not put in an appearance in Europe since they were first seen in 1861. Where did these creatures come from and why had nobody ever seen one before? It is the same with the larger species which are of economic importance and which are therefore watched for diligently and recorded carefully.

There have been seasons when whales were extremely scarce everywhere; there have been others like 1951 when even the most pessimistic professional whalemen broke down and admitted to the press they had never seen so many whales in their lives — so many, in fact, that the hard-bitten chaser captains had to wallow about among hundreds of the beasts for weeks on end without so much as touching one of them because their quotas were already filled and the international total of sixteen thousand blue-whale units was already taken. There is no doubt that the larger species, like the rights, the humpbacks, the finners, and the blues, have been reduced in numbers greatly and permanently not only in the Northern but also in the open waters of the Southern Hemisphere. It is equally certain that some species, like the sperm, have been making a healthy comeback. There is far less certainty as to the real extent to which the rorquals have been depleted in the Antarctic. Despite the overall international annual quota of sixteen thousand blue-whale units — to each of which there is either one blue, two finners, two and a half humpbacks, or six seis — which is taken every year, and usually somewhat exceeded through sundry dishonest practices, the whale stock has several times displayed a startling and incredible, though admittedly temporary, world-wide flare-up.

The rorquals are comparatively fast breeders, though they have an average of only a single calf every other year. The gestation period of whales, of course, varies greatly according to the species, but it is, in general, surprisingly short, being only 305 to 365 days for the finner and a year for the sperm. Most whales are of great size when born; they grow very rapidly, are weaned in short order, reach puberty in only a few years and full maturity soon after. Female rorquals have an astonishingly high reproductive capacity, so far as we can ascertain, since this is not an easy thing to investigate, and they seem to become impregnated and to give birth like clockwork from the day they become sexually able. The infant mortality seems to be surprisingly low; twin births are not uncommon; and even the young have few enemies or other natural deterrents to their growth and survival. Finally, whales are *not*, as was previously and for some inexplicable reason thought, short-lived. A killer, named affectionately "Old Tom," who could not possibly be mistaken, due to sundry physical peculiarities, haunted an Australian shore station for more than eighty years. He was the leader of a pack who deliberately assisted the owners of this whaling station in their daily hunting for years on end. The last of the pack to succumb, "Old Tom" was washed ashore in 1928 and his skeleton is now in the Eden Museum at Two-fold Bay in southern New South Wales.

Whales, with the possible exception of the rights, maintain, in fact, a steady and very strong reproductive pressure against all vicissitudes, and thus against attack by humans, which is at this time by far the most powerful force operating against their general welfare and natural increase. Thus, even a brief respite from depredations by men gives them a chance to rebound in an astonishing manner. But herein lies a very great danger. It takes at least four whales to make an additional whale each year. We don't know the total stock we now have available. If we did, any mathematician could tell us immediately how many we could safely kill per year in order either to keep the supply stable or to permit it to increase. The International Commission has settled on the purely arbitrary figure of sixteen thousand blue-whale units per annum,[1] and so far things have gone along all right, but we have no way of knowing what is going to happen when the time factor begins to take effect.

To my mind, there are two danger signals already flying, and the more significant of these is the strange irregularity in the apparent numbers of available whales. These variations are of exceedingly short term and cannot therefore be due to any normal rhythmical fluctuations in population, nor can they be explained by sudden spurts in reproduction. They come too suddenly and too often for even the fast-growing whale to bring about. This means there must be some place to which the animals retire either to breed or simply to avoid persecution, and from which they sometimes suddenly emerge in great numbers. The reason for their emergence is probably a temporary food shortage in these retreats. This, however, poses two further questions. First, do they *all* emerge at these times, or is a basic stock left there, as with lemmings, all the emergents of which die off but which leave a sufficient breeding stock behind to maintain the species? Second, did Captain Larsen find their only remaining retreat within the antarctic ice, or do the animals have other even less accessible strongholds to which they can retire? If the answer to both these questions is in the affirmative — namely, that all the remaining whales come out in times of food shortage and that

[1] Reduced in 1955 to 14,500 units.

all of them retire to the Ross Sea or other such retreat which we have found — both the whales and the whaling industry are probably doomed. If, on the other hand, either a sufficient breeding stock is left behind, or they have other inaccessible retreats where they can multiply unmolested, we may expect to be able to go on slaughtering whales forever, just as we have the worthy cow for several thousand years, and still have more available at the end of the process than we had at the beginning.

There is, however, one other factor that works in favor of the whales. This is a rather hard thing for those who are not specifically interested in biological matters to comprehend. It is even hard for those who are, unless they have had specific ecological experience in the field rather than in mere theory.

Just as there is a thing called "population pressure," the meaning of which should be obvious to everybody, there is also a very potent corollary force at work in nature which can be called "spatial tension." This means, that in order to keep life on this planet going, not only must a balance be preserved among all its parts, but an over-all "fullness" must be maintained just as if the whole habitable envelope of the earth were a vast sponge that had to be kept saturated; as the cliché has it: "Nature abhors a vacuum." Thus, if you clean all the whales out of a sea, others will come in from adjacent areas where there is a surplus, or some other creatures will fill the niche previously occupied. Furthermore, each of nature's niches has a specific volume, meaning that if you eliminate a hundred whales, aggregating "x" cubic feet of flesh, from any one area, there will be space for, say, a hundred million small fish which together add up to "x" cubic feet. If small fish are not available, large turtles, medium-sized sharks, countless shoals of tiny shrimps, or some other animal that can fill that particular niche will do just as well. The important point is that the greater the vacuum, the more urgently nature seems to advertise for new tenants. Moreover, nature is very direct in her actions, is a past master at cutting corners, and apparently has an unlimited number of tricks up her allegorical sleeve. One of her neatest ways of refilling a vacuum is to step up the breeding rates of the animals that have survived the persecution or catastrophe causing the reduction in their numbers.

Thus, provided we are sure there is a safe basic breeding stock of whales stashed safely away somewhere, nature will be able to keep working to fill up the vacuum we create in other areas. The danger is that we may already be tapping the last remaining reservoirs of this basic breeding stock, so that even the present quota permitted to be killed will defeat all nature's devices to fill the vacuum with whales.

This is perfectly obvious to anybody, and has for long been appreciated by whalemen, even the chaser captains, who are paid by the number of whales they kill. But those most concerned still adopt one or other of two quite contrary attitudes towards the problem. One may be stated simply as: "Let's kill as many whales as we can as quickly as possible and get as much cash as we can while they last"; the other may be summed up as: "Let's cut down our annual take, and thus our immediate returns, now, and so be able to keep the job longer or indefinitely, and eventually earn a great deal more."

The first attitude, most unfortunately, is not quite as silly as it sounds at the present juncture in history, for few people today are sure, in their innermost minds, just what chances they may have of being alive three years hence. In more normal times, if there ever were such, anyone advocating this behavior would be a criminal as well as an ass, because he would be robbing his children for personal gain; but in the present circumstances the likelihood of his or anybody else's children being around to benefit by his refraining from exterminating whales is no more probable than that he himself will be alive to suffer from his stupidity. Nonetheless, the saner and more forward-thinking attitude has fortunately prevailed, spearheaded by the American delegates to the International Whaling Commission sessions, the first of which was called in 1930 and sat in Sandefjord in Norway, and the most vital of which took place in Washington in 1946. As we mentioned in the last chapter, it was the Americans who finally not only forced the other signatory powers to ratify the international agreements they had drawn up almost twenty years before, but also got the industry as a whole, at least in some manner, to respect the authority of the Commission's scientific inspectors. There are times, in fact, when what other people often regard as childish "do-goodism" is founded on the greatest good sense and is backed with vigor by the American people though it may be of practically no concern to them specifically. America's part in international whaling today is as nearly altruistic as any international action could be for, apart from a small new sperming industry run by Norwegians, she prosecutes no whaling and uses very little of its products.

The results, even now, are not happy. Every whaling outfit — and there are about twenty during each season today — carries an inspector with assistants. Their duties are to inspect every whale and to check its measurements to see that it is neither a nursing mother, a protected species, nor below the prescribed limits of size. In addition this official advises — and he can never do anything else, poor fellow, since he is not invested with any executive or other real authority — the manager of the expedition against any physical encroachment upon the great oceanic reservations which have been set up among the southern sea-countries for the conservation of the whales, and he performs a lot of other watch-dog functions. He reports only to the Commission, and he is supposed to be empowered to recommend disciplinary action to be taken against any offenders, by the government under whose flag they are working when the offense is committed or by the government of the national concerned. In point of practice, not one single case of any such action has ever, as far as I can ascertain, been taken by any government as a result of any recommendation, and I do not know whether such a recommendation has ever been transmitted by an inspector to the Commission. At the same time, all the accounts of modern whaling, which admittedly are limited in number, in remarking upon this procedure seem to stress that the "suggestions" of the inspectors are noted with the greatest care by both whalemen and whaling companies, and their admonitions and advice are greatly respected. In the case of the whalemen, the inspectors have come to represent umpires. If they are vigilant and interpret the rules fairly and without bias, they become just as great a comfort to Captain Olsen by watching out for sharp practices by Captain Larsen when Captain Olsen is absent, as they do to Captain Larsen in watching the behavior of Captain Olsen when Captain Larsen's back is turned. So, in a strange kind of Anglo-Saxon way, the system is working, and, provided the Commission has lit upon a safe annual quota for the whales, experience and familiarity should crystallize the whole procedure into a whaleman's tradition; then all will be well. For the rest, it is up to the whales.

Now the bases of the second phase of modern whaling are two mammals — the finner, common rorqual, or finback whale and the blue, Sibbald's Rorqual, or sulphur-bottomed whale. Both have sundry other names of even less pertinence than the appellation "sulphur-bottomed" for the blue, which only applies to rare individuals that happen to have their undersides infested with a certain form of algae which, when spread in a thin film, looks yellow-green in sunlight. These animals are closely related, but the latter is much greater than the former.

The blue whale is, as far as we know, the largest living thing on earth today, but it is quite unwise to state, as it is a common practice to do, that it is the largest thing that *ever* lived on this earth. It is true that the record African elephant standing on the inner side of the skin of the belly of a blue whale would still have eight feet clearance above its head, and the largest dinosaur, say an *Atlantosaurus* could stand, with its mate, inside the hollowed-out skin of one, but both elephants and dinosaurs are aerial beasts and comparatively small. Bodies buoyed up by water can be much vaster, and even the record blue whale, measuring 113 feet and probably weighing as much as 170 tons, does not appear to represent the upper limit of size for an amphibious creature, and there may have been much bigger ones in the past. There are certain teeth of sharks found fossilized which could fit only jaws so much greater than any known today that the animals who possessed them must have had heads of positively monumental size. Sharks tend to have large heads, anyway, but the ratio of head to body could hardly have been much greater than that of a bowhead whale. Even if we allow for such grotesque proportions, the fishy owners of these fabulous teeth could well have exceeded the blue whale in bulk. This is a ghastly thought, for the size of this animal is quite staggering.

Whales have been measured for centuries, but have been weighed accurately only a few times. The first attempt was made in 1903 but gave results that are now highly suspect, since the weight came out at less than one ton per foot of the animal's length. Two females of eighty-nine feet in length have now been weighed scientifically. One was recorded by Lieutenant Waldon C. Winston on a Japanese whaler in 1949, and is stated to have weighed 136.40 metric tons (approximately 124 short tons of 2000 pounds, such as we use in America); the other, handled at Stromness shore station in South Georgia in 1926 and published by R. B. Robertson in his wonderful book *Of Whales and Men*, totaled 120 long tons (134 of our tons). These figures seem to confirm that the larger whales, at least, weigh about one and a half tons per foot of length — and not one ton per foot as previously thought. Some of the items noted in these records are, however, much more amazing than these colossal over-all figures.

We note, first, that fifty-six tons of "meat" are available from an eighty-nine-foot whale and that there then remains a residue of no less than twenty-two tons of bones, twenty-six tons of blubber, and such other delightful little items as eight tons of blood, one and a half tons of intestines apart from a half-ton stomach, a one-ton liver, and half-ton kidneys and heart. The tongue weighs over three tons, and the lungs over one ton. The baleen amounts to one ton also, and the remainder of the total is made up of such comparative minutiae as a uterus weighing over half a ton and a pair of twenty-five-pound ovaries.

The whole thing is on such a colossal scale that it becomes almost incomprehensible, and statistics, as usual, become pointless, so let me sum up by telling you that at the age of nine I performed the spectacular but rather pointless feat of wriggling through the main artery of a seventy-foot whale into the heart of the animal to entertain a group of Norwegian and Sheltie flensers at a shore station in the Shetlands. Whales are just so big you cannot appreciate them even when you see them. That is why a piece of rorqual skin that I have kept for years as a marker in a book on whaling always gives people such a surprise. They think it is a sheet of thin carbon paper! There are other surprises about rorquals. These vastest of living things feed, apparently exclusively in the case of the blue, on small crustaceous creatures related to shrimps and known to science as *Euphausia* and to whalemen as "krill." Over a ton of these may be taken from one stomach. The finner, however, also eats small fish, notably herring and, in the north, particularly a species known as *Osmerus arcticus*, of which up to a thousand have been taken out of a single stomach of this species.

The blue can plow along the surface of the sea at a steady fifteen knots when in a hurry, but the smaller, more streamlined finner, which seldom reaches eighty feet in length, can do even better. There is nothing quite so awe-inspiring as to look down upon an adult finner preceding a ship in clear water. I was once privileged to suffer the agonies of a cruise on an overpowered, overdecorated, and completely unseaworthy yacht of large dimensions and exaggerated design. Most of my time between meals, when everybody else, including the captain, slept, was spent lying up in the bows. My only companion there, and for three consecutive days, was a finner which I calculated to be about sixty feet long. It jetted along with its tail about four feet ahead of the vessel's knife-sharp prow for hours on end without any apparent effort or even discernible movement other than its inexplicable forward drive. But sometimes it just went away ahead so fast one could hardly catch its going. We were at times doing twenty knots, much to the discomfort of everybody aboard, and were being shaken along by twin screws of the most advanced design and by enormously powerful diesel engines. The finner maintained the same speed, with only an imperceptible twitching of its tail flukes, for hour after hour, day after day, and it could still dash off at twice that speed, at least, to grab a fish or something, apparently without even shifting gear.

This animal's behavior brings up another rankling question: namely, do whales sleep? Frankly, we don't know, and it would seem to neither matter very much nor be a question that is even amenable to any solution, for, as we have noted, mariners can fall asleep and still continue pulling rhythmically on a scull for hours. Perhaps the whale sleeps while on the move; perhaps he does so at other times when wallowing on the surface, as humpbacks appear to do; perhaps he gets along without resting at all, like so many other animals.

The rorquals, and this includes the sei, the little piked, and that odd species known as Bryde's Whale (*Balaenoptera brydei*), which seems to be a South Atlantic species, together with the humpback, display the curious feature of throat "pleats" extending from the chin to the navel. Although always called "pleats," these structures are really deep, parallel slits which look just as if the animal had been slashed with a sharp knife and the wounds had then healed over, but leaving the skin widespread. It is not known what purpose these structures may serve but, of all the theories I have encountered, one though fantastic might possibly warrant some consideration. This is that these animals have no means of braking or coming to a dead stop, but that they often have to do so to avoid enemies, flirtatious members of the opposite sex, or the sea bottom, or to come to grips with shoals of food. The theory is that, at such times of emergency, they open their mouths and throats so that water by the ton can rush in to both; whereupon the whole front end of the animal blows out like a parachute, due to the separation of the "pleats," and brings the two-hundred-ton submarine to a dead stop. It is a nice idea, but there is not a shred of evidence to support it. However, there is not an iota of real information about any other suggested use for these structures either. The finner has about one hundred pleats, and they first become visible in the embryo when it is only two feet long. The blue has about sixty.

The baby blue is some twenty-five feet long at birth, is nursed for seven months, and is over fifty feet long when weaned. Rather delightfully, it has a parody of a mustache consisting of just eleven hairs on the upper jaw and four on either side of the lower. Finner babies are only a little smaller than blues at birth, averaging about twenty-two feet, and they are stated to be weaned in six months. Both appear to become sexually mature at three years, but they seem to keep on growing throughout life, as do many amphibious creatures. This does not mean, however, that age is calculable by size alone, for whales vary in every imaginable way. No two are exactly alike any more than we are, and the degree of variety among even a single pod is excessive. Color, shape, the length and size of flipper, fin, and tail flukes, over-all bulk, color of baleen, number of pleats, and numerous other features are highly variable. Ancient ones may be of modest proportions; obviously young ones, of large size. The "experts" constantly state that both blues and finners have a life span of about twenty years, but, on the one hand, no marked individual has been retrieved after any such length of time, while, on the other hand, such knowledgeable people as the Eskimos maintain, though, of course, for no reasons that are acceptable to our mathematical universe, that these animals have exactly the same life span as men. The speed with which they grow casts doubt upon such an idea, for it does seem to be a rule that the faster an animal matures, the shorter time it lasts. Man and the Indian elephant have exactly the same rate of growth and the same life expectancy. Size has nothing to do with the matter.

The so-called blue whale is indeed a beautiful blue-gray color in life, darker above and so much lighter below as to be almost white, though the whole is basically dappled with pale gray, which, of course, shows more prominently on the light underside. The finner is dark slate gray above and glistening white below, but almost invariably displays a remarkable asymmetry of pattern. The right side of the head is usually lighter than the left, but there are also "left-hand" individuals. Bryde's Whale, which is a small (forty feet) slender creature, is blue-black above and pure white below, with a dusky bluish area under the throat and a gray band across the belly just in front of the navel.

The scientific naming of the blue and finner present the layman with almost insurmountable problems. If one is interested in whales at all, one ought at least to know what the two most important animals concerned in the business today might be, but if we should list all the names that have been applied to them in both popular and scientific literature, current and historic, we would fill three pages of text. The Blue is now known as *Balaenoptera musculus*, the Finner as *Balaenoptera physalus*, but all manner of other Latin names, both generic and specific, are extant for both. Make no mistake about the fact that there are two animals, which do not interbreed, both of which are found throughout the world, but mostly in cold waters, while one is large and the other is larger.

Both animals, like almost all other whales, migrate annually back and forth to north and south contrarily in the two hemispheres, though the movements of these two species are confined to voyages between cold and very cold waters, the animals going to the latter in the warm season and to the former in the cold season. Nevertheless, I have personally cruised past school after school of rorquals in the tropical Atlantic doldrums where the surface waters were so warm one could hardly cool off by falling into them from the canvas-shaded deck of a sun-drenched schooner under a cloudless sky. There is still a very great deal that we don't know about the habits of the commonest whales.

Another point that raises controversy about rorquals is their div-ing proclivities. Whalemen, especially professional harpooners, obvi-ously must know more of the true facts, but they seem not to have got their opinions into print or, if they have, the results have fallen prey to misrepresentation by "experts." It is categorically stated that blue whales when undisturbed breach about a dozen times at twelve-to fifteen-second intervals, and then sound for from ten to twenty minutes. Further, they are said to be able to stay below for as much as an hour. The *real* experts, namely the chaser skippers, will chuckle at this exposition, so let me add my humble observations. It takes a medium-sized blue whale well over thirty seconds to surface, blow (exhale), and submerge, which means to start coming to the surface at the front end, reach the blowhole, eject the air from its lungs, and then pass the remaining three quarters of its great body progres-sively to the surface, over, and finally under the water again. If you have ever held a Foyn gun trained on a rorqual and waited for that proper point between the blowhole and the fin to appear before let-ting go, you will know that no whale can breach, blow, and sub-merge in twelve seconds. Only the experienced whaleman can cor-rect me, but I contend that, when about their own business and undisturbed, rorquals are as irregular and unpredictable in their be-havior as a man on a vacation or any other animal at large. At the same time, they do prefer to breathe fairly regularly, and when at the surface they do so about a dozen times in quick succession on a rhythmical schedule, rising at about two-minute intervals and taking about a minute to roll under each time; then they go below, either deep or shallow, for from ten to thirty minutes. The slightest dis-turbance or worry upsets their behavior and may produce a wide variety of actions.

Finners are much more gregarious than blues and may assemble in composite schools of up to three hundred or more. They are also more cosmopolitan and are caught almost everywhere at all times, outside the equatorial latitudes, and they are not unknown even there. They are great travelers, but they do not congregate in polar seas near the ice to the extent that the blue whale does. The blow of rorquals is distinctive, though only a whaleman can tell that of the blue from the finner. Both are vertical and narrowly funnel-shaped, in still air. Whales, of course, do not spout water but forcibly eject body-heated air with a high water-vapor content which, on contact with the air, cools rapidly and forms mist.

Monumental tomes have now been written on these great beasts, references to which will be found in the appendixes and bibliography to this book, and yet very little is really known about them. Most of the best information is locked in the memories of professional whalemen, but none of those persons has so far put his real knowledge on permanent record, while half of what they tell others is pure balderdash, for the modern whaleman is just as strange a creature as his old Yankee counterpart, and no better understood than the whales he hunts. He lives in a world of rather magnificent but whimsical traditions, and carries on one of the most exacting jobs with a dispatch and efficiency never demanded of a factory or office worker or even of a farmer, and he grumbles more but complains less than almost any other exploited specialist. Today, he is caught in the clanking, chomping jaws of a monstrous mechanical Moloch that is one hundred per cent inimical to his whole mental and spiritual make-up and, if the apparently more reliable accounts are to be believed, the results are fraught with interest, to say the least. This is nothing new, for the Yankee greenhorns loathed sperming in the tropics just as fervently, and many of the British whaling crews were impressed against their will. Moreover, there does not seem to be anything that can be done about the situation, because nobody else either *wants* or is able to go whaling in the Antarctic, while a modern factory ship can only be run like a chemical plant. The whole business is equivalent to transporting a champion ice-skating team to the Central Sahara for eight months every year in order to mine subterranean ice to run a brewery.

The whaleman is a skilled hunter but hunting to a schedule devised to maintain a chemical plant is wholly foreign to his nature. And when you add to this various other strains, such as national frictions, impossible weather, a crushing quota system, the vagaries of such unpredictable animals as whales, the arbitrary fluctuations of world markets and raw material prices, and dull food combined with the total absence of women, you must inevitably encounter a curiously unstable situation.

Nonetheless, whaling still proceeds and at a tempo never before attained. Of the twenty-odd expeditions that sail to the Antarctic each year, half are Norwegian, three British, two Japanese, and one each Hollander, South African, Russian, German, Italian, and Argentinian. Almost all the actual whaling operations are, however, conducted by Norwegians, though they are nominally managed and controlled by the nationals under whose flag they sail. A very high percentage of the various engineering departments in this fleet are Scots, but the deck crews who actually sail the ships are almost invariably "Black" Scots, among whom the Shetland Islanders, or "Shelties," are most numerous. Curiously, almost all the expeditions are financed by British holding companies, despite protestations to the contrary by the Norsk, the Argentineans, and the American offices of the lone German outfit. This division of labor in the modern industry is interesting, to say the least, for in it we see the ultimate outcome of all the vast history of whaling that has preceded it. The Norsk do the whaling, the descendants of their ancient neolithic cousins (the Shetlanders) do the sailing, the Scots build the ships and maintain them and their engines, and the English pay for the whole business, use most of the products, and take most of the profits. The modern whaling expedition, however, carries also a polyglot crowd of technicians, who run complex machines like radar, assess chemicals, and prosecute purely scientific investigations.

The principal results of Captain Carl Anton Larsen's first experimental expedition to the Ross Sea were the proper organization of the whale hunting and the proper designing of appropriate factory ships. The latter began to come off the stocks in short order, culminating in the immense *Terdje Viking*. Despite the enormity of the initial outlay, the need was so great that the capital was immediately raised and for the most part in England.

The result is a number of small specialist fleets each consisting of an enormous floating factory with a slipway aft between her twin screws, and filled with a mass of tanks, cookers, chemical laboratories, and machinery, and an assortment of other craft which today includes as many as a dozen chasers to hunt and kill the whales, two or three buoy boats to collect and mark the catches and kill stragglers, two corvettes to tow them to the factory, and sometimes even a tanker to transport fuel and supplies to the fleet and take its finished products to the nearest shipping port. The whole thing is utterly fantastic, but it works.

The peak year since the Second World War was 1951 when 31,072 whales were taken, yielding 358,000 tons of oil alone, which, being valued at $475 per ton, represented the colossal total of some $170,-000,000. Despite the popular and widespread jibes constantly directed at the operating companies, even this huge gross, plus the proceeds of the sale of large amounts of fertilizer, bone meal, and several specialized products, cannot possibly represent much of a net profit, not only because of the enormous cost of fitting out and maintaining the fleets involved. Sometime the fleets themselves have to be paid for, and the floating factories are as big as large liners. They are also packed with incredibly expensive machinery, not just with state-rooms. Each ship costs millions.

The taking of the whales by the catchers is in no wise different from the method employed by those little ships when they worked from shore stations. The only innovations have been the electric harpoon, first successfully demonstrated in 1950 by catchers working from the British ship the *Balaena* but not yet universally adopted, and the introduction of little battery-charged radio transmitters that are now planted in the dead whales to give out continuous signals that can be picked up by the buoy boats and corvettes. This has almost eliminated the chance of losing a flagged whale even in the white vastnesses of the Antarctic. Airplanes have also been employed to spot whales and some rather loathsome experiments in bombing them are reported. The real innovations in the current practice, which distinguish it from the shore-based operations, are in the procedure aboard the factory ship.

The whales are left floating alongside by the corvettes and, when needed, are maneuvered around and attached, tail first, to the stern of the big ship. An enormous metal grab, known as a *hval kra*, or "whale-claw," slung on a complex of pulleys and steel cables, then descends dexterously upon the "neck" of one of the tails, and the vast corpse is hauled up a slipway. This ascends a tunnel in the "back" of the ship, between the twin propeller shafts and under the after-bridge structure, from which two funnels arise side by side, instead of fore and aft. As it arrives on the vast afterdeck space, over a hundred feet long, the head flensers leap upon it and make the primary cuts in the blubber, which is then hauled off in long strips by winches. When one side is clean, the corpse is rolled over and the other side attacked. The next job, also performed by the head flensers, is to cut the whole roof of the mouth out of the whale and with it the once so valuable baleen. Today, this is useless, and is just heaved overboard. The junior flensers cut the blubber into long strips about eighteen inches wide and ten feet long. These are seized by the blubberboys, who work with big metal hooks with a wooden cross handle and who tow the strips to open manholes on the deck. These lead directly down into the whirring choppers, which make a mighty pudding of the blubber and then spew it on down into the pressure cookers. These devices are the basic clue to modern whaling, for without their invention and perfection, the whales could not be processed fast enough to make the whole business pay.

They were invented by a Finnish engineer named Nils Kvaener and act just like vast editions of the housewife's pressure cooker, except that superheated steam under six hundred pounds' pressure is shot into them when they are filled with blubber, meat, or other material, and they are then kept running for various lengths of time according to whatever grade of whatever oil is needed and how the machines decide to do the job, for machines, like people, have striking individualities, however perfectly they may be constructed. The contents, when fully "cooked," are centrifuged in order to separate the oil from the residue which, in the case of the blubber, is only a little dirty water and useless muck called, like all other absolutely worthless parts of the whale, "grax," but which in the case of the meat and bone cookers consists of various "meals" that are then dried and bagged. If anything still remains, it is gone over again to take the last drop of oil out of it. Separate boilers handle rare materials like the livers, from which refined vitamin extracts are produced.

When the whale has been stripped of blubber and the "bada," or baleen, the flenser's work is done and the corpse is pulled through an archway to the forward deck where it is attacked by gangs known as "lemmers." These men are sort of superbutchers with an uncanny skill in dissecting the whale with the greatest dispatch but the utmost conservation of labor. The livers go to specialist lemmers who slice them in a certain way. The meat goes down one series of holes, the bones, when cut up by vast power saws, down others; only the stomach and a few parts of the guts are thrown overboard. Even the blood and all bits and pieces that may accumulate on deck are washed into a boiler and rendered, so that virtually the whole whale disappears into the cookers, and when the deck is sluiced down afterwards with power hoses, very little but dirty water goes overboard. But still, even this gruesomely efficient procedure has not as yet reached the peak of possible practicality.

I have a friend, a chemical engineer of considerable prominence, who has always been fascinated by sausage machines. He contends that flensers, blubberboys, and lemmers, except possibly the liver lads, could all be dispensed with if the whole business were redesigned, retooled, and tackled from quite another angle. His idea is to haul the whale into a structure like a huge coffin and then either cut it up with a power-driven super meat slicer, all blades going simultaneously, straight through the whale, after which the bottom of the box automatically drops all the slices into boilers or alternatively to seal the coffin and just boil the entire whale under pressure. In either case, improved chemical methods would be relied upon to separate whatever grades of whatever kinds of oil are needed from the resultant animal "crude oil." The whole thing is completely beyond my personal understanding, but if you can get perfume, gasoline, tar, and flavoring for ice cream out of petroleum, I must believe when I am told that chemists should be able to perform a similar miracle with a boiled whale. Perhaps, therefore, we shall still see the dawn of Modern Whaling — Phase III, in which the floating factory gives way to the floating cracking plant. Should this ever take place, it is my guess that it will have to be named American IV, and that it will write finis to the whole history of the pursuit of the whale.

# Part Seven

1955 A.D. TO 60,000,000 B.C.

## *The Posthistoric Period*

## 16

# Dark Is Before the Dawn

### (Zoological)

OUR LAUNCH with its little flotilla of canoes drifted gently towards the billowing greenery that cascaded from the bank of the river into its black waters. The thumping of the little engine died away in countless echoes between the towering walls of darker foliage that curved ahead and behind, so that we appeared to be drifting in a narrow lake sunk in a deep green canyon. The silence was absolute while we stood waiting for the sharp prow of the biggest canoe, which was lashed alongside, to poke in among the vegetation. The little boats, warped together side by side, had sufficient way to drive them far in among the tangled vegetation so that a mass of branches came fingering in beneath the roof of the launch like the writhing arms of some ephemeral green octopus. Wedged there in the silence, half in brilliant sunlight and half in the deep shade cast by the massed verdure that now hung eighty feet directly above us, nobody moved or spoke. Then, Guinapé, the Carib, let out a deep sigh like a grampus breaching. I remember reflecting at the time that it might look like this if we should ever reach the shores of Paradise. The "going away" of the noise of the engine, though itself a worthy little brute, had somehow taken with it all the cares of our clanking modern world of struggle and frustration, while we seemed to have drifted over some unseen threshold into a dream world of infinite beauty and peace.

The great equatorial rivers that wind for thousands of miles through virgin tropical forests as yet untouched by mechanically-minded man, and for the most part still unmarred even by the passing of primitive people, certainly come closer to man's idea of Heaven than any other places to be found upon this earth. There is no disease there unless you despoil it with your own parasitical hordes. There is food and water in abundance, and the moths do not corrupt; rather do they cleanse — along with the molds, fungi, and bacteria — by reducing all dead things, that might otherwise be nasty, to a beautiful, soft, brown fluffiness as sterile as the earth upon which it lies. This river was such a place, and, besides, the air was just below body temperature and fresh with the freshness of growing things, while the brilliant sunshine burnished the surface of the river until it looked like a black mirror.

One of my companions finally pulled himself together with a deep sigh and suggested that we go exploring in the smallest canoe to find a way through the vegetation to the bank so that Guinapé might cut a channel, pull the launch in, and start unloading the gear to make a camp. There was general agreement with this suggestion, so we clambered very carefully into the tiny dugout which was but seven feet long. It sank to within four inches of the water while we arranged ourselves fore and aft in its bottom and tied our machetes to its thwarts, a precaution we had learned in order to save these most valuable tools when capsizing or swamping, which was not infrequent in this rugged little cockle. Finally, we took up short paddles, backed out into the river, and then stroked upstream, searching for any dark tunnel under the bushes through which we might pull ourselves to the bank. This we confidently believed was hidden only a few feet beyond.

It was near the end of the rainy season, and the river was so high that the bushes bordering its banks were half submerged. The towering canopy of the forest reached many feet out over the bank, so that it cast a deep shadow about fifty feet over the waters. Only where this great breathing roof comes to a river does it descend to mingle with the walls of thin-branched bushes that line its banks, their roots dabbling in the waters. Thus, it was somewhat of a surprise when we found a narrow, winding passageway under these bushes, which, instead of leading us to the bank, continued on through a tangle of palms and finally debouched into the greenish half-light beneath this verdant roof. We found ourselves gliding along between the vast boles of the giant trees which rose from a continuous lake of placid, inky waters like the piers of some endless bridgework stretching in all directions as far as the eye could see. In considerable amazement, we held our paddles and just drifted, staring about at this gigantic natural cathedral.

The sight of this flooded forest was altogether awe-inspiring. The echoing silence and the unutterable stillness, with only the shafts of sunlight, all stabbing downwards at the same angle to disappear completely in the inky waters, engendered in us a sort of reverence that far surpassed anything either of us had ever felt in a man-made place of worship. Here, to me at least, was obviously where the Almighty concluded his labors on the sixth day by creating something very special where man, whenever he might gain true understanding, could come and contemplate all His other wonders. If the river had been Paradise on earth, this forest was the temple thereof. We finally turned, in silence, pushing with our paddles but not taking them out of the water lest their dripping disturb this gentle perfection. Then we made a remarkable discovery.

There was no bank at all at this point though the waters covering the natural levee which existed there, as it does almost everywhere along the lower reaches of great tropical rivers, were only about six inches deep. There was no place to make a camp, and as it was too late to go pounding up the river looking for a piece of dry land, and since we were, in any case, very comfortably installed aboard the boats, I decided without further delay that we should tie up for the night and take the evening off. We pushed the canoe up on to the inner, forest, side of the bank opposite the point from which the voices of the others were now coming from the river side beyond the bushes and called out to them about our plans. Our voices echoed just as in a vast cathedral and went rolling away, echo stumbling upon echo. When all was arranged, I proposed to my companion that we go back into the forest and paddle about a bit to see whatever we might see. Our reason for being in this wonderful place was primarily to study its wildlife, so how better could we occupy ourselves? He immediately agreed and we pushed off, paddling gently.

Experience had taught us years before that you can get lost in a tropical forest within a few yards of a large camp, even if you carry a compass. Everything looks alike and one always tends to drift to either one side or the other, and usually to the left for some unknown reason, every time one goes round any obstacle, such as a tree. The only safe way is to mark your trail, and this we now did, but every time we smacked at a passing tree with our machetes to make a clear sign, the forest rang with tortured echoes. The violent introduction of metal, something unknown to a virgin forest, seemed somehow sacrilegious, and we finally decided to just drift. By this time we were well over a mile from the river and in the depths of the forest.

Suddenly, the silence was disturbed, though not in any wise shattered, by a sound that can only be described as a monumental murmuration, just as if a very fat man were letting out a series of final sighs before expiring. My companion and I froze and stared at each other in amazement, for neither of us could tell even from which direction it had come. There followed several more similar gargantuan sighs in quick succession from right behind us, and then, within a few feet of the canoe, a number of shining pink things suddenly appeared out of the sherry-colored waters, each causing a gentle little wake to go weaving off between the trees. We stared at them in disbelief, while they passed beneath the canoe, rocking it ever so gently. They appeared again ahead, each blowing softly, and then, one after the other, dipped silently below the inky waters once more. And while we just sat there staring, they broke the surface still again, this time sighing deeply, and then they wheeled to the right and went off among the great tree boles. After they had gone and the waters had settled back to their mirrored perfection, something gave a gigantic slap upon their surface some way off, and there was a loud splash, after which there was only the silence.

That was all we saw, but it was a vision of the utmost significance, for we had witnessed something of very long ago, and possibly something of what the Africans call the first times, for what we saw that day, passing quietly along in the shallow waters below the forest, going about their own gentle business, was a small school of boutu. We saw nothing but a small portion of their heads above the water, but the outlines of their slender bodies were clear below. They were pink, like newborn Caucasian babies, or white pigs. The true significance of this strange sight will become apparent a little later.

WE STARTED to follow the whale from a rather vague and in some ways arbitrary date in Late Palaeolithic times, namely 16,000 B.C., because certain Stone Age men, living on the coasts of Portugal, were then using harpoons of such size that they would appear to have been useless for taking anything but whales. We have now followed the whale from that point to the present day. But this is only one side of the story, and we must now turn about and tell what is known of the other side by returning to that date and then following the whale to his beginnings. This will take us back in time some seventy million years to an age named by geologists the Cretaceous. If we were to omit this, our story would not be complete in many respects. This procedure may appear rather like putting the cart before the horse, or, we might say, the chaser before the whale, but had we begun in a tropical forest some seventy million years ago, the whole of what followed might well have become incomprehensible. Only after a rather profound introduction to the whales now living could anybody be expected to understand their real place in the scheme of life, and thus their humble beginnings. Our travel into the past will be rather rapid and will proceed with gargantuan strides in time.

The first step takes us to a point in what is called the Pliocene (see Appendix B) before our current ice age began. From the record of the rocks formed under the sea in that period, we know that many of the whales that live today were already around, though most of the actual species were different. Then, as now, they were clearly divided into baleen whales and toothed whales, and most of the subdivisions of both were already present, like rights and rorquals, on the one hand, and sperms, ziphioids, dolphins, and platanistids, on the other. So far none of the narwhal-beluga family or of the gray whales has yet been found in rocks of this age. In the later phases

of the Pliocene — which lasted from seven million to one million
B.C. approximately — this appears to have constituted the complete
whale population *in the seas and oceans*, but we do not know what
whales may have lived in rivers or in fresh-water lakes during that
time. And this is very important. When we move back into the
lower strata of the Pliocene, however, we encounter the remains of
two families of whales that are not, at least as far as we know, represented by living examples on the earth today.

These have been given long Latin names (*Acrodelphidae* and
*Hemisyntrachelidae*), the first of which may be loosely translated as
the "Sharp-fronted Dolphinlike Ones" and the other of which will
be ignored because it is not germane to our story. To make matters
simpler, I shall refer to the first as the Acrodelphids. They had a history of about fourteen millions of years, according to the dates of
the rocks in which their remains have been found, but logic demands
that we assume they were around somewhere long before that time.
These are very remarkable creatures.

The Acrodelphids constitute a family of whales somewhere between the ziphioids and the true dolphins of today. They were small
animals, about ten feet long, and they retained a number of characters in their skeletons that are regarded as very primitive, notably a
completely symmetrical arrangement of the bones of the skull so
that one side mirrored the other. As we have seen, modern whales
show a great tendency to be lopsided in this respect. What is more,
these Acrodelphids had real nosebones, like dogs, ourselves, and
other land animals, and their nostrils appear to have been placed far
forward on their snouts rather than on the top of their heads like
the blowholes of modern whales. Finally, these creatures had loosely
connected vertebrae in their necks, so that they must have been able
to turn their heads right around, like sea lions. The earliest Acrodelphid, named *Argyrocetus patagonicus*, found, as its latter name
implies, in the southern Argentine in lower Miocene rocks, was about
nine feet long and had the most extraordinary upturned snout, unlike any other known mammal, living or extinct, yet another Acrodelphid, named *Agabeus*, found in association with it had, most surprisingly, already lost all its teeth, a condition of affairs that we
otherwise regard as a final stage in the evolution of whales.

Acrodelphids were not by any means the only whales of early

Pliocene times. Palaeontologists have come across the teeth, skulls, and skeletons of a number of other completely extinct forms that are of considerable interest. The rights made their first appearance sometime during this period, but rorquals flourished throughout. The best known is called *Plesiocetus*, of which an almost complete skeleton has been found. One species was sixty feet long. Then there were strange animals apparently halfway between rorquals and rights, typified by one called *Mesoteras* which had a skull eighteen feet long. But much more extraordinary creatures have been discovered in rocks of this age in the extreme south of South America. One was a kind of sperm known as *Physodon* which had a ten-foot skull with a crest obviously devised to hold a spermaceti tank, but which had twenty-two teeth on either side of the upper jaw, as well as twenty-four in each side of the lower. The shape of the head must have been more like that of the little pigmy sperm than of the greater species living today, since it had a short rostrum, or beak.

When we reach down into the next level of the rocks, known as the Miocene Period — which lasted from nineteen million to seven million B.C. — we enter for the first time a distinctly different cetacean world. Some very primitive rorquals, a sort of generalized group of sperms, and creatures that may be distinguished as ziphioids and true dolphins make their first appearance, but the seas were for the most part populated by Acrodelphids and no fewer than four other families of extinct primitive whales. One of these is known as the *Eurynodelphidae*, which, being translated, means the "Broadened Dolphins" and is just about the silliest description possible, since the majority of them were pronouncedly the exact opposite. These were the most numerous whales of the time, it would appear, and they were in many ways far ahead of their time. They had long, toothless bills like those of storks, either entirely without teeth or with toothless front beaks and numerous teeth in the hinder part of both jaws. Another group we find here for the first time — going backwards, of course — are called the Cetotheres.

These are ancient and rather primitive baleen whales, combining many features of all the present-day families of those creatures. Their discovery caused a great deal of debate extending over many years as some palaeontologists thought they had at last found, in them, a missing link between the baleen and the toothed whales. However, thousands of specimens of no fewer than two dozen quite different genera of Cetotheres have now been unearthed, and it is plain that, although they are indeed very primitive, they are still distinctly Baleen Whales, or *Mysticeti*. They lasted about twenty-two million years, and then died out suddenly. They appeared just as suddenly and apparently from nowhere. Like all other groups of whales, they must have evolved somewhere where no deposits were laid down — either in the real oceans or in lakes and rivers. A third group of whales that are found in the Miocene rocks are equivalent in standing to the Cetotheres among the *Mysticeti*, but they are Toothed Whales, or *Odontoceti*. These are the *Squalodontidae*.

The Squalodonts were even more peculiar. They were a dying race during the Miocene, and they retained some altogether unwhalelike characters. Their skulls were typically cetacean and not unlike those of some dolphins, but their teeth were sixty in number and were clearly divided into twelve simple, peglike front teeth, or incisors, four recurved eyeteeth, or canines, sixteen holding teeth, or premolars, with double roots, and twenty-eight triangular, triple-rooted grinding teeth, or molars, with one serrated upper edge. This is the division of teeth found in the average land mammal, but at the same time it displays the multiplication of premolars and molars that is typically whalelike and which, in its ultimate form, gives rise to the tremendous, continuous rows of teeth, all alike, that are seen in certain whales today. The Squalodonts are placed among the *Odontoceti*, or Toothed Whales, but they form a sort of missing link between them and an entirely different major group of whales, which also became extinct in the Miocene, called the Zeuglodonts.

Now, these animals are so unlike any whales living today, either *Odontoceti* or *Mysticeti*, that they have been placed in a separate suborder called the *Archaeoceti*, or the "First Whales." In their day they were very common creatures and their remains have been found in considerable quantities in North and South America, in western Europe, the Caucasus, New Zealand, and Australia. Some grew to a length of seventy feet. Their skulls, though obviously cetacean, are still more like those of other mammals. They had normal nasal bones and their nostrils were in the ordinary mammalian position at the tip of the snout and were probably not blowholes in the technical sense. Their neck vertebrae were long and joined like those of seals so that the head could be freely turned about. Most important of all, their teeth were only thirty-six in number and were also differentiated, like our own and those of most other land animals, into groups — simple front teeth, pointed eyeteeth, or canines, and complex grinding teeth, or molars. The skull and skeleton also retained many other nonwhale and typically terrestrial mammalian features. The bones of the upper arm, for instance, were proportionately much longer than in other whales. Zeuglodonts, in fact, fit quite well into an evolutionary series from land animal to marine whale, though we know nothing of their soft parts, and so cannot tell exactly at what evolutionary point they may be placed. Their real significance is the arrangement and number of their teeth, especially when considered in conjunction with those of the Squalodonts which are, in some respects, intermediate between them and the modern toothed whales.

The next step backward takes us into the Oligocene Period, one of some sixteen million years' duration, between thirty-five million and nineteen million B.C. In the rocks laid down under seas of this period we find only extinct forms — Cetotheres, Squalodonts, and Zeuglodonts. The rights, rorquals, grays, and porpoises have not yet been evolved, and we have no evidence of sperms, ziphioids, dolphins, or platanistids. There is very good reason to suppose that they or their immediate ancestors were around somewhere, but they either did not get themselves fossilized, or did so in strata that we have not yet unearthed. The gray whale of today must be very like the first rorquals, and the two groups may merge ancestrally somewhere between the late Oligocene and the early Miocene. The ziphioids of today appear to be even more primitive, and they may have had a common ancestry with Acrodelphids. The sperms are a very ancient and most distinct family that must have had a long evolution before their appearance in the Miocene. The little platanistids, which today live in fresh water, appear suddenly in the lower Miocene. Nothing is known of their ancestry prior to this time, but they are even more likely to have been around, and for longer than all the other present-day groups. From this point backward our steps can be only few and rapid.

Before the Oligocene comes a twenty-million-year period called the Eocene. Whales from this time are all either very primitive Squalodonts or Zeuglodonts. The former make their first appearance about the middle of this immense stretch of time, the latter in its earlier phases. When we move back again to the Palaeocene, a five-million-year period marking the earliest phase of the Age of Mammals (the Tertiary, or Caenozoic Age of geologists), we encounter a complete blank as far as whales are concerned. Our pursuit of the whale backwards in time thus comes to a dead stop about fifty million years ago in the Eocene Period, as far as the fossil record is concerned. This, nevertheless, is by no means the only avenue of pursuit open to us. There is an entirely different channel along which we may follow the whale to very much greater distances in time, if not to its very beginnings.

Despite their weird, fishy external form and, for mammals, strange habits, almost everything about whales points to their ancestors' having once lived on land. The only alternative that might be suggested is that they could have been developed directly from some warm-blooded marine reptiles independently of all other mammals. This latter idea is quite untenable for a number of reasons, simple little things which might appear unimportant but which have to be explained. First, whales breathe air, like mammals, birds, reptiles, and amphibians in their adult stage, so their ancestors must have been air-breathers; this precludes fish. The only alternatives are amphibians or reptiles, but these are cold-blooded. Second, they bear their young alive, and then suckle them with milk. Such a process was obviously developed by animals living on land, not in water. Third, many whales have a few hairs left about their jaws and heads, and many more have quite a number before they are born. Hair is an efficient covering for the bodies of land animals, but it is not satisfactory to aquatic creatures. Why, therefore, develop hairs only to get rid of them again? Finally, there are still traces of hind limbs and hip girdles buried in the bodies of some whales, while they have well-developed internal ears and many other anatomical structures which are typical of land animals but which could not be developed directly from the equivalent structures — if any — found in fish, amphibians, or reptiles.

If whales are descended from terrestrial mammals, the questions which immediately arise are, from what land animals, and are any of them either still living today or known from fossils? While, as we have seen, the answer to the latter is unfortunately in the negative, there is very good reason to believe that the answer to the former is in the positive. When you come to sum up all the characteristics of whale anatomy, especially certain of their peculiarities — like their complex multiple stomachs and simple livers — and compare them with those of the other existing orders of mammals, you will find, and this is perhaps most surprising of all, that they have more in common with the order called the *Artiodactyla*, or the "ungulates with an odd number of toes," which is composed of the horses, tapirs, and rhinoceroses. The evidence for this is both logical and plain to palaeontologists and anatomists, but may well sound farfetched to others. Therefore, I will attempt to sum it up briefly.

Let us start with four of the major groups or "orders," of living mammals — the whales, the hoofed mammals with an odd number of toes, the hoofed mammals with an even number of toes (pigs, deer, cattle, antelopes, and so on), and the carnivores, or flesh-eaters (cats, dogs, bears, raccoons, hyenas, and weasels). Of these four, the two groups of hoofed animals appear, at first glance, to be the most closely related, while both seem to be very different from the carnivores, and all three apparently have practically nothing in common with the whales. However, the collection and examination of hundreds of thousands of fossil bones of thousands of different kinds of animals from rocks laid down during the past sixty million years, plus two centuries of anatomical researches into the bodies of almost all living members of these four groups, now clearly show that the even-toed ungulates are much more closely related to the carnivores than they are to the odd-toed ungulates and, in fact, have a common ancestry with them, while the direct ancestors of the odd-toed ungulates, which are called *Condylarthra*, or "Knuckle-jointed Ones," show much closer affinities with the earliest Zeuglodonts, which were, of course, whales.

The common ancestors of the even-toed ungulates and the carnivores are called Creodonts. They were simple little doglike creatures, the earliest having five fingers and toes, and a long tail. What *they* arose from we do not yet know. We also do not know the common ancestor of the Zeuglodonts, on the one hand, or of the *Condylarthra*, on the other. Nevertheless, there must once have been both such creatures, and it is a positive axiom that those two in turn must also have had a common ancestor in still earlier times, probably in the Cretaceous Period. Thus we get a family tree that goes like this:

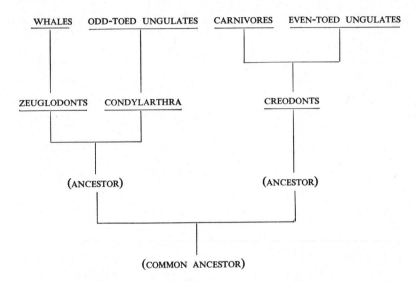

After looking at such an heraldic device, many people tend to observe that the science of palaeontology should stick to facts and avoid conjecture. There is nothing conjectural about this, however, unless you do not believe in evolution, for the animals we *do* know must have arisen from something that we do not know, and these, in turn, from something before those; and the farther we work back along, or down, any such family tree, the more the ancestral types converge and come to resemble each other.

Although we know these ancestors of the whales existed somewhere and at some time, we unfortunately do not know what the original land-living forms looked like. Yet, our pursuit is not ended. There is still one last place where we may look for clues, and this, strangely, is among the existing whales themselves. Anent this, however, a most pertinent question arises: namely, whether this land animal, from which whales were descended and which we will call the "First Ancestor," lived by the sea or on the banks of inland lakes and rivers. Was it, in fact, a shore dweller or a swamp dweller? Did it take to salt water off rocky coasts, as the sea otter and seals seem to have done, or did it go searching for food in swamps bordering lakes or along the banks of rivers? A second important question is: did this take place in a hot or a cold climate — that is to say, in cold temperate or polar regions during an ice age or in the tropics during such a period — or did it take place when the whole world was at *normal* temperature, and thus tropical? These are not easy questions to answer without becoming conjectural, but there are some very distinct pointers to guide us, and all of these seem to direct us towards one conclusion — namely, that the "First Ancestors" lived on the banks of rivers or lakes in tropical forests. The evidence is as follows:

When primitive man "returned" to the sea, he did so by two quite distinct routes, as was noted early in our tale. On the one hand, he floated down rivers to gulfs and then crept along coasts, the riverine-gulfine mariner; on the other, he struck out boldly from headlands to islands offshore or vice versa, thereby becoming the peninsular-insular sailor. In this he was only recapitulating an immensely ancient pattern ofttimes followed by all sorts of land animals. The manatee and iguana lizards are of the former breed; the sea lion and the sea snakes of the latter. While there is no distinctive pattern distinguishing one from the other, the whales display a greater conformity to the former type than to the latter, quite apart from their features in common with the odd-toed ungulates. Rather, it is certain aspects of their external form that give us pause to consider.

There is a wonderful animal living today in the tropical forests of South America, known as the *Saro*, or the Giant Otter (*Pteroneura braziliensis*). This animal is almost wholly aquatic, and its legs have been reduced to little stumps that cannot support its five-foot, flattened, alligator-shaped body on land, so that it slithers along like a snake. Its muzzle has become shovel-shaped and extends forward over the mouth, which opens below like that of a shark. What is more, its tail has developed flanges along either side, so that, when looked at from on top, it has the shape of a broad spear (see Appendix C). The whole creature is devised for diving into streams and rivers, and its tail for getting down to the bottom and back up to the surface again with as little effort and as great dispatch as possible. Maneuvering from side to side is, to this and other riverine hunters, only of secondary import.

In the same area where the *saro* is found, live also those mysterious, complacent, purely aquatic mammals known as manatees. These creatures have lost almost all their hair, except for a pronounced "Old Bill" mustache; their hind limbs have entirely disappeared; their forelimbs are reduced to dwarf arms and their fingers are joined by complete, solid webs, so that, although they can hold their babies to their breasts, they cannot use their forelimbs for much else. Their tails have become curious paddles for going up and down, but these are nothing more than a further development of those of the *saro*. The next step may be seen in the tail of the manatee's only living relative, the dugong of the Indian Ocean shores. In this beast, these side flaps have been further extended outwards to form triangles and have then curved backwards a little at their tips. With this shape of tail, a semirotary, or sculling, motion becomes possible, and this will drive the animal forward as will the propeller of a ship.

Now, any animal thus driven will immediately tend to be thrown into a rotary motion itself, just as the blades of a helicopter, being forced to go round one way, set the body of the machine going round the other, so that a little additional vertical propeller has to be set in motion on the tail to counteract the effect. The dugong is a comparatively sluggish beast, and can get about slowly without going into a spin. Some whales, however, which are comparatively fast swimmers have encountered this problem and, to counteract it, have developed as stabilizers a series of fore-and-aft bumps running along the ridge of their backs. The next stage is to be found in the swift dolphins, where perfect stabilizers in the form of tall, triangular dorsal fins hold the beasts steady on their headlong course. The ultimate exaggeration is seen in the predaceous killer, who depends on sudden bursts of great speed for swift maneuver. He has truly falcate tail flukes, and an enormous dorsal stabilizer, sometimes over six feet tall and so slender that the tip turns over like the ear of a dog. The purely mechanical evolution of the aquatic mammalian tail, ending in that of the killer, when traced backwards, almost inevitably leads us to a riverine ancestor.

This alone, however, would mean nothing were it not for other facts discovered by embryologists. As everyone now knows, unborn baby animals go through the whole history of their race from the amoeba to their own father and mother. Not only do unborn whales have hairs, indications of external ears, tiny teeth in their gums, stumps of hind limbs, and nostrils on the front of their noses, they also display the whole development of the tail just as we have told it, and finally, their dorsal fins first show as a narrow ridge along the crest of their hinder back. Before the *saro*-like flanges appear on the sides of their tails, moreover, they are practically indistinguishable from dogs or even ourselves at certain stages of embryonic development. They are, in fact, pretty good imitations of the "First Ancestors," in miniature. They sometimes also display another feature that comes as a great surprise.

Dotted about the embryonic skins of several species may be found strange little coinlike plates of tissue containing bone-building cells. Sometimes these are rectangular in shape and form contiguous checkerboards covering specific areas, notably the top of the head, the sides of the forebody, and the mid-back. The common porpoise is often dotted with scattered bony tubercles set under the skin, and a row of them may line the fore edge of the dorsal fin. The Finless Porpoise (*Neomeris phocaenoides*), which is found round the coasts of India, has several rows of these tubercles extending along the ridge of its back from behind the head to the tail. They are squarish, set close together, have roughened centers, are developed in the skin, are calcified — that is, are true bone — and are thus morphologically the same as the bony scutes that make up the "shell" of armadillos. Even more significant in this respect is an extinct dolphin known from complete skeletons and named *Delphinopsis freyeri*. This has whole regions of its body covered by a complete and regularly arranged armature of these little, interlocking, bony scutes. Similar structures have been found in association with the skeletons of some of the Zeuglodonts.

From this it would appear not only possible but quite likely that the land-living "First Ancestors" of the whales were not just hairy beasts but, rather, specialized types covered with an armor of bony plates, like the armadillos, but with hair about the face, beneath the body, and probably on the limbs. If they were not, the development of such bony scutes and their subsequent loss by all sorts of whales constitutes an even more senseless procedure than the development and loss of hair.

The strongest argument in favor of a tropical riverine origin for the whales, nonetheless, remains right before our eyes today, in South America, in West Africa, in India, and in China, in the form of the little platanistids and certain aberrant forms of true dolphins, notably those called the Irrawaddy dolphin and some species of the genus *Sotalia*. These dolphins live in fresh water, some near the mouths of great rivers, some at their heads thousands of miles away from the sea, some in tiny streams or in flood waters covering the floor of the jungle, and some in fresh-water lakes. One of them apparently feeds exclusively on vegetable matter.

From time to time throughout what has gone before, we have referred to dolphins, and we have described a few of them in some detail. The name "dolphin" presents us with several difficulties which must now be disposed of without further delay. First, there has recently arisen an altogether preposterous notion that the name dolphin should be applied only to a kind of fish, and that all dolphins be called "porpoises." Nothing could be more inaccurate according not only to the laws of scientific precedence, but also to two thousand years of linguistic tradition and, I would also point out, to plain common sense. This is an example of the worst kind of misrepresentation, such as is today so widely disseminated under the guise of scientific fact, even by the more responsible sections of the press.

There is a small group of fishes known as the *Coryphoenidae* which grow to a length of six feet and feed on flying fish. When these were classified in the last century, they lacked a popular English name and were dubbed quite arbitrarily "dolphin-fish" by somebody. This name is unknown to tropical mariners or fishermen, who mostly seem to call them "carries." Then again, some of the strange, primitive, cartilaginous fishes known as chimaeras (*Chimaeridae*) have for somewhat longer been referred to by some sailors as "dolphins" because of their resemblance to the mythical dolphins of classical and neoclassical statuary, with pronounced triangular dorsal fins. But nobody who has been to sea has ever called any fish a "dolphin." Further, our word dolphin comes straight from the Latin *delphinus*, which in turn comes directly from the more ancient Greek *delphinios*, or *delphoi*, and has been in world-wide use for a thousand years for these small whales. But even worse than the practice of calling some fish a dolphin is the quite inexcusable suggestion that dolphins should be called porpoises. The porpoises, and there are several, are not just specialized forms of small dolphins; they are quite different animals constituting a separate family called the *Phocaenidae.*

Dolphins of popular terminology are included in a family of whales rather obviously called the *Delphinidae.* Here, however, comes a second complication, because this family includes a variety of animals (see Appendix E for complete list), among which are the killer, the false killer, and the pilot whale or blackfish, as well as the true dolphins. This family is today organized by zoologists into fourteen genera and contains, all told, about sixty quite distinct animals, among them some very strange creatures which are most pertinent to our story. The majority are of interest only to specialists. If anyone should be interested further, he can find their names by reference to the illustrations in Appendix E, and then pursue detailed information on them in the works listed in the appropriate portion of the bibliography.

Finally, there is the quite distinct little family of tiny whales known as the *Platanistidae,* sometimes popularly known as Freshwater Dolphins, which are of the utmost importance to our story. Quite a number of marine dolphins, and all the porpoises, will enter the mouths of rivers and pursue fish inland into purely fresh water. They remain, nevertheless, basically marine animals, and they return to the sea to breed. There are others that dwell always in great rivers, and almost every large tropical river system appears to have some special breed of little whale, either a dolphin, a porpoise, or a platanistid.

Starting in South America, the La Plata has one platanistid called *Pontoporia blainvillei;* the Amazon complex has the Boutu (*Inia geoffroyensis*) and three different kinds of *Sotalia,* called locally the Tucuxi (*Sotalia tucuxi*), the Buffeo Blanco (*Sotalia pallida*), and the Buffeo Negro (*Sotalia fluviatalis*). The rivers of the Guianas have besides the boutu, still another species named *Sotalia guianensis.* In the Cross River of the Cameroon, West Africa, lives an animal called *Sotalia teuszii* which is unique in that nothing but grass, mangrove leaves, aquatic plants, and some fruits have ever been found in its stomach. In the Ganges and Indus rivers of India is found the Susu (*Platanista gangetica*), which we have already described in detail as a result of its mention by Pliny. Then, in the Irrawaddy is found *Orcaella brevirostris*, a true dolphin, while in China we have, first, the pure-white *Sotalia sinensis* of the coastal waters which ascends the larger rivers, and, second, the altogether different *Lipotes vexillifer*, a true platanistid which dwells only in Tung Ting Lake, six hundred miles up the Yangtze River in Hunan Province.

The Irrawaddy dolphin and the *Sotalias* are true dolphins and belong to the family *Delphinidae*. They are most probably, if not assuredly, animals that originated in the sea and have returned to the rivers in search of food and to escape enemies. Only the Cross River dolphin, its stomach filled with vegetable food, is quite unique among whales, and gives us pause to think. It is indeed odd that an animal with millions of years on an animal diet behind it and anatomically devised to live on such food should suddenly change its ways in a river teeming with animal life, both great and small, as the writer can personally attest. It is just possible that the *Sotalias* were developed in tropical rivers and then went to sea, while this species alone remained behind. This does not, however, fit into the general pattern displayed by almost all other whales and their fossil ancestors. The Irrawaddy dolphin is another matter. This is very definitely a marine type that has wandered up the river and its tributaries. It is about seven feet long, dark slate gray in color, and has a blunt head with bulbous forehead. There is a small, recurved dorsal fin, and the flippers are pointed and slender. It eats fish, crayfish, and shellfish and has about fifteen tiny teeth, less than a quarter of an inch long, on either side of both upper and lower jaws. Altogether, it looks rather like an unborn bottle-nosed whale. The remaining species are not really dolphins, or *Delphinidae*, at all, but platanistids. To define these is not easy.

There is in this tiny group of little, geographically scattered, apparently useless, retiring, and wholly inoffensive beasts an intrinsic interest to the zoologist that might stand as an example to all thinking men. In their quiet, obscure way, puffing about in the muddy shallows of their lukewarm streams and pools, they provide, for any of us who would trouble to go and investigate them, an object lesson in the art of living and a living demonstration of something so incredibly ancient that its significance is not at first comprehensible.

The little La Plata *Pontoporia* has never been known to exceed six feet eight inches in length for the male or six feet two inches for the female, or to weigh more than eighty-eight and seventy pounds respectively. It is pale brown, has a pronounced triangular dorsal fin, a rather speedy-type tail, and broad flippers which it can fold up like a fan. It has a distinct neck and a rounded head from the front of which protrudes the most exaggerated beak of any living whale. This is narrow, tubular, and blunt-ended, and no fewer than two hundred small sharp teeth, all alike, are arranged along each side of its upper and lower jaws, averaging about fifty a side. This strange animal goes about in small family parties, wandering out into the sea and up and down the southeast coast of South America, entering all the rivers, great and small, but always keeping to the north in the southern winter or going far inland away from the antarctic cold at that season.

The boutu of the Amazon is quite a different beast. It averages between six and seven feet in total length, and also has a long, slender beak, but one shaped more like that of a stork. Its tail is more subdued in outline, and instead of a dorsal fin it has an extraordinary, elongated ridge stretching from the neck to the tail base and rising gently to a rather abrupt peak about amidships. The flippers are even larger than those of its La Plata cousin and it uses them to cross mudbanks, like a sea lion galumphing over a beach, raising its forequarters off the ground when completely out of water. Its eyes are tiny, but its ear openings are rather large, and it has acute aerial as well as subaqueous hearing. There are only thirty teeth per side in each jaw, but some of those at the back have dual crowns and sometimes even double roots, which is distinctly reminiscent of the early Squalodonts. In color they run the whole gamut from an over-all baby-pig pink through beige, various smooth browns, grays, and slates to a rather startling indigo. All colors may be seen together when large parties join up in the big rivers. Normally, two of about the same color (and this may be a feature of age) travel together. They extend right up the mighty Amazon even into the tributaries that flow from the eastern escarpment of the Andes, but they also occur in the rivers of the Guianas and in the Orinoco, and have been caught at sea immediately along the coast. Their final oddity is that they can turn their heads around, and have pronounced necks, the skin on the back of which is thrown into wrinkles like that of a walrus.

The Chinese lake platanistid is an even more remarkable animal. It is found only in one lake, Tung Ting, where it concentrates in considerable numbers in the winter when the water is low, but it goes up little streams only a few feet wide to breed in the spring. It is about seven feet long, weighs up to three hundred pounds, and is bluish gray above and pure white below. It also has a beak, over a foot long with an average of thirty-five teeth per side in both upper and lower jaws. This beak is curved upwards, but not to the same extent as the extinct Acrodelphid, *Argyrocetus*, of Patagonia.

With the living evidence of these strange little whales before us — animals that have mouthfuls of teeth, some of them even showing signs of differentiation, that can move their heads about and even crawl out on to mudbanks, and that have skeletons more like normal land mammals than any other whales — it is permissible to suggest that the "First Ancestors" lived along the borders of great tropical rivers. The present-day platanistids may be only the remnants of oceanic creatures who retreated into these rivers for protection but, in view of all their primitive characteristics and their way of life, it is perhaps reasonable to suppose that they have been living there ever since the beginning. Behind them, historically, stands a complete geological void, as we have seen, but in behavior, at least, they certainly fill one of the blanks between the earliest marine whales and their *saro*-like "First Ancestors."

There is an immensity of research still to be done, not only on the little platanistids, but on all whales, and if only the time is vouch-safed to modern educated man, this may in due course be prosecuted. To approach the whale is not easy; even to see him is sometimes almost impossible. There may be a thousand platanistids within two miles of your launch in almost any tropical river, but you will never even know that they are there. A little puffing whistle is the only indication they may give of their presence, and this, as in the case of the boutu, is usually so gentle that it is altogether blanketed by the whirring, buzzing, fizzing, chirruping, and croaking of the myriad insects and frogs, not to mention the roaring of howler monkeys and greater creatures, the thunder of the equatorial rains, and the rushing of the wind as it breaks in waves over the massed foliage. What new types of old animals remain to be found in the waters of tropical rivers simply cannot be conceived.

I have often sat on the banks of such a river and, wondering how deep it might be, have tried to calculate the cost of having a large enough net constructed of wire cable to stretch completely across it from side to side and from three feet above its surface to its bottom. Having computed this cost and accepted it as theoretically possible, I have then many times considered the recruiting of sufficient labor to transport the net there and sink it, together with a similar net farther upstream, and then bombing the intervening water with some novel form of depth charge. I then considered, further, the assembly of a fleet of small river boats, with trained crews, to drag the upstream net down to the downstream net and join the two. Finally, I contemplated the purely mechanical problem of getting the resultant mass — weighing a minimum of fifty tons, I once estimated, in the case of a very small river — to either bank for examination. These are nice mental exercises, for although such projects could presumably be devised and carried out, who is going to pay for them? Yet without such an elaborate effort, repeated over and over again, we will never really know just what *does* live in the great, muddy, tropical rivers. Natives once brought me a giant rayfish, measuring ten feet across, from a river on the banks of which I had lived for six months and by which other Europeans had dwelt for some time and the natives for thousands of years. None of us had ever seen anything like it before, and the locals were just as amazed as I was. Perhaps there are Acrodelphids still cruising the oceans, Zeuglodonts browsing in lakes, lochs, and fjords, the ancestors of these in tropical rivers, and even some "First Ancestors" on their banks.

Let us not forget that only one state in this great Union is properly mapped — Massachusetts, that the island of Corsica proved to be dozens of miles out of place on all maps when used as a starting point for bomb runs on Italy in the last war, that there are swamps over twenty thousand square miles in extent in Africa and in South America that have never even been penetrated by man, and finally, that almost three quarters of the surface of our entire earth is covered by oceans which are, on an average, about two and a half miles deep while only half a dozen men have ever been below half a mile anywhere in this vastness. Let us also realize that the dot on an "i" in the word "Pacific" on a map of that ocean in the average school atlas would actually measure four hundred miles from side to side if it were put down on the surface of that ocean. We don't know much about our earth, for all our delvings and diggings, and comings and goings. We know still less of what we *don't* know, despite all our theories and hypotheses and our erudite writings and pompous pronouncements.

After at least ten thousand years in pursuit of the whale, we still know very little about him, and we don't really understand those of our own kind who have followed him.

*Appendixes, Bibliography
and Index*

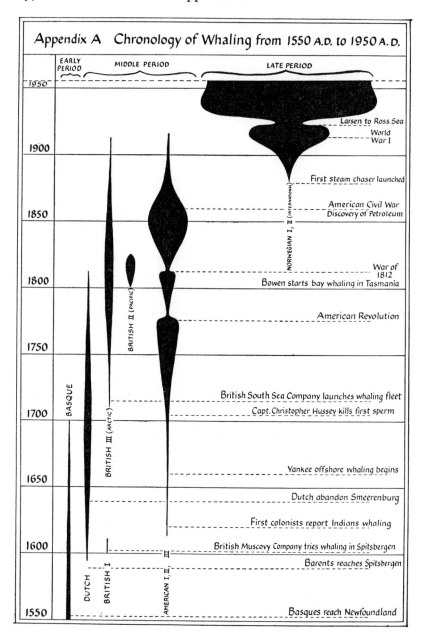

Appendix A    Chronology of Whaling from 1550 A.D. to 1950 A.D.

EARLY PERIOD    MIDDLE PERIOD    LATE PERIOD

1950

1900 — Larsen to Ross Sea
World War I

1850 — First steam chaser launched
American Civil War
Discovery of Petroleum

1800 — War of 1812
Bowen starts bay whaling in Tasmania

1750 — American Revolution

1700 — British South Sea Company launches whaling fleet
Capt. Christopher Hussey kills first sperm

1650 — Yankee offshore whaling begins

Dutch abandon Smeerenburg

First colonists report Indians whaling

1600 — British Muscovy Company tries whaling in Spitsbergen
Barents reaches Spitsbergen

1550 — Basques reach Newfoundland

BASQUE

DUTCH

BRITISH I

BRITISH III (ARCTIC)

BRITISH II (PACIFIC)

AMERICAN I, II

NORWEGIAN I, II (INTERNATIONAL)

# The Chronology of Whaling
## from 1550 A.D. to 1950 A.D.

THE chronology of modern whaling, which may be said to have been initiated about the middle of the sixteenth century when the British and Dutch entered the business, can readily be displayed from the historical or temporal point of view. Exact dates and a wealth of statistics are available. However, when we attempt to show the *volume* of the whaling prosecuted, we immediately encounter insurmountable difficulties.

Upon what criteria are we to base our assessment? Various alternatives are equally permissible, namely, the number of ships employed, the tonnage of those ships, the number of people employed on them or in the industry as a whole, the number of whales taken, the volume of oil and other products produced, landed, or sold, the value of those products, or even the dividends paid. None of these is wholly satisfactory, and for none do we have over-all figures, because at different times and in different countries different methods of assessment were used. Moreover, during long periods no proper records were kept at all. Thus, the best we can attempt is some composite picture based on a general assessment of the amount of activity in this field by any one people at any one time. The results are displayed in the accompanying chart.

As basic criteria in composing this we have taken certain historical statements found in records of later Basque whaling, on the one hand, and in the official statistics given by the International Whaling Commission of the post-World War II period, on the other. From these it would appear that, whereas the Basques, even at the time of their most industrious enterprise, probably never landed more than a hundred whales in any one year, the modern industry has taken as many as twenty thousand in a similar period. The comparative activity is shown in these proportions on the accompanying chart, but it must be clearly understood that the volume, variety, and value of the products produced today far exceed those derived from the boiled blubber of the black right whales tryed-out by the Basques on the high seas.

The actual volume of Dutch, British, and American whaling is similarly hard to assess and still more difficult to demonstrate visually, and it must be pointed out that the apparently slender Dutch effort probably represents a much greater investment and far greater monetary returns than either of the others. The number of ships employed has usually been used as a basic criterion, but a modern factory ship attended by a dozen chasers and other craft takes whales at such a rate that the efforts of the Yankee spermers, even when extending over three-year voyages, pale into insignificance. There are about two hundred and fifty chasers working today, as against some eight hundred sailing ships in 1850, but they take four times as many whales and produce from them several hundred times the volume of products.

Finally, it must be stressed that while the effects of war are shown on the American and modern industries, they have been ignored with respect to the British and Dutch. Those nations were just as radically affected by their endless squabbles, both with each other and with outsiders, and this produced a bewildering rise and fall in the size of their whaling fleets and the annual accomplishments thereof, but these details were deliberately eliminated in order to present a simplified overall picture of the chronology of whaling during the last four hundred years by the five leading operators and contestants – the Basques, Dutch, British, Americans, and Norwegians.

At the same time, it must not be overlooked that the French, Spanish, Germans, and, to a lesser extent, the Danes and Portuguese were also whaling throughout this period with varying degrees of industry, while in other parts of the world all manner of maritime peoples were always busy at small offshore whale-fishing efforts and stranded whales continued to represent a boon to almost all coastal peoples.

# APPENDIX B

# *The Chronology of Whales*
## *from 60,000,000 B.C. to 1950 A.D.*

THE past history of the whales themselves presents us with many fascinating and quite unexpected surprises. The difficulties presented by time, on the geologic or cosmic scale, to creatures such as we with our very limited span of life have already been mentioned on two separate occasions, first, with regard to our own paltry history and, second, with respect to the age of the rocks comprising the surface of our earth. Sixty million years are really quite incomprehensible to us; a mere million of anything is almost beyond our reasoning.

Whales are rather primitive animals, but they are mammals, and these are the least primitive of living things. Their origins obviously were in the dim past, but when we come to plot all that we have discovered of that past, in the form of fossils, we find that it extends back hardly at all into the vast sweep of our planet's history. The earliest whale that we know definitely is not older than some fifty millions of years, and this is comparatively young for mammals as a whole.

One most primitive-appearing type of whale, the gray whale, is not known from before the current ice age, and four of the existing groups — the platanistids, the beaked whales, the sperms, and the dolphins — appear simultaneously only some twenty million years ago. These, moreover, are the oldest of existing whales. On the whole, the baleen whales appear to be the most recently developed, though the primitive forms known as Cetotheres have a venerable history, as shown on the accompanying chart. The majority of toothed whales, and even the extinct forms, appear more recently. Only one group, known as the *Agorophidae*, are of comparatively great age — as great, in fact, as the earliest of the ancient whales, the Zeuglodonts. There is some doubt as to the true position of these agorophids, and there is considerable mystery involved in the complete absence of any intermediate types, either in time

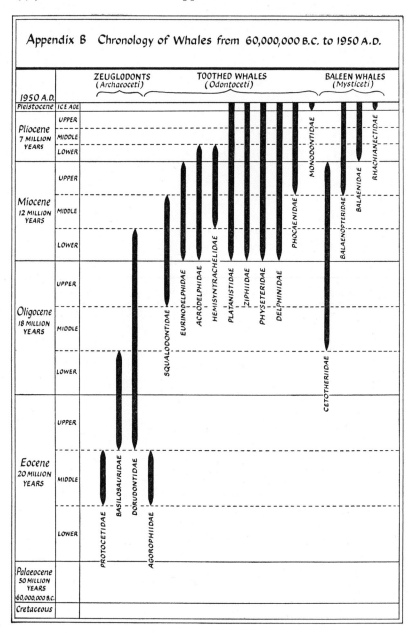

Appendix B  Chronology of Whales from 60,000,000 B.C. to 1950 A.D.

or in structure, between them and their nearest relatives first found in the lower Miocene age, some twenty-three millions of years later.

The Zeuglodonts, now totally extinct as far as we know, are definitely more primitive than any existing known whales but, in some respects, link all of them to their common terrestrial ancestors. Yet the Zeuglodonts are still whales and their history does not extend backwards beyond the middle Eocene, some fifty million years ago.

The accompanying chart displays the time sequence proportionately, but the *subdivisions* of the major ages — of the Pliocene, Miocene, Oligocene, and Eocene — are not proportionate but simply diagrammatic. They represent differing periods of time in almost every case, but the exact number of years by which they differ has not yet been adequately agreed upon in all cases, and this precludes any definite pictorial breakdown and renders any attempt at generalization unwarranted. Further, the arrival upon the geologic scene or the disappearance therefrom of any form does not necessarily occur at exactly the beginning or end of any one subdivision of the periods as herein shown. Animals do not just spring spontaneously into existence, so each group must have had ancestors. Similarly, they did not all just disappear overnight and we may assume that they lingered on somewhere, though no longer leaving skeletons entombed in the rocks, or doing so in strata that we have not yet investigated. Substantially, this chart represents our present knowledge of the past history of the whales, but it may well be greatly altered at any time by new discoveries.

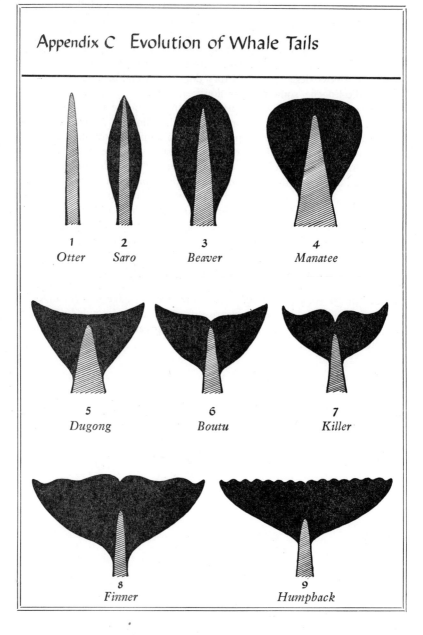

# Appendix C  Evolution of Whale Tails

**1**
*Otter*

**2**
*Saro*

**3**
*Beaver*

**4**
*Manatee*

**5**
*Dugong*

**6**
*Boutu*

**7**
*Killer*

**8**
*Finner*

**9**
*Humpback*

# APPENDIX C

# *The Evolution of Whale Tails*

WHILE the evolution of the cetacean tail must remain purely theoretical until fossil evidence ascertains whether whales are descended from terrestrial animals and, if so, by what intermediaries, we are entitled to conjecture its beginning with a paddle-shaped rudder like the tail of the living saro, or giant otter, of the Amazon. Starting from this point, we can progress readily via the broad paddle of the beaver, to the virtually circular paddle of the manatee, thence to the tail of the dugong, and from this to the somewhat similar organ of the boutu. From this point onward, the stages of development became various and involved.

It would appear that, while the actual proportionate length of the tail to that of the animals involved — that is to say, the tail proper as defined by the bones of the vertebral column — did not decrease, the side flaps, or paddle blades, or flukes, became progressively shorter from front to back as they became longer and more widely spread to either side. Actually, these flukes retreated progressively along the tail until they extended well beyond its extremity, like the tail fin of a fish. The form, or outline, that they adopted in doing so, however, did not follow a single line of development.

Examination of a large number of photographs of whales' tails, undertaken during the search for data for this book, brought to light the rather surprising fact that little if any comparative research has been conducted on the form of this organ in the various groups of whales. Further, the shape of the flukes, as displayed in photographs, was very often at variance with the shape shown in hand-drawn text figures in monographs and other precise works, while we could find no record whatsoever of the tail shape of many species. Also, the most cursory review of what photographs are available showed immediately that there is a quite extraordinary amount of variation in the proportions, shape, and size of the tail flukes even within any one species. In fact, this aspect of cetacean morphology presents a wide field for study that would well warrant investigation.

There are species that display the most exaggerated tail-fluke forms, notably the gray whale wherein the forward edge is concave on either fluke and the hind edge widely convex, so that the whole is fan-shaped with a deep central notch. This may be an ultimate development of the main evolutionary trend that is depicted in the accompanying chart; it might equally well have been developed very long ago from quite another line of change stemming almost directly from the paddle of the manatee stage. The susu, and to some extent also the boutu, has a tail that appears to be at least partially collapsible, more like the combined hind flippers of a seal, but this again may be an offshoot of the main trend, which would appear to be as shown in the chart.

While the side flaps, or flukes, were widening and ever retreating, their combined hind edge appears to have become, first, convex, then, straight, and finally, concave. From this point on, a form of fluting set in, starting with the backward extension of two flaps immediately to either side of the central point, which remained static and thus caused a notch. Such a condition is seen in its primitive form in the tail of the boutu. By further development of this trend, we reach the fluke form of many oceanic dolphins, notably that of the killer, in which the median notch is very deep. When we come to the rorquals, we encounter a further complexity in the development of an additional pair of convexities on either side of the hind edge of the combined flukes, and the ultimate form appears to be that found in the humpback, where, by reduplication, these convexities and intervening concavities have produced an irregular *fluting*, or *slotting*, comparable to that developed by aeronautical engineers on the hind edge of the wing of certain airplane models.

The whole development is undoubtedly a mechanistically controlled reaction to ever increasing speed and maneuverability. It must be borne in mind that the drive of a whale is transmitted from the enormous muscles within the tail proper, which lies inside the body ahead of the flukes, to the water via a most remarkable semirotary, or sculling, action of the flukes. While the "tail" appears simply to go up and down as a whole, each fluke bends once, twice, or even more times along its fore-aft axis at each stroke, and the right fluke has an exactly opposite cycle to that of the left. The motions are enormously complicated, quite impossible to describe in text, and so fast they can hardly be seen with the naked eye even in the clearest water and at close range. The net result, however, is that every part of the surface of both tail flukes, above and below, continuously exerts a powerful tangential push against the water throughout every phase of the up-and-down vibration of the tail as a whole. The dorsal fins and fore flippers of the marine whales are only stabilizers to keep the body from going into a spin if one tail fluke exerts greater pressure than the other.

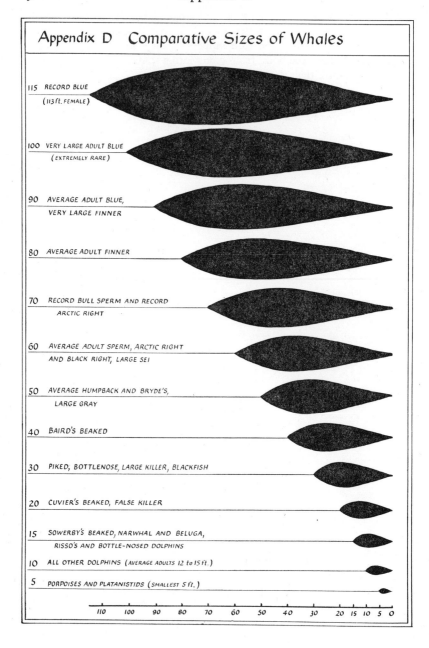

## Appendix D    Comparative Sizes of Whales

115  RECORD BLUE
  (113 ft. FEMALE)

100  VERY LARGE ADULT BLUE
  (EXTREMELY RARE)

90  AVERAGE ADULT BLUE,
  VERY LARGE FINNER

80  AVERAGE ADULT FINNER

70  RECORD BULL SPERM AND RECORD
  ARCTIC RIGHT

60  AVERAGE ADULT SPERM, ARCTIC RIGHT
  AND BLACK RIGHT, LARGE SEI

50  AVERAGE HUMPBACK AND BRYDE'S,
  LARGE GRAY

40  BAIRD'S BEAKED

30  PIKED, BOTTLENOSE, LARGE KILLER, BLACKFISH

20  CUVIER'S BEAKED, FALSE KILLER

15  SOWERBY'S BEAKED, NARWHAL AND BELUGA,
  RISSO'S AND BOTTLE-NOSED DOLPHINS

10  ALL OTHER DOLPHINS (AVERAGE ADULTS 12 to 15 ft.)

5  PORPOISES AND PLATANISTIDS (SMALLEST 5 ft.)

110  100  90  80  70  60  50  40  30  20 15 10 5 0

# APPENDIX D

## Comparative Sizes of Whales

MANY astonishing facts become evident from a chart such as that shown opposite. First, it may come as a great surprise to find that the average whale hunted throughout the ages until the introduction of the modern steam chaser was, comparatively speaking, a "small" whale in point of length and much more so in point of bulk. The average sperm, black right, and even arctic right seldom exceeds sixty feet in length, while the record blue was only a few feet short of double that length. The rights are excessively bulky for their length but, on the grounds of solid geometry, their volume is still less for their over-all size than is that of the mighty rorquals.

Second, we will see that there are two notable gaps in standard whale size. One is the hundred-foot length and the other the seventy-foot. Although whales of both dimensions are recorded, there are none that normally grow to these sizes. This may seem strange, even to the biologist, but not quite so strange to engineers or mathematicians. If the volume of spindle-shaped objects such as whales be plotted on a graph adjusted to take into account a number of known factors, it will be found that significant changes in shape, proportions, and dimensions are called for about these as well as at other less important points. There are, in fact, at least four kinds of whales, from the point of view of mere size — the tiny, which are nothing more than land animals adapted to an aquatic existence; the small, from fifteen to twenty-five feet in length, which are really giant mammals buoyed up by the water; the large, from twenty-five to fifty-five feet in length, which use volume to overcome certain difficulties of size; and the giant, from sixty to ninety feet in length, which keep down their geometric bulk by increasing their length and adopting another form. Over and above these, there can be the supergiant, which, if common, would constitute a fifth class, but which are today, as far as we know, only exceptions. There presumably is no limit to size in the oceans, but there probably are limitations on form as one moves up in length. If there are two hundred-foot creatures as yet undiscovered in the sea, they will probably prove to be greatly elongated or serpentine in form, whether they be seals, whales, or other mammals, or even fish.

The third remarkable fact to be gleaned from such a pictorial representation of the whales is that the vast majority are singularly insignificant in size, more than half being of the two smallest classes, under fifteen feet in length. The difference in bulk between the smallest and the greatest whale known is of the order of ten thousand to one.

# APPENDIX E

## *Illustrated List of Living Whales*

## BALEEN WHALES
### (*Mysticeti*)

### I RIGHT WHALES (*Balaenidae*)

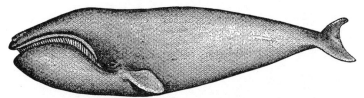

Black Right Whale (*Balaena biscayensis*)

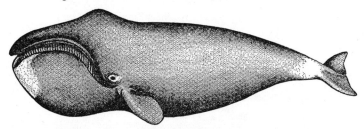

Arctic Right Whale (*Balaena mysticetus*)

Pigmy Right Whale (*Neobalaena marginata*)

## II Rorquals (*Balaenopteridae*)

Blue Whale (*Balaenoptera musculus*)

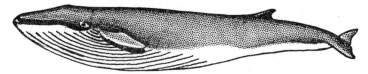

Finner or Common Rorqual (*Balaenoptera physalus*)

Sei or Rudolphi's Rorqual (*Balaenoptera borealis*)

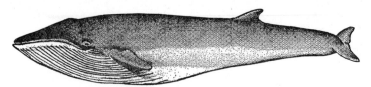

Bryde's Rorqual (*Balaenoptera brydei*)

Piked or Lesser Rorqual (*Balaenoptera acutorostrata*)

### III  HUMPBACKS (*Megapteridae*)

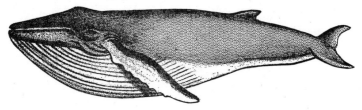

Humpback (*Megaptera nodosa*)

### IV  GRAY WHALES (*Rachianectidae*)

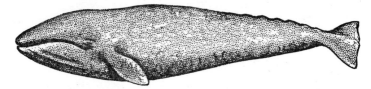

Gray Whale (*Rachianectes glaucus*)

## TOOTHED WHALES
### (*Odontoceti*)

### I  SPERM WHALES (*Physeteridae*)

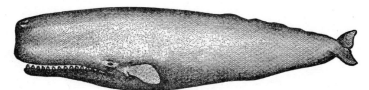

Sperm Whale (*Physeter catodon*)

Pigmy Sperm (*Kogia breviceps*)

## II Beaked Whales (*Ziphiidae*)

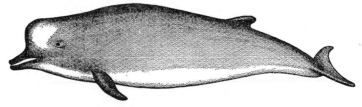

Northern Bottle-nosed Whale (*Hyperoödon rostratus*)

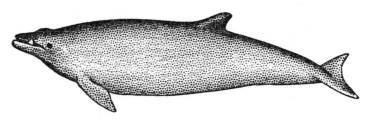

Sowerby's Whale (*Mesoplodon bidens*)

Gray's Whale (*Mesoplodon grayi*)

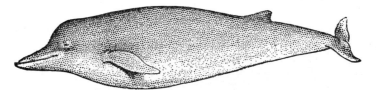

Baird's Whale (*Berardius bairdii*)

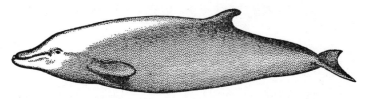

Cuvier's Whale (*Ziphius cavirostris*)

## III WHITE WHALES (*Delphinapteridae*)

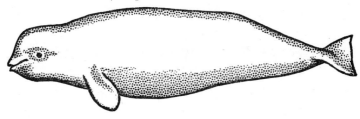

Beluga (*Delphinapterus leucas*)

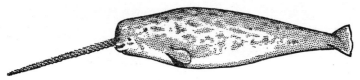

Narwhal (*Monodon monoceras*)

IV DOLPHINS (*Delphinidae*)

Killer (*Orcinus orca*)

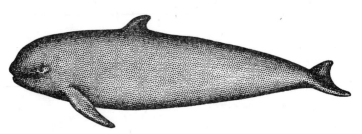

False Killer (*Pseudorca crassidens*)

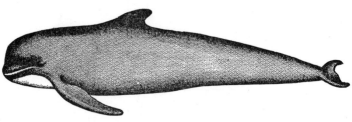

Blackfish or Pilot Whale (*Globiocephalus melas*)

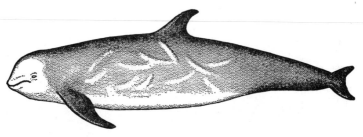

Risso's Dolphin (*Grampus griseus*)

Northern Right-Whale Dolphin (*Lissodelphis borealis*)

Southern Right-Whale Dolphin (*Lissodelphis peronii*)

Common Dolphin (*Delphinus delphis*)

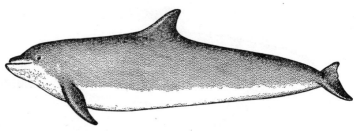

Northern Bottle-nosed Dolphin (*Tursiops truncatus*)

White-sided Dolphin (*Lagenorhynchus acutus*)

White-beaked Dolphin (*Lagenorhynchus albirostris*)

Peale's Dolphin (*Lagenorhynchus australis*)

South Pacific Dolphin (*Lagenorhynchus crucigera*)

Dusky Dolphin (*Lagenorhynchus obscurus*)

Heaviside's Dolphin (*Cephalorhynchus heavisidei*)

Hector's Dolphin (*Cephalorhynchus hectori*)

Commerson's Dolphin (*Cephalorhynchus commersoni*)

Rough-toothed Dolphin (*Steno rostratus*)

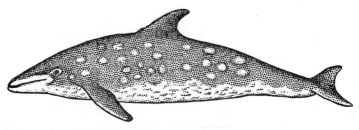

Spotted Dolphin (*Stenella graffmani*)

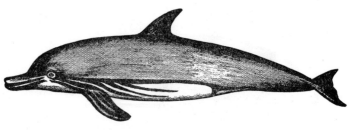

Slender Dolphin (*Prodelphinus attenuatus*)

Gadamu (*Sotalia gadamu*)

Guianan River Dolphin (*Sotalia guianensis*)

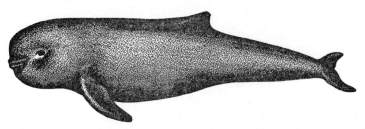

Irrawaddy Dolphin (*Orcaella brevirostris*)

## V PORPOISES (*Phocaenidae*)

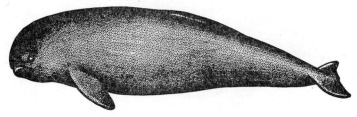

Finless Porpoise (*Neomeris phocaenoides*)

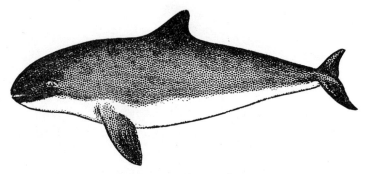

Common Porpoise (*Phocaena phocaena*)

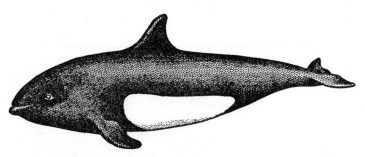

Harbor Porpoise (*Phocaena dalli*)

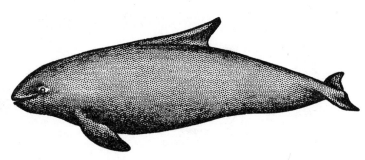

Burmeister's Porpoise (*Phocaena spinipinnis*)

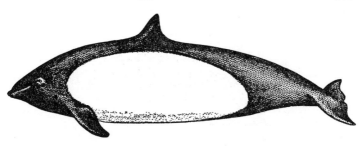

True's Porpoise (*Phocaena truei*)

Spectacled Porpoise (*Phocaena dioptrica*)

## VI PLATANISTIDS (*Platanistidae*)

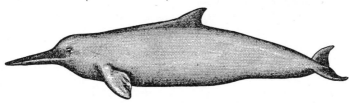

La Plata Dolphin (*Pontoporia blainvillei*)

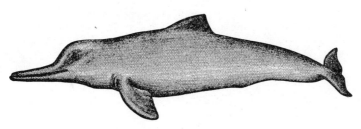

Chinese Lake Dolphin (*Lipotes vexillifer*)

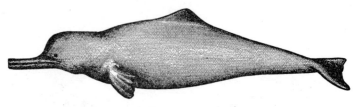

Susu (*Platanista gangetica*)

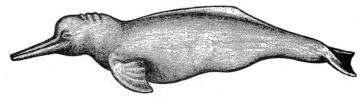

Boutu (*Inia geoffroyensis*)

# Bibliography

The following list of works does not purport to be either a complete bibliography of whaling — any such would fill a large volume in itself — or even a complete list of works consulted during the ten years of research for this book. It is offered, rather, as a condensed list of further reading on the main theme and subsidiary subjects covered in the foregoing text. It is for this reason that the items are not arranged in the customary manner, by author, or even alphabetically. As far as possible they follow the text but are grouped according to subject.

## PREHISTORIC

*Early Man, International Symposium on*, Ed. by George Grant Mac-Curdy, J. B. Lippincott, Philadelphia, 1937

*Guide to Northern Archaeology*, Ed. by the Earl of Ellesmere, Royal Society of Northern Antiquaries, J. Bain, London, 1848

*The Primaeval Antiquities of Denmark*, by J. J. A. Worsaae, Tr. by William J. Thomas, J. H. Parker, London, 1849

*Prehistoric Times*, by Sir John Lubbock (Lord Avebury), Henry Holt and Co., New York, 1913

"Whales as an Economic Factor in Prehistoric Europe," by Grahame Clark, *Antiquity*, Vol. XXI, No. 82, June 1947, Gloucester, England

"Seal-Hunting in the Stone Age of North Western Europe," by J. G. D. Clark, *Proc. Prehistorical Soc.*, XII, 1946, pp. 12–48, Cambridge, England

*Undersögelser i Geologisk-Antiquarisk Retning*, by G. Forchammer, J. Steenstrup, and J. Worsaae (Six Reports on Kitchen-Middens), Acad. Sci. of Copenhagen, *Oversigt Over*, Nos. 5 and 6, 1854.

## ANCIENT

"Jonah's Whale," by Paul Haupt, *Proc. Amer. Phi. Soc.*, Vol. XLVI, p. 151, April 1907

*The Persian Gulf*, by Sir Arnold T. Wilson, Clarendon Press, Oxford, 1928

*Arrian's History of Alexander's Expedition*, Tr. by Mr. Rooke, Vol. II, p. 257, T. Worrall, London, 1729, 2 vols.

*The Cuneiform Name of the Cachalot*, Annual Meeting of the American Oriental Society, held at Philadelphia on April 5, 1907

*The Cambridge Ancient History*, Vol. I., Macmillan and Co., London, 1928

"Die Wasserfahrzeuge in Babylonien," by von Armas Salonen, *Studia Orientalia Edidit Societas Orientalis Fennica*, VIII, 4, Helsingfors, 1939

*Arabia Before Muhammad*, by De Lacy Evans O'Leary, Trubner's Oriental Series, Kegan Paul, Trench, Trubner and Co., Ltd., 1927

*A Guide to the Babylonian and Assyrian Antiquities*, Trustees of the British Museum, London, 1922

*Ancient Records of Egypt*, Ed. and Tr. by J. H. Breasted, Vols. 1–5, University of Chicago Press, Chicago, 1906–1907

*An Egyptian Hieroglyphic Dictionary*, by Sir E. A. Wallis Budge, John Murray, London, 1920

The Bāveru-Jātākā, No. 339, *The Jātākā*, Ed. by Prof. E. B. Cowell, Cambridge University Press, England, 1897

*Intercourse Between India and the Western World*, by H. G. Rawlinson, Cambridge University Press, 1916

*India and the Indian Ocean*, by K. M. Panikkar, George Allen and Unwin, London, 1945

*Ancient India, The Cambridge History of India*, Ed. by E. J. Rapson, Vol. I, Cambridge University Press, 1935

*Ancient India, As Described in Classical Literature*, Ed. and Tr. by J. W. M'Crindle, A. Constable and Co., Ltd., Westminster, 1901

*The Geography of Strabo*, Tr. by H. C. Hamilton and W. Falconer, 3 vols., H. G. Bohn, London, 1854–1857

"Sea-Trade in Early Times," by James Hornell, *Antiquity*, Vol. XIV, No. 59, September 1941, Gloucester, England

*Unrolling the Map*, by Leonard Outhwaite, John Constable and Co., London, 1935

*A History of Egypt*, by James Baikie, A. and C. Black, London, 1929

"On the Mammalia of the Assyrian Sculptures," by William Houghton, *Trans. Soc. Biblical Archaeo.*, Vol. V, Pt. 2, pp. 229–383, London, 1877

"The First Polar Expedition – 325 B.C.," by Rev. Dr. M. A. Eitel, *Proc. Roy. Geog. Soc. of Australasia*, Vol. VII, pp. 30–47, Adelaide, 1903–1904

*The Dolphin in the Literature and Art of Greece and Rome*, by Eunice Burr Stebbins, George Banta Publishing Co., Wisconsin, 1929

*The Aegean Civilization*, by Gustav Glotz, Alfred A. Knopf Inc., New York, 1925

*The Ancient Explorers,* by Max Cary and E. H. Warmington, Methuen and Co., London, 1929

*Early Ivories from Samaria,* by J. W. and Grace M. Crowfoot, Palestine Exploration Fund, London, 1938

"The Megiddo Ivories," by Gordon Loud, Chicago University, *Oriental Inst. Pubs.,* Vol. LII, 1939

"Historia Animalium," Bks. I, II, VI, VIII, IX, Tr. by D'Arcy Wentworth Thompson, *The Works of Aristotle,* Ed. by J. A. Smith and W. D. Ross, Vol. IV, Clarendon Press, Oxford, 1910

"The Natural History of Fishes," Bks. I–IX, Tr. by John Bostock and H. T. Riley, *The History of Pliny,* Bohn's Classical Library, Vol. II, George Bell and Sons, London, 1890

*A Dictionary of the Bible,* Ed. by James Hastings, Vol. II, p. 750, C. Scribner and Sons, New York, 1899–1904


## NORSE

*A Description of Europe,* by King Alfred, Tr. by Rev. J. Bosworth, 3rd Pr., p. 7, 1855

*The Vikings,* by Allen Mawer, *Cambridge Manuals of Sci. & Lit.,* Cambridge University Press, England, 1930

*Northmen of Adventure,* by Charles Marshall Smith, Longmans Green and Co., London, 1932

*Viking Settlers in Greenland,* by Paul Nørlund, Cambridge University Press, England, 1936

*The Discovery of Muscovy,* by Richard Hakluyt, p. 176, Cassell and Co., Ltd., London, 1904

"Animal Bones from the Norse Ruins at Gardar," by M. Degerbøl, *Medellelser an Grønland,* Vols. 76 and 88 (3), 1936.

*The King's Mirror,* Tr. from the Old Norwegian by Laurence Marcellus Larson, The American-Scandinavian Foundation, New York, 1917


## JAPANESE

*Japan Times and Mail,* Aquatic Industries Number, 1935

*Japanese Whaling Prior to 1946,* by William M. Terry, Rep. 126, Nat. Resources Sect., G. H. Supreme Commander for Allied Powers, Tokyo, 1950

*Special Exhibit of Whaling Pictures* (catalogue), from the Collection of Allan Forbes, Peabody Museum, 1919

"Skin Boats: A Study of Ancient Ships of Japan," by Shinji Nishimura (Four Brochures), pub. by Soc. of Naval Architects, Tokyo, 1931 (see Prof. Shōgorō Tsuboi, *Jour. Anthrop. Soc.,* Vol. XXIII, No. 263, p. 162, Tokyo)

"Arabic and Chinese Trade in Walrus and Narwhal Ivory," by Berthold

Laufer, *T'oung-Pao*, Vol. XIV, Oriental Printing Office, E. J. Brill, London, 1913

*Prehistoric Japan*, by Neil Gordon Munro, Yokohama, 1908

*Illustrated History of Japanese Marine History*, Japanese Min. of Communications, 1911

"Early Japanese Whaling," by F. C. Frazer, *Proc. Linn. Soc. of London*, 1937, pp. 19–20

*The Account of the Western Trip*, by Shiba Kotan, 1790, 5 vols.

*Pictures of Whaling — Yugyotoru Eshi*, by Yamada Yosei, 1829

"On Maritime Enterprise in Japan," by H. A. C. Bonar, *Trans. As. Soc. of Japan*, Vol. XV, 1887


## BASQUE

"On the Whale-Fisheries of the Basque Provinces of Spain," by C. Markham, *Proc. Zool. Soc.*, p. 969, London, 1881

"Whaling," *Diccionario Historico de los Artes de la Pesca Nacional*, by Sanez Reguart, Vol. 3, Madrid, 1792

"Cétacées du Sud-Ouest de la France," by M. Fischer, *Actes Soc. Linn.*, XXXV, 4th Series, V, pp. 5–219, Bordeaux, 1881

*A Book of the Basques*, by Rodney Gallop, Macmillan and Co., London, 1930

*Historia del Ilustre País Bascongado*, by Joaquim Landazuri y Romarate, Tomo. 7, Vols. 1 and 2, A. P. Cardenal, Bilbao, 1901–1902

"Petite Histoire du Pays Basque Français," by Joseph Nogaret, *Bull. Soc. des Sciences, Lettres, Arts, et d'Études Regionales de Bayonne*, 8°, pp. 1–96, Bayonne, 1923

*Revue Historique et Archaeologique du Béarn et du Pays Basque*, Pau, 1910

*Corsarios y Colonizadores Vascos*, by Michel Iriart, Editorial Vasca Elkin, Biblioteca de Cultura Vasca, Buenos Aires, 1945

"L'Atlantique et les Basques," by William D'Abartiagne, *Courrier, Bull. Société des Sciences, Lettres, et Arts de Bayonne*, pp. 262–273, 1937

"Pre-Columbian Discovery by Basques," by Louis D. Scisco, *Proc. and Transac. Roy. Soc. of Canada*, Series 3, Vol. 18, Sect. 2, pp. 51–61, Ottawa, 1924

*Histoire Maritime de Bayonne; Les Corsaires sous l'Ancien Régime*, by Édouard Ducéré, E. Hourquet, Bayonne, 1895

*Primitivos Navegantes Vascos*, by Enrique de Gandiá, Editorial Vasca Elkin, Buenos Aires, 1942

"Sellos Medioevales de Tipo Naval," by Ramon de Berraondo, *Revista Internacional de los Etudios Vascos*, Vol. XXIII, No. 1, San Sebastian, 1932

## BRITISH — NORTHERN

*A Whaling Cruise to Baffin's Bay and the Gulf of Boothia,* by A. H. Markham, S. Low, Marston, London, 1875

*The Arctic Whalers,* by Basil Lubbock, Brown, Son and Ferguson, Glasgow, 1937

*Journal of a Voyage to Greenland in the Year 1821,* by George William Manby, G. W. B. Whittaker, London, 1822


## BRITISH — SOUTHERN

*Whalemen Adventurers,* by William John Dakin, Angus and Robertson, Ltd., Sydney, 1934

"Whaling in New Zealand Waters," by Ronald McIntosh, *The New Zealand Railways Magazine,* Vol. 12, No. 12, March 1938, Wellington

*The Old Whaling Days,* by Robert McNab, Whitcombe and Tombs, Ltd., Christchurch, N. Z., 1913

*A Voyage to the South Atlantic and around Cape Horn into the Pacific Ocean for the Purpose of Extending the Spermaceti Whale Fisheries and Other Objects of Commerce,* by Captain James Colnett, W. Bennett, London, 1798

*The Natural History of the Sperm Whale,* by Thomas Beale, 2nd Ed., John Van Voorst, London, 1839

*Discovery Reports,* Vol. 7 (Contains complete history of New Zealand whaling from 1770–1933)


## AMERICAN

*The Real Story of the Whaler,* by A. Hyatt Verrill, D. Appleton and Co., 1916

*A Whaling Voyage in the Bark Willis — 1849–1850,* by Samuel Millett, Boston, Mass., 1924 (priv. print.)

*Whale Off,* by Everett J. Edwards and Jeanette E. Rattray, Frederick A. Stokes and Co., New York, 1932

*The Yankee Whaler,* by Clifford W. Ashley, Houghton Mifflin Co., Boston, 1926

*Whale Ships and Whaling,* by George Francis Dow, Marine Research Society of Salem, Mass., 1925

"The Way of the Sperm Whalers," by Robert Cushman Murphy, *Sea Power,* Vols. 2 and 3, 1917

*The American Whaleman,* by E. P. Hohman, Longmans, Green and Co., New York, 1928

*Whaling Cruise,* by J. R. Browne, Harper Bros., New York, 1846

*Incidents of a Whaling Voyage,* by Francis Allyn Olmstead, D. Appleton and Co., New York, 1841

*Whaling and Fishing,* by Chas. Nordhoff, Dodd Mead and Co., New York, 1895

## MODERN

*Whaling in the Frozen South,* by A. J. Villiers, Bobbs-Merrill Co., Indianapolis, 1925

*Whale Hunting with Gun and Camera,* by Roy Chapman Andrews, D. Appleton and Co., New York, 1916

*Whales and Modern Whaling,* by Travis Jenkins, Witherby and Co., London, 1932

*Ends of the Earth,* by Roy Chapman Andrews, G. P. Putnam's Sons, New York, 1929

"A History of Whaling," with a Résumé of the Whaling Industry of the U.S. 1937–40 (Mimeo'd), U.S. Dept. of the Interior, Bureau of Fisheries, *U.S. Vital Statistics,* 1942

"Twentieth Century Whaling," by Charles H. Townsend, *Bull. N. Y. Zoo. Soc.* Vol. XXXIII, No. 1, 1930

*International Whaling Statistics,* Pub. by Comm. for Whaling Statistics, Oslo, Norway, Vols. I–XIII, 1930–39

"Finwhale Fishery off the North European Coast," by A. H. Cocks, *Zoologist,* 3rd Series, Vols. X to XIV (off the Lapland coast, 1886–1890)

*Whaling and Whale Oil During and After World War II,* by Karl Brandt, Food Research Inst., Stanford University, Stanford, Calif., 1948

"Los Grandes Cetáceos del Estrecho de Gibraltar, su Pesca y Explotación," by Angel Cabrera, *Trabajos del Museo Nacional de Ciencias Naturales,* Série Zoológica, No. 52, Madrid, 1925

*Of Whales and Men,* by R. B. Robertson, Alfred A. Knopf, New York, 1954

"Whaling in Scotland and Shetlands," by R. C. Haldane, *Ann. Scot. Nat. Hist.,* No. 54, April 1905, No. 59, July 1906, No. 61, January 1907, No. 66, April 1908, No. 70, April 1909, No. 73, January 1910

## LOCAL

"Longshore Whaling in the Grenadines," by Frederick A. Tenger, *Outing,* Vol. 61, New York, 1913

"Arctic Giant Killers," by Charles Lanius, *Collier's,* November, 9, 1946, p. 11

"The Indians of Cape Flattery, at the Entrance to the Straits of Fuca, Washington Territory," by James G. Swan, *Smithsonian Contributions to Knowledge,* No. 220, Washington, 1889

"Whale Hunting in the Faroes," by Svere Patursson, *The Trident* (Brit. mag.), Vol. 8, No. 90, p. 426, 1946

"Ethnological Results of the Point Barrow Expedition," by J. Murdock, *IXth Ann. Rep. Smithsonian Inst.*, Washington, 1892

"The Whaling Equipment of the Makah Indians," by T. T. Waterman, *Un. of Washington Pubs. in Anthropology*, Vol. I, No. 1, The University, Seattle, Wash., 1920

*A Description of the Western Isles of Scotland*, by M. Martin, Stirling, 1934 (originally published London, 1703)


## GENERAL HISTORICAL

*A History of the Whale Fisheries*, by James Travis Jenkins, H. F. and G. Witherby, London, 1921

*Whalers and Whaling*, by E. Keble Chatterton, T. F. Unwin, Ltd., London, 1925

"The History of Whaling," by Sir Sidney F. Harmer, *Proc. Linn. Soc. London*, 140th Session, Pres. Inaugural Address, 1927–1928


## MISCELLANEOUS

"The Sinking of the Bark Kathleen," by Frederick Booth, *St. Nicholas Magazine*, Vol. 36, pp. 676–679, 1909

*Sailing Ships and Their Story*, by E. Keble Chatterton, Sidgwick and Jackson, Ltd., London, 1923

*La Nave Nel Tempo*, by Michele Vocino, Luigi Alleri, Milano, 1942

*Neue Luther Kirchenzeitung*, 1895, p. 303 (story of a man swallowed by a whale)

"Whaling and Fishing in the North Atlantic," by Johan Hjort and Johan T. Rudd, Extract of 123 pages from *Conseil Permanent International pour l'Exploration de la Mer*, Copenhagen, 1929


## ZOOLOGICAL

*The Marine Mammals of the Northwestern Coast of North America*, by Charles M. Scammon, J. H. Carmany and Co., San Francisco, 1874

*A Book of Whales*, by F. E. Beddard, G. P. Putnam's Sons, New York, 1900

*U. S. Navy World Chart*, 1853 (showing distribution of sperm and right whales)

"Fossil Whales," by E. D. Cope, *American Naturalist*, July 1890

*Aquatic Mammals*, by A. Brazier Howell, Charles C. Thomas Co., Springfield, Ill., 1930

*Giant Fishes, Whales, and Dolphins*, by J. R. Norman and F. C. Frazer, Putnam, London, 1937

*General Information for the Ready Identification of the Principal Types of Whales*, U. S. Coast Guard, U. S. Gov. Print. Off., Washington, 1937

"Preliminary List of Works and Papers Relating to the Orders of Cete and Sirenia," by J. A. Allen, *U. S. Geolog. and Geog. Surv. of the Terr. Bull.*, Vol. 6, No. 3, Gov. Print. Off., Washington, 1882

*Guide to the Whales, Porpoises, and Dolphins*, by R. Lydekker, Trustees of the British Museum, London, 1909

"The Porpoise in Captivity," by Charles H. Townsend, *Zoologica*, I, No. 16, June 1914, New York

"Whales and Whaling," by L. Harrison Matthews, *Endeavor*, Vol. V, No. 19, London, 1947

"Observations on the Auditory Organ in the Cetacea," by Sir William Turner, *Proc. Roy. Soc. Edinburgh*, Vol. XXXIV, Pt. 1, No. 2, 1914

"Documents sur les Cétacés et Pinnipèdes Provenant des Campagnes du Prince Albert I de Monaco," by Jules Richard, Fascicule XCIV, Oceanographic Inst., Monaco, 1936

"On Whales Landed at the Scottish Whaling Stations, Especially During the Years 1908–1914," by D'Arcy Wentworth Thompson, *The Scottish Naturalist*, September 1918

*Discovery Reports*, Vols. 1, 2, 5, 6, 7, 15, 17, 19, and 22

"Whales, Giants of the Sea," by Remington Kellogg, *The National Geographic Mag.*, Vol. LXXVII, No. 1, January 1940

"Monographs of the Pacific Cetacea," by Roy Chapman Andrews, *Mem. of the Am. Mus. Nat. Hist.*, New Series, Vol. I, Pt. V, pp. 289–388, 1914

"The Genealogical History of the Marine Mammals," by Prof. O. Abel, *Annual Report of the Smithsonian Institute*, 1907, p. 473

*Wonders of Animal Life*, by R. V. Daniel, Vol. II, Ch. LXVIII, p. 731

"On Zeuglodont and Other Cetacean Remains from the Tertiary of the Caucasus," by R. Lydekker, *Proc. Zool. Soc. Lond.*, 1892, p. 558

"The Reproductive Organs of Cetacea," by A. Meek, *Journ. of Anatomy*, Vol. LII, p. 186, Macmillan and Co., London, 1918

*Report on Cetacea Stranded on the British Coasts*, by Sir Sydney F. Harmer (seven parts), Brit. Mus. Nat. Hist., 1914–1920

"Contribution to the Natural History of the Cetaceans, A Review of the Delphinidae," by Frederick W. True, *Bull. U. S. Nat. Mus.*, No. 36, 1889

"Observations on the Anatomy and General Biology of Some Members of the Larger Cetacea," by D. G. Lillie, *Proc. Zool. Soc. Lond.*, 1910, pp. 789–792

"Sowerby's Whale on the American Coast," by Glover M. Allan, *The American Naturalist*, Vol. XL, No. 473, Boston, 1906

*A Text-Book of Palaeontology — Mammalia*, by Karl A. von Zittel, revised by Max Schlosser, Vol. III, Macmillan and Co., London, 1925

"The Principles of Classification and a Classification of Mammals," by George Gaylord Simpson, *Bull. Am. Mus. Nat. Hist.*, Vol. 85, 1945

## ECONOMIC – INDUSTRIAL

"Whale Oil – An Economic Analysis," by Karl Brandt, *Fats and Oils Studies*, No. 7, Food and Research Inst., Stanford University, Stanford, Calif., 1940

*Whales and Porpoises as Food*. Bureau of Fisheries Economic Circular, No. 38, U. S. Dept. of Commerce, 1918

*Whalebone – Its Production and Utilization*, by Charles H. Stevenson, U. S. Bureau of Fisheries Document, No. 626, Gov. Print. Off., 1907

*The Whale Fishery and Its Appliances*, by James Temple Brown (Great International Fisheries Exhibition, London, 1883), Gov. Print. Off., Washington, 1883

# Index

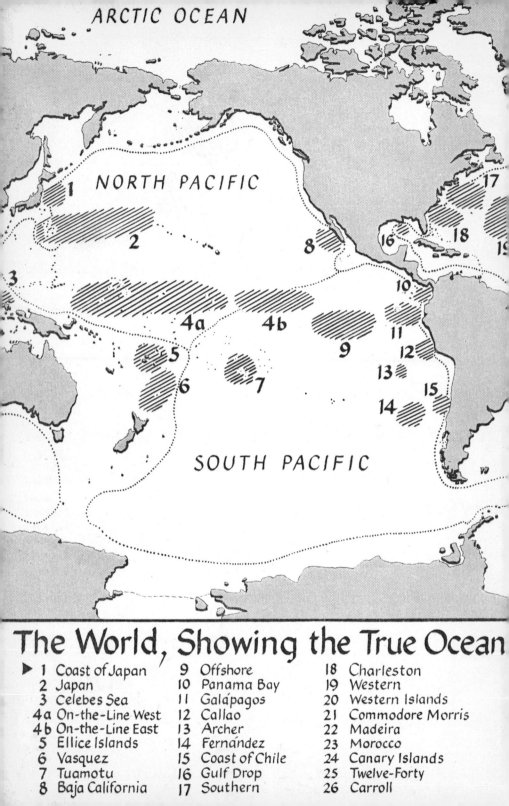

ARCTIC OCEAN

NORTH PACIFIC

1

2

3

8

16

17

18

19

10

4a    4b

5

6    7

9

11

12

13

15

14

SOUTH PACIFIC

# The World, Showing the True Ocean

▶ 1  Coast of Japan
2  Japan
3  Celebes Sea
4a On-the-Line West
4b On-the-Line East
5  Ellice Islands
6  Vasquez
7  Tuamotu
8  Baja California

9  Offshore
10 Panama Bay
11 Galápagos
12 Callao
13 Archer
14 Fernández
15 Coast of Chile
16 Gulf Drop
17 Southern

18 Charleston
19 Western
20 Western Islands
21 Commodore Morris
22 Madeira
23 Morocco
24 Canary Islands
25 Twelve-Forty
26 Carroll